OPERATIONS RESEARCH SOCIETY
OF AMERICA

Publications in Operations Research
Number 6

PUBLICATIONS IN OPERATIONS RESEARCH

Operations Research Society of America

Editor for Publications in Operations Research

DAVID B. HERTZ

No. 1.   QUEUES, INVENTORIES AND MAINTENANCE
Philip M. Morse

No. 2.   FINITE QUEUING TABLES
L. G. Peck and R. N. Hazelwood

No. 3.   EFFICIENCY IN GOVERNMENT THROUGH SYSTEMS ANALYSIS
Roland N. McKean

No. 4.   A COMPREHENSIVE BIBLIOGRAPHY ON OPERATIONS RESEARCH
Operations Research Group, Case Institute

No. 5.   PROGRESS IN OPERATIONS RESEARCH, VOLUME I
Edited by Russell L. Ackoff

No. 6.   STATISTICAL MANAGEMENT OF INVENTORY SYSTEMS
Harvey M. Wagner

STATISTICAL

MANAGEMENT OF

INVENTORY SYSTEMS

HARVEY M. WAGNER

ASSOCIATE PROFESSOR OF BUSINESS ADMINISTRATION,
INDUSTRIAL ENGINEERING, AND STATISTICS
STANFORD UNIVERSITY

CONSULTANT TO:
THE RAND CORPORATION
MCKINSEY & COMPANY, INC.

NEW YORK · LONDON, JOHN WILEY & SONS, INC.

⌐1962⌐

TO RUTHIE

PREFACE

THE NEED FOR INTENSIVE research in the subject of designing control devices for multi-item and multi-echelon integrated inventory systems was brought to my attention in the early part of 1958 during my consulting efforts for The RAND Corporation's Logistics Department. RAND Logistics had made substantial progress in devising scientifically based methods for stocking inventories within the United States Air Force. Concomitant interest was engendered in the possible interactions that the stockage policies would have with the variety of financial control devices that were being either used or proposed. These financial controls have been widely adopted in military and commercial establishments, purportedly to assist in managing large and partially decentralized logistics complexes. It was not then clear to what extent scientific inventory rules and financial controls were mutually consistent. In addition, the potentialities for effecting control by means of statistical indices had not been explored in any degree of thoroughness. Consequently, I undertook a study of such questions, and the present monograph summarizes the findings.

The reader will discover that this monograph is essentially a mathematical approach to problems of management control of complex systems. He may legitimately ask: "What insights to such problems can mathematics offer?" By the very nature of the analysis, all that can be expected is an exploration of fundamental and hopefully general properties of management control mechanisms. The management scientist who wants to apply the results of the research to particular real situations is, therefore, required to synthesize the elemental findings. In this process he will find that the mathematical analyses do not provide answers to every important issue. Perhaps this is because the current state of the art is too primitive;

but in all likelihood it is because there will always be a collection of management control problems which do not yield completely, if at all, to mathematical analysis. Consequently, the operations researcher must look to other disciplines, such as the behavioral sciences, to complement and perhaps modify the findings provided by mathematics. The approach is not unlike that found in the physical sciences: basic principles are evolved which motivate experimental studies and structural designs; the principles are rarely of practical use in their *raw* form, but nevertheless they provide the key observations for applied efforts.

The reader may also have questions concerning the content and level of this book, such as:

What is the significance of the book's title? What is the relation of this study to other publications in the field of inventory control? The guiding theme of this monograph is an exploration of how managerial control can be exercised in the operation of a large-scale inventory system; in particular, the methods embraced are those based on statistical aggregates and indices. With hardly an exception, I have not treated any problems of finding optimum inventory rules; I have assumed that management has available operations research techniques for arriving at desired policies. This study can, in a sense, be viewed as starting where most other treatises on inventory control end. Management has already selected procedures for dealing with inventory changes, and now wants to ensure that such procedures are followed and not modified, except when external conditions properly require that revisions be made. The only managerial control devices I investigate are those which measure operating characteristics of the *system's* behavior.

What is the technical background required? Although I have endeavored to maintain a consistent mathematical level throughout the monograph, I suspect that not all passages are of equal difficulty, and some sections rely more heavily on a background of probability theory, some more heavily on a knowledge of mathematical statistics, and others more heavily on a familiarity with sequential decision theory. The reader needs an understanding of the basic ideas in inventory theory, which can be found in such books as [FD, H, HMMS, M, Wh]. The probability theory prerequisites are at the level of [KMST, KS] and the non-esoteric parts of [Fe]. A knowledge of statistics at a level somewhere between that of [BL] and of [Cra, K] is required. References to decision theory are at the level of [B, CM, LR, and Sch]. The over-all mathematical sophistication is probably more comparable to [Mo] than to [AKS].

What is the nature of the results? Since I have included introductory and summary sections throughout the monograph, I shall not comment here on the substance of the results. Rather, I shall turn to that aspect which might be termed presentation format. The reader will quickly ascertain that this monograph is not a handbook—I have not attempted to state and organize the results so that the reader has a quick and easy guide to the design of control systems. On the other hand, I have avoided, for the most part, propositions that might be classified as "existence theorems," the principal exception being Chapter 1 which is meant to be expository. I have, in the main, confined the mathematical analyses to propositions capable of numerical calculation, albeit some of the calculations do require the use of a large-scale electronic computer. Throughout I have tried to give numerous examples. In addition to providing specific numerical illustrations, these examples enable the reader to check computational schemes of his own devising, based on the mathematical results of this study. Furthermore, the examples may be helpful in testing new optimizing and approximating techniques in the solution of inventory problems. Because the monograph represents a research study rather than a textbook, I have cross-referenced rather than repeated results and conclusions that have bearing in several sections of the book.

How generally valid are the conclusions? Of course this is a controversial question. It would be presumptuous to attempt to answer it here. But I do want to give my arguments in support of my concentrating on (s, S) inventory policies [AHM] and stationary probability analysis.

Savants of inventory theory are aware that methodological disputes presently exist among the various schools of thought. Two criticisms commonly made are that "so-and-so's approach is to treat inventory theory essentially as a branch of mathematics," and "such-and-such a result is based on a very special set of assumptions." Although such criticisms are difficult to refute, it is noteworthy and ironic that each school of inventory theory seems to level them at the results of the opposing schools. I feel we come closer to the core of the dispute if we adopt the view expressed earlier—that inventory theory, as we know it today, provides mainly a set of idealized models which, like idealized models in the physical and engineering sciences, offer insights to the solutions of real problems. As time elapses, more information on the comparative properties of these models will become available. While this is happening, each scientist must decide which idealized model best suits the purpose of his investigation, and clearly a single approach (chosen from among those we know today) is not likely to be universally best.

I have employed the class of (s, S) policies because I felt that it entailed the weakest set of assumptions among the competing approaches, but at the same time encompassed the essence of the control problems I wished to explore, and the associated mathematics proved tractable. As this is not the place to embark on a detailed comparative analysis of mathematical approaches, I shall ask the reader to decide only after studying the book's contents whether the transition from the model in this monograph to other inventory models seems immediate and, in particular, whether there is reason to believe that the substance of the current results will be greatly affected after such a transition.

My defense of stationary probability analysis is, at least in part, of a different character. A major issue here is: does the use of stationary analysis bias the essence of the results? Stationary analysis unquestionably makes mathematical manipulations easier. Be that as it may, the approach has to be justified on logical grounds as pertinent to the study of control mechanisms; I attempt such a justification in Section 2.1.5 and shall not repeat that material here. But I add that, given the nature of the questions I studied, I believe the stationary probability analysis is defensible. To be specific, my results concerning the inconsistencies arising from controls such as quarterly budgets are, if anything, reinforced when stationary probability analysis is dropped and transients are introduced.

I am most grateful to Charles J. Zwick, Albert S. Cahn, and Glen H. Craig of The RAND Logistics Department for their active support and interest during the greater part of this research effort. The comments of Kenneth J. Arrow, Stanford University; Theodore K. Matthes and Willard I. Harriss, The RAND Corporation; Robert M. Solow, Massachusetts Institute of Technology; Allen V. Butterworth, General Motors Corporation; and David B. Hertz, McKinsey and Co., Inc., on earlier versions of the manuscript were invaluable, as have been the criticisms of numerous colleagues at The RAND Corporation. I am also indebted to Marcia Minier, Elizabeth Graef, and Deborah Hopp, The RAND Corporation; and to Milton R. McGuire and Alfred E. Story, Stanford University, for their assistance in the preparation of the numerical examples; and to Jean R. Scully, The RAND Corporation, for her help in preparing several preliminary drafts of the manuscript.

Stanford, California   HARVEY M. WAGNER
June 1962

CONTENTS

INTRODUCTORY SUMMARY

TO A LARGE extent Operations Research literature focuses on problems and techniques of economic optimizing. A central assumption is that the principal elements of an actually functioning system can be mathematically modeled, and subsequently the system's decision mechanism can be optimized. We well may ask whether evolving a technique of solution is sufficient for a complete and successful application of an Operations Research model. Experience has amply shown that more than a method is essential for full implementation. Staying within the context of inventory control, this monograph explores an important facet of the implementation phase, namely, to determine whether a decision mechanism predicated on a proposed Operations Research model is consistent within the milieu of an existent management control system, and to design control mechanisms for adequately supervising a new Operations Research oriented segment of the system. It is easiest to clarify these goals by rephrasing them as inquiries about a multi-item inventory complex:

Will a set of newly proposed stockage policies be able to operate under previously existent managerial controls, such as quarterly budgets? Is a previously operative management objective of a high inventory turnover consistent with the implied policy decisions of the suggested stockage rules? Under the proposed inventory model, how can control limits be placed on the dollar value of inventory on hand? Is the objective of staying within such limits in keeping with the aims of the stockage policies?

If there are reasons to believe that operating personnel might not fully observe the inventory policies, can a control scheme be devised which will adequately audit the degree of compliance, and yet will not require that the individual records be examined in detail? If the environmental conditions assumed within the Operations Research model do in fact change,[1] can a procedure be designed which will detect the alteration, and which will not necessitate an individual review of each inventory component?

[1] By environmental conditions, we mean the set of demand probability distributions.

1

These are the kinds of inquiries studied in the present monograph. Almost needless to say, in order to arrive at substantiated answers we necessarily confine our investigation to a particular class of managerial environments, inventory situations, and control devices. In brief, we deal with an organization in which some actions are to be taken on the basis of the over-all inventory system's behavior; the drains on inventory are probabilistic, and replenishment can be instituted only at fixed intervals of time; the control data aggregate and summarize the fluctuations in the detailed item-by-item behavior; and the system's operating characteristics are to be viewed according to their long-term properties. Although such a configuration obviously is not universal, nevertheless it represents the essence of an important class of situations and well approximates many others.

In summary form, the conclusions of the study are:

1. It is possible to follow a formalized procedure to evaluate the economic worth and efficacy of proposed control schemes. Such a procedure also goes far toward classifying and resolving specific issues raised when control devices are imposed.

2. It is possible in principle to design a control device which will strongly motivate operating personnel to observe recommended inventory rules. The scheme usually cannot be fragmentary, that is, it cannot look at only one aspect of the inventory operations, such as inventory on hand. Rather, the control indices must encompass simultaneously several characteristics of the inventory operations. The scheme typically cannot be of a quota type, such as limiting the total expenditures on replenishment for a specified period of time. Instead, it must directly reward or penalize the operating personnel according to the variance between actual and targeted amounts, a device which we term barometer control.

3. It is possible to design a control device which properly motivates operating personnel to be economical in their withdrawals of inventory. A barometer mechanism based on the total amount withdrawn will be consistent with the objective, whereas a quota limitation on this aggregate amount may not be.

4. It is possible to design statistical indices which aggregate detail fluctuations, and which potentially will indicate whether the environmental conditions have changed.

The difficulty attached with quota controls is worthy of emphasis for at least two reasons. First, most commonly used control devices are of the quota type. Secondly, although it is usually possible to design consistent barometer control schemes, they are only infrequently used in practice, and even when nominally employed, they often turn out to be of the quota type—if the penalties accumulate to too large a sum (the quota) within a period of time, the operations of personnel are reviewed.

Within this monograph we seek to quantify precisely the preceding qualitative statements. There is the obvious danger associated with generalizing from the particular. But because of the mathematical nature of the arguments supporting the forgoing conclusions, we feel that such results will also be valid for other inventory systems. Although the mathematical derivations are necessarily specific to the particular class of inventory situations we employ, the approach in terms of analyzing the behavior and interactions of important inventory and control system operating characteristics is general.

The logical structure of the monograph is predicated on the notion of "first things first." Chapter 1 sets the organizational and conceptual framework for the study. Chapter 2 provides the mathematical tools needed to analyze control devices. ' Chapter 3 investigates control mechanisms directed at the actions of operating personnel, the underlying assumption being that the environment leading to inventory withdrawals is not changing. Chapter 4 introduces the complications associated with a changing environment. As a consequence of this order of presentation, a reader may wish first to study selected topics in the final two chapters before concentrating on the details in the earlier chapters. To assist in this process, each chapter and each major section (such as Section 1.1, 2.3, 3.4, etc.) contain a brief summary of the material to follow.

Chapter 2 deserves a special comment, as it fulfills a threefold purpose. It provides the mathematical methods needed in the analysis of particular control schemes considered in Chapters 3 and 4. It also develops the analytic tools requisite for studying other kinds of control mechanisms. Finally it derives the long-run operating characteristics of the important class of inventory schemes which assumes periodic review. Therefore, a reader may be interested in the chapter's results in order to verify the analysis in the subsequent chapters, to devise and evaluate control mechanisms of his own making, and to study, for example, the various optimizing methods or the behavior of particular stockage rules. Because of the detail contained in this chapter, we suggest that a first reading be a skimming of the subsection summaries, so that the reader gains a perspective of the chapter's contents.

With regard to Operations Research methodology and, in particular, to the development of an implementation theory, one fundamental conclusion seems to be warranted from this study: it is a serious and non-trivial problem to incorporate a decision model within a control system so that the composite operations are consistent. We firmly believe that increased attention will be devoted to the formulation of a theory of implementation, and we hope the present monograph will serve as one step forward in this developing area.

Chapter 1

MANAGEMENT CONTROL
BY STATISTICAL INDICES

1.1 INTRODUCTION

THE PURPOSE OF this monograph is to examine, through mathematical and economic analysis, the manner in which statistical aggregates or index numbers may be employed to improve inventory management. Significant progress has been achieved during the past decade in developing and applying scientific approaches in inventory management [AHM, AKS B, DKW, FD, H, HMMS, M, Mo, Wh]. With only a few exceptions, (Sections 2.5.3 and 3.2.4) we are not concerned here with any specific methods for deriving recommended stockage rules, and, in keeping with our intended purpose, we forgo an extensive discussion of the current progress in computing optimal policies when demands for inventoried items are viewed as being random.[1] We assume the reader is acquainted with the basic notions in this area, and we treat the rules, however computed, as part of the input to our analysis. This approach gives us wide latitude in our study, for, as cited above, there are a multitude of mathematical methods, all of which lead to the same class of decision rules; since only these rules are of importance to us, it is not essential to know the specific method by which they were obtained. What does concern us is a collection of statistical inference problems which are intimately associated with managerial control and which arise when scientific inventory policies are operative. Aside from Chapter 1, which is expository and establishes the framework for the subsequent analysis, this monograph is devoted almost exclusively to a detailed exploration of the mathematics and statistics underlying the inference problems.

We begin by establishing the general organizational setting in which the inference problems occur, Section 1.1.1, and postpone giving a detailed

---

[1] Throughout our study we adopt the hypothesis that demands for inventoried items are described stochastically.

hypothetical illustration to the end of the chapter, Section 1.3. We next define *control* as we shall employ the term in this study, Section 1.1.2. Finally, we outline the development of the remainder of the monograph, and briefly summarize the principal findings, Section 1.1.3.

1.1.1   Organizational Setting

We focus our attention on large and complex organizations in which inventory management and operational responsibilities are partially divided and decentralized.   Upon top management falls the task of guiding the organization so that its inventory operations meet the accompanying requirements in an economic fashion.   In such complexes, it is reasonable that top management concentrates mainly on such indices as aggregate holding costs, depletion penalties, purchase expenditures, etc. To say so is really tautological, of course; if top management had the same interest in detail as the operating echelon has, then, from an inventory control point of view, there would be little distinction between the two echelons.[2] Another factor reinforcing top management's proclivity for index number evaluation is that top management may, in turn, be controlled by, say, supreme management through means of aggregate financial restrictions.   In a business enterprise, for example, a vice-president responsible for company-wide inventory stockage may be given a total budgetary restriction on expenditures by the Board of Directors.   Consequently, top management may find it essential to devise control schemes which, in their turn, reflect analogous restrictions on other echelons.

The assignment of attending to such detailed inventory operations as deciding when and how much of each item to reorder falls upon lower management.   Although top management by its very function is not able to undertake detailed supervision, it is typically able to offer unequivocal policy recommendations with which lower management is expected to comply.

In some actual inventory systems, it may not be easy to identify a particular individual who is solely assigned top management responsibility. It is certainly possible that an inventory manager might have access to both detail and summary data.   Nevertheless, a top management *function* is likely to exist, that is, at least one individual probably takes action on the basis of aggregated information.   Rather than employ the perhaps more universally applicable phrases "top management function" and "lower management

[2] In terms of modern statistical decision theory [BG, CM, Sch, Sa], we are claiming that employing an aggregate ought to imply that top management's "utility function" has the probability distribution of the index number as its argument, rather than the underlying joint distribution of the individual components.

function," we have elected the convenience of presenting the analysis as if individuals in the inventory system can be classified as either higher or lower management. But having adopted this verbal convention, we call the reader's attention to the point that the usefulness of the following analysis transcends what might seem to be an overly idealized organizational structure.

For a variety of reasons to be discussed in Section 1.1.2 and illustrated in Section 1.3.2, top management commonly desires control devices in order to ascertain the degree to which changes in inventory are being economically met and the extent to which lower management is acting in consonance with the recommended policies. We emphasize at the outset that the employment of such controls is not meant to imply a supersedure of item-by-item quantity controls; the need for the latter is usually conceded. Therefore, a primary objective of this monograph is to find whether statistical aggregates can be beneficially employed by top management to supplement existing single-item control by lower management.

In particular, we examine the aspects of

1. Establishing a method whereby control schemes may be economically evaluated.

2. Deriving the probabilistic behavior of the important characteristics of an inventory system.

3. Exploring whether commonly used aggregate control devices, such as expenditure budgets and limitations on inventory on hand, are consistent with recommended inventory policies.

4. Determining whether aggregate control schemes can be devised which are consistent with item-by-item stockage rules.

Clearly a complete evaluation of any specific kind of control mechanism depends on factors peculiar to the actual situation; but this monograph provides the mathematical and statistical tools to be embodied in a complete evaluation, and it also demonstrates the important qualitative behavior of significant control schemes, all of which are capable of being quantified by means of the tools provided.

For large-scale inventory systems, in addition to the complexities due to the attendant institutional structure, there are the complications arising because of the multitude of different items stocked. If an inventory system were comprised of a single item, there would be little, if anything, to be gained by transforming physical quantity data, such as stock on hand, quantity backordered, amount purchased, number of orders, etc., into index data such as inventory holding charges, depletion penalties, purchase costs, ordering costs, etc. But if the system encompasses stocks of more than one item, a conversion from quantitative to, say, financial data allows top management to aggregate item-by-item detail into summary indices.[3]

This aggregation potentiality commonly leads top management to rely on statistical indices which presumably mirror the effectiveness of the current detailed operations with some degree of accuracy. The actual determination of the items aggregated in a single index may involve such criteria as

1. A common demand pattern.
2. Identical stockage costs, such as holding charges, stockout penalties, purchasing and ordering costs.
3. Utilization characteristics, such as stationery, tires, hardware.
4. Personnel allocation.
5. Geographical location.

Indices of primary interest include

1. Value of inventory on hand.
2. Value of inventory on order.
3. Value of inventory on hand and on order.
4. Number of orders placed.
5. Number of orders outstanding.
6. Number or value of current purchases.
7. Number or value of shortages.
8. Number or value of backorders.
9. Number of outages.

Indices of this sort, in addition to giving information about the important system stockage costs, are intimately connected with the operation of the stockage policies. Since the drains on the inventory of a single item are conceived as occurring in a probabilistic fashion, in general, the level of such inventory, the number of lost customers or backorders, or other characteristics of the item's stockage, are then also envisaged in terms of random variables. *A fortiori* index numbers based on the operations of a multitude of items or control policies founded on such index numbers must be described stochastically, and we usually can expect perturbations of the probability distributions of demand or of the stockage policies to have an effect on an index's pattern of fluctuations. In this monograph we explore just how well devices based on these types of indices do fulfill the requirements of top management to maintain control.

[3] It is often convenient to refer to these aggregates as financial indices, even though they do not always involve actual cash-flow expenditures.

1.1.2 Definition of Management Control

Throughout we shall be primarily concerned with two aspects of control:

1. Given a set of management standards—for example, as to the utilization, procurement, and stocking of inventory—does the mechanism being examined guarantee or at least encourage the fulfillment of these standards? Figuratively, we may say this is *management by rule.*

2. Given a set of management standards, as before, does the mechanism ensure or at least make likely the detection of deviation from these standards? We may call this *management by exception.*

In Chapter 3 these standards are defined in terms of lower management's observance of recommended stockage policies. In such a context, management by rule is fostered insofar as the control schemes employed motivate lower management to follow the stated objectives; management by exception arises when the control devices signal top management that there is statistical evidence pointing to violations of the specified rules. One possible cause of failure to observe standards is that lower management is subject to strong pressures and commitments which are at variance with those imposed by top management; another reason is that, because of the decentralized structure of the organization, lower management may not be sufficiently well informed about top management's true objectives, a condition which might be alleviated by the imposition of a control scheme designed to indicate these objectives properly. In Chapter 4, standards are characterized in terms of the utilization and depletion of inventory— changes which are caused both by requirements generated by activities within the organization and by requests from outside customers. Lack of fulfillment of these standards may be due, in some real situations, to personnel in the organization who draw on stocks in a partially unauthorized fashion, and, in other real situations, to factors leading to a change in customer demands, which are beyond the immediate control of the establishment. Succinctly, management by rule, when appropriate, is the encouragement of personnel to be economical in the utilization of inventory; management by exception is the detection of utilization and depletion occurring at rates not anticipated by top management.

As we mentioned above, we do not dwell on the derivation of recommended stockage policies. Our analysis might be viewed as beginning after top management has arrived at its stockage objectives. The justification for this approach is that, whatever the factors influencing the selection of an inventory policy for an item, the resultant rule implies a certain pattern of fluctuations in any operating characteristic of the inventory system; for control purposes, it is this implied pattern which is of principal interest.

1.1.3   Summary Outline of Study

The remainder of Chapter 1 is devoted to describing the elements required to undertake a complete evaluation of control schemes, and to constructing an example that illustrates how control problems arise and how the evaluation process can be applied. In general terms, we give the steps to be followed in an economic study of control procedures and the associated entities to be identified. The objective here is not to provide a computing technique for arriving at an optimal control scheme (although such a method can be made explicit from our formulation), but to highlight the features which are essential in an economic evaluation. In the hypothetical example, several important control problems are sketched, and a simple device for solving each one is explained. Then the previously suggested framework of analysis is employed to suggest how each device might be evaluated. An important outcome of the analysis in Chapter 1 is a listing of those aspects which are suitable for mathematical investigation. The framework of the chapter consequently provides both a motivation for the effort in the subsequent chapters and a classification with which the implications of these later results are more readily perceived.

Given our primary aim of investigating the usefulness of statistical aggregates for inventory management, we may approach the subject in either of two ways; the first is a study of the properties of the aggregates per se, without regard to the details of composition; the second is a study of the properties of the individual components, followed by an examination of the effects of aggregation. We have chosen the latter approach. As a consequence, preliminary to our investigation of aggregate control, we derive the specific operating characteristics associated with the inventory policies; this task is accomplished in Chapter 2. The inventory model employed involves (s, S) policies [AHM, AKS, DKW, Scar] for items having probabilistic demand. The (s, S) inventory rule is to review periodically the amount of inventory on hand and on order, and to place an order whenever this amount falls below s, so that, after the order, the amount equals S; often s is called the reorder point and S the reorder or impress level. The important factors describing a particular inventory model include the demand distribution; the replenishment sequence, including the possibility of delivery lags; and the rule determining whether unfilled demand is backlogged. The mathematical analysis herein deals primarily with stationary probabilities of the system's operating characteristics, such as inventory on hand, on order, and backlogged; amount and number of purchases; amount of shortages; net demand; number of and interval between orders. Included in the derivation of the stationary probabilities is an analysis of the probability distribution of sums of these characteristics, measured during consecutive time periods. The development in Chapter 2 is both theoretical and empirical, in that the mathematics underlying the random processes are first explored and numerical examples are then provided to illustrate the mathematics.

Although our own purpose for deriving the results of Chapter 2 is to provide the inputs to the analysis in the following chapters, the subject area is important in its own right, especially for management scientists engaged in determining recommended stockage rules. Such persons will find the contents useful as a manual and guide to the probability characteristics of (s, S) policies; many of the results are essential for a derivation of optimal inventory rules in cases where management's objective is stated in terms of stationary evaluations.

Our analysis of the effectiveness of specific control schemes starts in Chapter 3. There we view an inventory system comprised of a large multitude of items. We assume the probability demand for each item to be known to top management which, accordingly, specifies a set of recommended (s, S) policies. The problem of control stems from ensuring that lower management is in fact observing the recommended policies. A control scheme which properly encourages lower management to adhere to the suggested rules is termed "consistent." Most management devices include as elements barometer and quota controls. Barometer control rewards or penalizes lower management according to its performance, measured by an aggregate index, as compared to a management-determined target figure. Quota control penalizes lower management whenever the aggregate index figure exceeds a management-determined critical limit. In Chapter 3 we show how barometer schemes can be constructed to yield consistent control, but how, for the most part, quota schemes produce inconsistent controls. This analysis is illustrated both by mathematical and by numerical examples. At the end of the chapter, we draw policy conclusions from these results and review the implications in terms of the general model formulated in Chapter 1.

We do not assume in Chapter 4 that the demand probability distribution for each item is known to top management. As in Chapter 3, we devote considerable attention to ascertaining whether specific control devices are consistent. The first control problem we consider deals with the case of demand being generated by personnel or operations under the responsibility of lower management; such drains on inventory may not be entirely authorized, and top management desires to institute a control which reduces unauthorized demand to a minimum. We find that an index based on the value of purchases leads to consistent control if used in a barometer scheme, or if used in a quota scheme, provided the lower echelon cannot store inventory from one period to the next; if it can, a quota system yields an inconsistent control.

The second control problem arises when the stockage policies being followed are known to top management (they may be incorporated into a computerized inventory system), but top management needs to ascertain whether the composite of actual demand distributions agrees with a set of hypothesized ones. Such a problem is meaningful if, for example, top management desires to undertake a thorough review of the currently operating (s, S) policies only when previously made assumptions concerning the demand distributions are seriously in error. What is needed in this example, provided an aggregate index technique is to be adopted, is a statistic which does not confound various shifts in the demand distributions. In Chapter 4 we examine several such statistics, and the non-confounding property forces us to reject the use of so-called sufficient statistics.

Finally, we consider the control situation present when top management has no certain knowledge of either the (s, S) policies actually being employed or of the demand distributions. The results are analogous to those in Chapter 3: we find that in many real situations it is possible to devise a consistent barometer control which will encourage lower management to adopt economical stockage policies, but that it seems extremely difficult to devise a consistent quota control based on the kind of statistical indices used by top management. We also demonstrate how to construct an aggregate index for which it is not necessary to know the actually operating (s, S) policies, an index that can be employed to test hypotheses concerning the set of demand distributions.

We initiate each major section of the monograph with a nontechnical summary of the content, thereby enabling the reader who initially wishes to skim the mathematical details to do so with sufficient ease.

1.2   FOUNDATIONS FOR ANALYSIS OF AGGREGATE CONTROL SCHEMES

We now seek a formulation which embodies the essential elements to be considered in an evaluation of control schemes. Section 1.2.1 gives a general description of six steps to be followed in such an evaluation. These are the establishment of the operations which potentially warrant control, the ascertainment of action possibilities, the assignment of organizational responsibilities, the evaluation of economic worths emanating from system operations, the determination of a specific control system's operating characteristics, and a synthesis of the previous information. Subsequently, in Section 1.2.2 these ideas are expressed in precise mathematical form, which bears close resemblance to a statistical decision theory model, and are illustrated by several simple examples. Of particular note is the necessity to revise the usual statistical decision theory model to account for game theory elements. In this discussion we also exhibit the various forms the criterion function may assume for evaluating the worth of a control scheme.

1.2.1 A Framework for Evaluation of Control Systems

In examining a particular control system, six interrelated stages of analysis are essential. First, it is necessary to decide what operations *potentially* warrant control. This entails establishing operating standards that define the meaning of "in control," and ascertaining whether there is significant freedom of decision so that an "out of control" state is a real possibility. The standards for "normal" or "satisfactory" operations must not be so broadly defined as to encompass all eventualities (unless we desire to vitiate completely any potential for control).

Second, the action possibilities available to constrain such decisions must be ascertained, with a view toward encouraging certain decisions and discouraging or prohibiting others. Even if an "out of control" state frequently occurs, the notion of control is meaningless unless it can be either prevented or corrected by appropriate action.

A third important consideration is deciding to whom the various responsibilities associated with control are to be delegated. Since our intention is to offer only an economic and mathematical analysis of inventory control systems, we shall limit our discussion of this question, which is primarily oriented toward political and organizational issues. But, almost needless to say, the controversies stemming from this consideration may very well be crucial in determining the ultimate adoption of a control system.

The fourth stage is an economic evaluation of the worth of ensuring that the standards are met, of detecting when they are not, and of making mistakes in the process of controlling.[4] Although such evaluation is perhaps the most difficult task in the analysis, it is fundamental to the establishment of a beneficial control system. To some extent the task is aided by the very analysis which leads to the development of economic inventory stockage policies. In certain cases a precise evaluation of worth may not be necessary, since the criterion for selecting a control system may be insensitive to fairly large changes in the worth values assumed.

---

[4] The interdependence of the stages of analysis is clear here, for the worth of ensuring minimal standards is usually low as compared to that of ensuring comprehensive standards, whereas the costs of control in the latter case are usually high.

Clearly, these economic evaluations may differ among various viewers of the system. In a business corporation, for example, it is conceivable that the stockholders at large, the board of directors, operating management, and personnel in the field operations may have differing evaluations, each leading to a different conclusion concerning the merit of instituting a certain control.[5]

In our discussion so far, the stages of investigation have not depended on the specific control system being analyzed. In the fifth stage it is necessary to examine the operating characteristics of the system. These include the related aspects of the very feasibility[6] of the plan, of the rules to be followed for taking managerial actions depending on data emanating from the system, of the cost of maintaining the control system, and of the important concomitant benefits not directly attributable to control *per se*. The latter may contribute largely to the desirability of the system, but by definition are obtainable even if the control aspects are ineffective.[7]

The sixth stage is the synthesis of the previous information to yield an economic evaluation of the entire control system. Even if the evaluation provides a favorable indication, it is usually advantageous to compare the suggested system with other possible alternatives.

1.2.2   A Mathematical Description of the Elements of a Control System

We now formulate for subsequent reference a mathematical model which we believe is sufficiently general to embody the important aspects of a management control device. By studying the interconnections among the somewhat abstract entities comprising a control scheme, we seek a better understanding of the issues which may arise in an analysis of specific proposals. We stress that the model below, even though it may be too cumbersome for obtaining explicit numerical solutions to control problems, provides a framework from which useful approximate methods may evolve.

---

[5] It is beyond the scope of our present discussion to comment further upon the normative issues involved. In all likelihood, the decision of whether or not to institute control will probably be based on the evaluations of those personnel who are entrusted with the responsibility for making such a decision. In contrast, the development of operating procedures for the system, if instituted, will probably be based on the evaluations of those personnel who are entrusted with the responsibility of actually imposing control. Since the two sets of evaluations need not be the same, the possibility for mutual disappointment may be very real.

[6] For example, availability of personnel and other resources necessary for the scheme's operations, establishment of responsibilities within the plan in the framework of the organization, and internal consistency of the control device.

[7] These benefits may be referred to as external economies.

We utilize to a large extent the conceptual framework of "statistical decision theory" [CM, L, Sa, Sch] to define the elements of a control system. There are other possible models which compete with our formulation, two notable ones being "non-cooperative" and "cooperative" games [LR]. We believe, however, that in controlling phenomena which are described in terms of large statistical aggregates (for example, the total number of raw-materials purchases made during a month in a sizeable manufacturing plant), little is gained by viewing the process as a "game" among dozens of players and management. But our particular view of the operations, that is, as a type of statistical process, requires certain modifications of the familiar statistical models in order to account for some of the "gaming" effects which are too important to be ignored.

Throughout this section we structure the dynamic, i.e., multi-period, control problem in a fashion suggested by the theory of recursive functions [Be]; for the current control period, we separate its entire economic consequences into present effects and future consequences. Since the analysis is to provide, not specific optimal procedures [BG, W], but a framework within which we may orient the results of the subsequent chapters, this characterization will suffice to explain the issues involved.

We say there exists a potential for control over some operation if the operation may be defined as being in one of several situations, say, N_1, $N_2, \cdots, N_i, \cdots, i > 1$; and without the imposition of control, it is not a certainty that the operation is in a particular situation. (If being in a particular situation were a random phenomenon, we would be assuming that there is no situation whose probability of occurrence is unity.) One aspect of the latter assumption is that, to some extent, it is a subjective matter to define the collection $\{N_i\}$; as we remarked in Section 1.2.1, if the defining "standards" are too broad, then the operation with near certainty will be in one particular situation, even without the imposition of control. A related aspect is that having defined the $\{N_i\}$ there must be a real possibility for the operation to shift from one N_i to another; otherwise there would be no need for control. We elaborate on this definitional aspect in Section 3.4 and Section 4.3.

A subtle facet to the specifying of the set $\{N_i\}$, which is to be a mutually exclusive and completely exhaustive categorization of the possible modes of operation, is that it may be necessary to envisage each N_i as a vector with two or more dimensions. For an illustrative example, consider a mail-order merchandising company investigating the possibility of instituting a system to effect control over average stockage levels. Suppose, to keep our discussion simple, that there are two possible average levels of inventory. $500,000 and $400,000, the latter being the company's preferred amount, A dimension of importance other than average inventory level may be the average time lag between the day an order is received from a customer and the day the material is shipped. Suppose, again for simplicity's sake, that there are two possible average lag times, 3 and 5 days, the former being preferred. How should $\{N_i\}$ be defined? If there is any possibility that a particular control system, even though aimed at maintaining the $400,000 standard, might have a distinguishable secondary effect on delivery lags, the situations should be {($400,000; 3 days), ($400,000; 5 days), ($500,000; 3 days), ($500,000; 5 days)}. It is impossible in a general discussion such as this to offer a set of infallible rules for determining the number of dimensions that ought to be included in the definition of $\{N_i\}$.[8] The point to be made here is that a false or incomplete evaluation of a control system may result if certain important dimensions to the control environment are unwittingly confounded in the enumeration of the $\{N_i\}$.

We next must define the set of actions, the elements of which are mutually exclusive and completely exhaustive, $a_1, a_2, \cdots, a_j, \cdots, j > 1$, available to the agency responsible for control. Just as the N_i may be multidimensional, each element of $\{a_j\}$ may also represent a complex of decisions, and similarly there is the problem of deciding on the number of relevant dimensions.

To continue our example of the mail-order merchandising company, the principal focus of the control system may be to decide whether or not the purchasing agent should be required to obtain specific management approval for each purchase order issued to outside vendors. If tight control is instituted, the delivery time-lag may increase as a result of the time-lag imposed in the purchase of replenishments. In addition to considering the imposition of the control device, the company may also be contemplating the installation of a streamlined data processing system, which, *ceteris paribus*, would decrease delivery time-lag. It may be that decisions on both questions ought to be made simultaneously, that is, that the $\{a_j\}$ should be {(ordinary control on purchasing agent; present data processing system), (ordinary control on purchasing agent; new data processing system), (tight control on purchasing agent; present data processing system), (tight control on purchasing agent; new data processing system)}. We illustrate the details of this definitional aspect in Section 3.4 and Section 4.3.

Presumably the actions $\{a_j\}$ potentially have some capability of causing the operations to change from one N_i situation to another or to be maintained.[9] We denote by $R(N_i, a_j)$ the function describing the real effect of

---

[8] Discussion of a parallel subject in statistics, viz., the definition of a "sample space," may be found in [Fe].

[9] It is here only that we introduce some influence of the current control period's decisions on operations in the subsequent period. We note that this is one instance of where our statistically oriented approach must be modified by a "gaming" aspect.

taking action a_j when the operation is in situation N_i; for example, R could be a *bona fide* probability distribution over the situations (depending on the parameters N_i and a_j). We are only interested in situations where $R(N_i, a_j)$ does not equal N_i for all a_j and for each N_i.[10] If this assumption is ill-founded, then the idea of control is meaningless; of course, the device may be of value as an information system yielding data leading to actions in other realms of activity. We stress here that we are viewing the conceptualization of these actions $\{a_j\}$ independently of any particular control system; i.e., we postulate that these actions are available under any control system. As we shall discuss momentarily, the role of the control system is to guide the decision agency toward taking beneficial actions.

It is necessary to make an economic evaluation of the occurrence (N_i, a_j) which we denote as $w(N_i, a_j)$. The function w embodies the benefits and disadvantages concomitant with taking a_j if the operation is in situation N_i. We encompass within w both the economic effects for the present period and the expected economic effects for the remaining future. Since we have the function R, these future evaluations are well defined upon applying the method of recursive functions [Be, BG, W]. Of course the task of the actual calculation to yield this future component is severe, but it is nevertheless inconsequential to our present purpose, which is merely to construct a meaningful framework for analysis. We focus attention on situations where for some N_i there exist j' and j'' such that $w(N_i, a_{j'}) \neq w(N_i, a_{j''})$. If the latter were not true, there would be little economic reason for considering a control device even though control might be a meaningful notion. Given N_i, there is at least one action a_j which maximizes $w(N_i, a_j)$. What makes the control problem a difficult one is that an a_j which is economically optimal for N_i, may be very poor for $N_{i''}$, and the true mode of operation N_{i*} is unknown. Even if for some N_i, $R(N_i, a_j) = N_i$ for all a_j, it does not follow that one action is as good as another. For example, one action may erroneously call for management review of an operation which does not need a review; the action itself may not cause any change in the operation, but the review may have incurred a cost needlessly.

As we noticed in the previous section, two important pertinent political or organizational issues are the specification of who is to operate the control system, and whose preferences are to be taken into account in determining the economic evaluations. With respect to these considerations,

---

Whereas "Nature," who selects a situation N_i in the "statistical decision theory" model, is assumed to be passive and indifferent to the action taken by the statistician, we cannot assume in our discussion that the state of operation in the following control period is completely independent of the action taken in this control period.

[10] Equivalently, there exists an N_i and a_j such that $R(N_i, a_j)$ does not equal N_i.

our model is "open ended," in that it sheds no light on how to solve such questions but definitely is affected by their resolution.

Consider the following commercial example illustrating the above ideas. A manager of a local distributorship is contemplating the imposition of some monthly control device for encouraging his stock clerks to follow certain inventory stockage policies. For simplicity of exposition, suppose he classifies each clerk's operations as either $N_1 =$ the clerk is following

TABLE 1.2.1
$R(N_{ik}, a_j)$

	a_1	a_2
N_{11}	N_{11}	N_{12}
N_{12}	N_{12}	N_{12}
N_{21}	N_{12}	N_{12}
N_{22}	N_{22}	N_{12}

prescribed policies, or $N_2 =$ he is not. Let us further assume that the manager may take either action $a_1 =$ allow the clerk to continue his operation without any supplementary managerial direction, or action $a_2 =$ audit the clerk's records and reprimand him *if* any violations of the rules have occurred. Suppose $R(N_1, a_1) = N_1$, $R(N_1, a_2) = N_1$, $R(N_2, a_1) = N_2$ and $R(N_2, a_2) = N_1$. Although $R(N_1, a_1) = R(N_1, a_2) = N_1$, it is reasonable to believe that $w(N_1, a_1) > w(N_1, a_2)$, because if a_2 is elected, a needless audit has been taken. If the manager knew whether N_1 or N_2 were the true mode of operations, he would pick a_1 or a_2, respectively. His difficulty rests in the fact that he does not have full information as to whether N_1 or N_2 is occurring.

We may further complicate the situation by noting that another important dimension is the clerk's speed of operation. There may be reason to believe that action a_2, even if warranted, will cause the clerk to reduce his rate of speed; and the imposition of a control device may do the same thing. In this case we may define $N_{11} =$ clerk is following policies at normal rate of speed, $N_{12} =$ clerk is following policies at reduced rate of speed, $N_{21} =$ clerk is not following policies, but is operating at normal rate of speed, and $N_{22} =$ clerk is not following policies and is not operating at normal rate of speed. The actions a_1 and a_2 are as before. The reaction function $R(N_{ik}, a_j)$ may be that in Table 1.2.1.

As evidence that the new dimension may make a difference in the proper choice of action, Table 1.2.2 presents a hypothetical set of values for $w(N_{ik}, a_j)$, which reasonably indicates the preference order of various possibilities. Assume it is likely that the clerk is following the prescribed policies with probability 2/3, and that this value is independent of the likelihood of normal or reduced speed of operation. We postulate that the correct action to take is that which offers the largest expected value of w [BG, CM, LR, Sa, Sch].

In particular, if the supply manager believes the clerk is operating at normal speed, then situations N_{11} and N_{21} are possible, occurring with the

TABLE 1.2.2
$$w(N_{ik}, a_j)$$

	a_1	a_2
N_{11}	9	7
N_{12}	8	7
N_{21}	4	7
N_{22}	3	7

assumed probabilities 1/3 and 2/3, respectively. We calculate the corresponding expected value for w:

Average w for action a_1 assuming normal speed
$= (2/3)(9) + (1/3)(4) = 22/3$.
Average w for action a_2 assuming normal speed
$= (2/3)(7) + (1/3)(7) = 21/3$.

Action a_1 is the preferred decision.

If instead the supply manager believes the clerk is operating at reduced speed, then situations N_{12} and N_{22} are possible, occurring with the same assumed probabilities 1/3 and 2/3, respectively. We calculate the corresponding expected value for w:

Average w for action a_1 assuming reduced speed
$= (2/3)(8) + (1/3)(3) = 19/3$
Average w for action a_2 assuming reduced speed
$= (2/3)(7) + (1/3)(7) = 21/3$.

Now action a_2 is the preferred decision. This example thus demonstrates the essentiality of including within the definition of a situation all the dimensions relevant to the selection of an action.

Finally, we shall demonstrate the importance of specifying the set of a_j so that it adequately reflects the entire scope of possible actions.

Suppose it is possible to add new personnel, and that doing so would increase the speed of operation should it be below the normal rate. Then we may define a_{11} = allow a continuation of present operations, maintain present work force; a_{12} = allow a continuation of present operations, increase present work force; a_{21} = audit current operations, maintain present work force; a_{22} = audit current operations, increase present work force. In Table 1.2.3 we exhibit a reasonable set of assumptions about R, and in Table 1.2.4 a set of numerical evaluations for w.

TABLE 1.2.3
$R(N_{ik}, a_{jh})$

	a_{11}	a_{12}	a_{21}	a_{22}
N_{11}	N_{11}	N_{11}	N_{12}	N_{11}
N_{12}	N_{12}	N_{11}	N_{12}	N_{11}
N_{21}	N_{21}	N_{21}	N_{12}	N_{11}
N_{22}	N_{22}	N_{21}	N_{12}	N_{11}

TABLE 1.2.4
$w(N_{ik}, a_{jh})$

	a_{11}	a_{12}	a_{21}	a_{22}
N_{11}	9	8	7	8
N_{12}	8	8	7	8
N_{21}	4	5	7	8
N_{22}	3	5	7	8

It is clear from Table 1.2.4 that action a_{22} dominates actions a_{12} and a_{21}; it does not dominate a_{11} because, if N_{11} is the true situation, adding new personnel would merely increase the cost of current operations without improving them. Maintaining the assumption that the probability is $2/3$ that a clerk is following prescribed policies, we now find that if the supply manager believes the clerk is operating at normal speed, he should take action a_{22}.[11] Thus the addition of another area of decision may change the action that ought to be taken with respect to the operation of primary interest.[12]

[11] Average w for action a_{11} assuming normal speed = $(2/3)(9) + (1/3)(4) = 22/3$. Average w for action a_{22} assuming normal speed = $(2/3)(8) + (1/3)(8) = 24/3$.

[12] At first glance, the result of the example seems surprising, since even under the assumption of normal speed the optimal action is to add new personnel. The reason for this result is that there is a $1/3$ chance of an audit being necessary, and, if it is, it will cause a reduction of speed in the next period unless new personnel are added.

There are several distinct approaches [BG, Le], each with its own merits, leading to the selection of an action, regardless of whether statistical data are available and a control scheme has been instituted. We now illustrate a few such approaches. With reference to the first example, in which there are two situations and two actions, suppose no control device were instituted in the present period. The manager of the local distributorship then has the option of taking the action a^* such that:

$$\text{maximum}_{j=1,2} \left[\text{minimum}_{i=1,2} w(N_i, a_j) \right] = \text{minimum}_{i=1,2} w(N_i, a^*);$$

or assuming that the average or expected value of w is a relevant criterion, he may select action a_1 with probability p^*, and action a_2 with probability $(1 - p^*)$, where p^* is chosen such that:[13]

$$\text{maximum}_{0 \leq p \leq 1} \left[\text{minimum}_{i=1,2} pw(N_i, a_1) + (1 - p)w(N_i, a_2) \right]$$
$$= \text{minimum}_{i=1,2} p^*w(N_i, a_1) + (1 - p^*)w(N_i, a_2).$$

If, without imposing a control device, the manager has *a priori* beliefs about the likelihood of a situation being in force—say, the probability of N_i being q and of N_2 being $(1 - q)$—then (continuing our assumption as to the relevancy of expected values) he should pick the action a^* such that:[14]

$$\text{maximum}_{j=1,2} \left[qw(N_1, a_j) + (1 - q)w(N_2, a_j) \right]$$
$$= qw(N_1, a^*) + (1 - q)w(N_2, a^*).$$

In each of the aforementioned cases, the imposition of the control device proves valuable if it is able to provide criteria for actions which are likely to increase the resulting value over that possible without the device.

Let $\{c\}$ denote the class of possible control schemes. We let $W(N_i, a_j, c)$ denote the composite evaluation when situation N_i occurs, and action a_j is taken under the imposition of a particular control device c. Utilizing the terminology of inventory control systems, $W(N_i, a_j, c)$ will include (1) the value stemming from the utilization of information for purposes other than control *per se*, e.g., in annual budget accounting; (2) those costs attributable to the control system that vary with the mode of operation, e.g., the number of documents processed if inventory reorders are of too small a magnitude;[15] (3) the costs assignable to the disrupting of the control system operations by taking action a_j; and (4) joint costs, such as those due

---

[13] This approach is usually called *minimax* [BG].

[14] This approach is usually called *Bayesian* [Le].

[15] This cost is analogous to that in certain industrial experimentation where an item is subjected to a test of strength. Well-produced items meet the test and may be used subsequently; poorly produced items are destroyed, thus adding to the cost of experimentation.

to taking corrective action within the control system in the event that a below-standard operation is ascertained. As was true of $w(N_i, a_j)$, the value of $W(N_i, a_j, c)$ is the sum of economic factors both in the present period and in the remaining future; thus again a numerical evaluation must use the method of recursive functions [Be, BG, W].

Some of the costs encompassed are out-of-pocket expenses, e.g., clerical work, computer facilities, and communications.[16] There also may be other economic costs[17] due, for example, to the allocation of certain limited resources (possibly personnel) to the control activity rather than to other competing activities.

A control device may be thought of as functioning in the following manner: depending on the true situation N_i, the control induces a probability distribution[18] for taking actions a_j. We may denote these distributions as $p(a_j \mid N_i, c)$. Then the average evaluation $\overline{W}$ of a particular control system, given that N_i obtains, is

$$\overline{W}(N_i, c) = \sum_j W(N_i, a_j, c)p(a_j \mid N_i, c).$$

To outline the approach we would use in ascertaining the value of imposing a control system, suppose there are *a priori* reasons to believe that with this system c in force the probability of N_i obtaining in the current control period is $q_i{}^*(c)$, $\sum_i q_i{}^*(c) = 1$. An interesting phenomenon, often occurring with the imposition of a control device, is that the very adoption of the scheme may cause a shift in the state of operation. This effect is distinct from that embodied in the function R; in the latter, a particular action a_j, which is defined independently of any particular control scheme, may cause a shift in the situation occurring in the following control period. The current phenomenon, which is independent of any action taken, is fostered by the "threat" of scrutiny not previously present.[19] Much of our

---

[16] Without letting our discussion wander very far afield, we mention that ascertaining out-of-pocket expenses may be an intricate problem itself, for in the short run many expenses that might be charged to control operations are often fixed and/or joint with other operations.

[17] Various terminology is used to refer to these quantities, such as "shadow" or "opportunity" costs.

[18] Of course we include the possibility of distributions, conditional on N_i, specifying that a_j is taken with certainty.

[19] We contrast the situation with that in the usual model of "statistical decision theory:" in the latter model, in which the statistician is envisaged as playing a "game against nature," it is not meaningful to contemplate nature's selecting a strategy that depends in part on whether or not the statistician is going to take a set of sample observations. There are, of course, classical examples of statistical models in which such interaction may very well be present; e.g., in statistical quality control applications, the imposition of a sampling plan may have a beneficial effect on the quality of the product, even though, perhaps, the plan itself is incapable of yielding much useful information.

analysis in Chapter 3 is directed toward establishing how the $q_i^*(c)$ do in fact depend on the particular type of control scheme adopted; a device which encourages $q_i^*(c)$ to equal unity for that i representing the system's being in control is termed consistent. The over-all average evaluation of the control system is then

$$\sum_i q_i^*(c)\overline{W}(N_i, c) = V^*(c).$$

The control device is of net value if

$$V^*(c) > \max_{a_j} \sum_i q_i w(N_i, a_j) \equiv V,$$

where the $\{q_i\}$ are the *a priori* probabilities if the control scheme is not instituted. Given q_i and $q_i^*(c)$, the control device c^* to be selected must satisfy[20]

$$\sum_i q_i^*(c^*)\overline{W}(N_i, c^*) = \underset{\{c\}}{\text{maximum}} \sum_i q_i^*(c)\overline{W}(N_i, c) > V,$$

and control c' is better than control c'' if $V^*(c') > V^*(c'')$.

The problem to be faced is that a control device may be beneficial when given one set of q_i, but may be uneconomical when given another set. Despite the difficulty of the problem, it nevertheless represents the crux of the issue of determining the adoption of a control scheme.

1.3   AN ILLUSTRATIVE MODEL

We prepare for the mathematical analysis to follow in Chapters 2, 3, and 4 by outlining an illustrative model of a complex inventory system. The model we have devised is hypothetical, but is complex enough to high-light many details that are crucial to a study of the use of aggregates for management control of inventory.

We first give the organizational structure of the example, including the manner in which inventory is stocked and replenished, Section 1.3.1. Then we exhibit three specific control problems and how they arise in the organization, Section 1.3.2. In brief, these relate to the budgeting of funds to finance inventory replenishment, the encouragement of lower management to adopt recommended stockage policies, and the controls imposed to induce personnel to draw upon inventory in an economical fashion. Finally, in Section 1.3.3 we discuss the six steps of analysis outlined in Section 1.2.1 as they pertain to these specific control questions.

---

[20] In this monograph we are ignoring such mathematical details as the existence of a device which attains a finite maximum for V^*. The qualifications necessary for a rigorous treatment would mainly affect the details of the discussion and not its tenor.

1.3.1 Organizational System

Suppose our organization resembles a city-wide department store chain with a structure like that in Fig. 1.3.1. We picture the main office, which purchases items from factories for the entire chain, serves as a warehouse for some items, and also performs a number of retail functions on its own premises. The retail stores have several departments which either sell merchandise or perform the store's accounting, receiving and shipping, delivery, truck maintenance, etc. The main office has top management responsibility, as defined in Section 1.1.1, for the operations of the retail stores, and the store managers have analogous responsibility for the operations of the subsidiary departments. At the stores, the supplies of most items of inventory are kept in the departments; supplies of the remaining items—those used by several departments—are located centrally within a store. As mentioned above, there may be additional stocks at the main

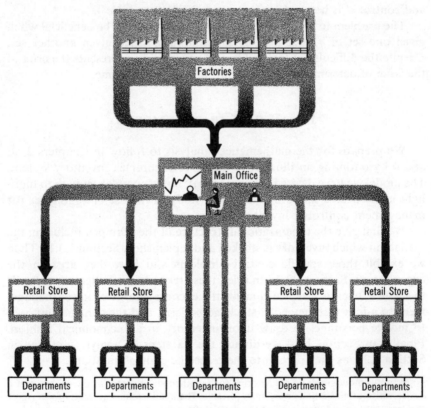

Fig. 1.3.1

office. Departments replenish their inventories by submitting requisitions to their store management. For convenience, we postulate that all requisitions are placed at the end of a specified time period—a day, or a week, or a month, etc. In Chapters 2, 3, and 4 we term this length an inventory review period.

For store j and item k, store management has designated s_{kj} as the inventory reorder point, and S_{kj} as the stockage reorder level. Letting $x_{kj}(t)$ be the amount of stock on hand and on order at the end of period t, inventory of item k is to be requisitioned if $x_{kj}(t) \leq s_{kj}$, and the corresponding order quantity is $r_{kj}(t) = S_{kj} - x_{kj}(t)$. Stock on hand and on order is diminished through the occurrence of demand $\xi_{kj}(t)$ generated either by customers or internal needs; whenever more than one department in store j uses item k, we lump all the drains together into $\xi_{kj}(t)$. In Chapters 2, 3, and 4 the demands $\xi_{kj}(t)$ are characterized in terms of a stochastic process. In real situations, it is necessary to specify additional details about the system's operations, such as whether all demands $\xi_{kj}(t)$ are eventually filled and whether delivery delays accompany replenishment requisitions; these factors are given careful attention in Chapter 2 and need not be introduced for the purposes of our present discussion.

Associated with each item is a purchase price $C_{\text{pur}(k)}$ charged by the supplying factories. If all requisitions in period t are filled, the organization contracts a total expenditure of

$$R_p(t) = \sum_j \sum_k C_{\text{pur}(k)} r_{kj}(t).$$

If all demands are eventually filled, the total organizational replacement accruing from the goods demanded is

$$R_s(t) = \sum_j \sum_k C_{\text{pur}(k)} \xi_{kj}(t).$$

1.3.2 Control Devices

In our illustration, we distinguish three requirements for aggregate controls. The first is that of the main office management who must budget and plan for inventory purchases. This echelon needs information based on the value of $C_{\text{pur}(k)} r_{kj}(t)$, summed over various subsets of k and j; such information may be a forecast of this sum for the following period. The second and third are those of each retail store management. This echelon (1) desires to ensure that the departments are following stated stockage objectives (i.e., are observing the rules implied by the values of s_{kj} and S_{kj}), and to detect violations, and (2) attempts to encourage those departments actually consuming inventory to do so economically.

A multitude of statistical indices may be employed to meet the above requirements; we discuss a number of these in Chapters 3 and 4. Here, since we shall limit ourselves to presenting only three illustrative examples, we strongly caution the reader that the discussion to follow is intended merely for illustration and carries no implication as to the relative merit of the devices for the situations outlined; such an evaluation is reserved for the remaining chapters.

Management of the main office may classify the situations $\{N_i\}$ in terms of the expected value [Cra, Fe] of a sum of $C_{\text{pur}(k)} r_{kj}(t^*)$ for the period t^* of interest, the sum being taken over a subset S of the possible values of k and j. The actions available are, say, to maintain a previously established budget for the replenishment purchases of items included in S, or to revise such a budget. We let the statistic used be

$$\bar{R}_p = \frac{\sum_T \sum_S C_{\text{pur}(k)} r_{kj}(t)}{T},$$

where the $r_{kj}(t)$ are the orders occurring in the previous T periods. Here, as in the paragraphs to follow, T represents the control period of Section 1.2.2. If $\bar{R}_p$ exceeds a preset limit L_p, then management of the main office revises its previous budget; that is, if the statistic $\bar{R}_p$ is sufficiently large as compared to a specified number, the value of which is set with reference to a probability and economic analysis suggested in Section 1.2.2, the main-office management is encouraged to revise its previous budgetary plans.

For stockage control purposes, the management of retail store j may aggregate various items, perhaps according to the criterion of their being used in a single department; we let K denote one such set of items. Management may then view its objective of having its recommended stockage policies actually observed for the items in set K as tantamount to having the statistic

$$\bar{N}_j = \frac{\sum_T \sum_K C_{\text{pur}(k)} [\xi_{kj}(t) - r_{kj}(t)]}{T},$$

which is computed after T consecutive periods, approximately equal zero; the underlying rationale is that, for each item k, the bracketed term, which we call net demand, ought to approach zero over a large number of consecutive periods, provided the recommended policies are being adopted. The presumption which is investigated in Sections 2.6.1 and 3.3.4, is that if the recommended policies are violated, $\bar{N}_j$ will be significantly different from zero, the usual assumption being that $\bar{N}_j$ will be negative. Thus the control operates by defining the situations $\{N_i\}$ as the possible expected values of $\bar{N}_j$, noting whether after T periods the observed value of $\bar{N}_j$ falls short of a preset limit $L_n(<0)$, and if $\bar{N}_j$ is not sufficiently large, making an audit of the associated department's requisitioning policy.

For inventory-consumption control purposes, the management of retail store j may once again aggregate various items, one such set being K'. After T consecutive periods, management penalizes or rewards the associated department by the amount

$$I_j = \theta \sum_{K'} C_{\text{pur}(k)} \left[\frac{\sum_T \xi_{kj}(t)}{T} - \bar{\xi}_{kj} \right], \qquad \theta > 0,$$

where the values of $\bar{\xi}_{kj}$ are preset constants. Here the motivation is that the constants are set so that the expected value of I, is zero, provided the department is economically utilizing inventory. Thus control is imposed by motivating the department to minimize its consumption of the items in K', and management's actions consist of penalizing or rewarding by employing I_j as a measure of the department's effectiveness.

1.3.3 The Evaluation Process

We are now ready to present a selected set of issues arising when control devices of the sort suggested in Section 1.3.2 are proposed. We organize these issues according to the evaluation framework of Section 1.2.1.

Steps one and two of the evaluation of proposed control schemes entail distinguishing the possible situations the inventory system may be in and the action possibilities available to management. For the problem of the main office, the question arises whether, despite the observed value of the suggested statistic, it is in fact possible for conditions to change at the retail stores, thereby necessitating a revision in the budget. Even if such changed conditions do occur, we must ascertain whether it is actually feasible to alter the previous budget. For the stockage problem of the retail store, we must establish whether there is any possibility for department personnel to alter the (s_{kj}, S_{kj}) directives; in some real situations, these policies may be automated by means of electronic data processing equipment. For the consumption problem of the retail store, we must learn whether personnel have any discretion in the utilization of inventory; to illustrate, we might investigate whether there is significant option in the retail clerks' consumption of order books. These aspects in the establishment of potentially possible situations and actions are relatively easy to manipulate. More difficult issues arise when management finds it necessary to include notions such as customer service in the definition of the situations. Such a necessity may occur, for example, if the retail store is able to make speedier deliveries to its customers by allowing some waste in the consumption of repair parts in the maintenance of delivery trucks.

The third step, an investigation of organizational issues, may uncover problems involved with ascertaining the responsibility for out-of-control situations and with implementing corrective procedures. Further, the resolution of these issues may have an important influence on that dimension of $\{N_i\}$ associated with quality of service.

At step four, the subsidiary function $R(N_i, a_j)$, Section 1.2.2, is specified, and the worths $w(N_i, a_j)$ are evaluated. One realm of issues involves the criteria to be utilized for selecting items encompassed under a single control scheme. The main office, perhaps, need not be closely concerned with the budgeting arrangements for items representing a relatively low total expenditure. The same may be true for retail store management with respect to the observance of stockage policies and consumption practices for certain low total-cost items. Another realm of issues involves the benefits and costs associated with taking (1) a corrective action when it is needed; (2) no corrective action when it is needed; (3) a corrective action when it is not needed; and (4) no corrective action when it is not needed. The extent to which value will accrue to management from control depends in part on the sensitivity of the $w(N_i, a_j)$ function to a_j. Once again the importance of carefully defining $\{N_i\}$ has its impact, for a fragmentary view of the elements describing $\{N_i\}$ leads to an incomplete evaluation of $w(N_i, a_j)$.

In the fifth and sixth steps the characteristics of each potential control scheme are investigated, and the alternative schemes are compared. We cite three aspects of the issues arising here. One concerns questions of operating detail. For example, certain items may enter and others leave the inventory system during a control period; purchase prices may vary; existing stocks may be reallocated among departments and stores; errors and delays in the accounting system may occur. The manner in which these events are to be resolved in each control scheme must be settled.

A second aspect is the evaluation of $W(N_i, a_j, c)$, Section 1.2.2. A control scheme may provide useful management information in addition to that utilized in the control device. For example, insofar as the budgetary process for inventory affects other operations of the firm, the main office may derive extra benefits from the information stemming from the imposed control. Economic utilization of inventory in various retail store departments may lead to second-order efficiencies in the allocation of existing stocks among these departments. At this stage of evaluation, the direct costs associated with personnel, paperwork, and communications needed to operate the particular control scheme must be ascertained.

A third aspect is related to the operating characteristics of potential control schemes. Management must know the value of $p(a_j \mid N_i, c)$, i.e., the probability of taking action a_j when given the situation N_i and the control scheme c (Section 1.2.2), and also the *a priori* probabilities $q_i^*(c)$ of the situation N_i occurring if control scheme c is adopted. Furthermore, management needs some guidance in exploring various control devices conceivably suitable to its needs. These topics may be approached through analytic techniques, as we demonstrate in the remaining chapters. Upon resolving the issues outlined in this section, which are of a nonmathematical nature, and then applying the probability analysis of the subsequent chapters, management can perform a final evaluation and select a control system by means of the process suggested at the end of Section 1.2.2.

STATIONARY OPERATING
CHARACTERISTICS
OF (s, S) MODELS

U NDERLYING AN ANALYTIC study of control devices and a computing procedure for optimal stockage policies is the determination of various operating characteristics of an inventory system; this chapter provides the probability distributions of interest. As stated in Chapter 1, the approach of our analysis is to examine the system's behavior through studying the influence of each of the individual items stocked; the subsequent aggregation process is undertaken in Chapters 3 and 4. We concentrate primarily on stationary, that is, steady-state, distributions, the justification for which is given in Section 2.1.5.

Because of the detail contained in this chapter, we suggest that a first reading be a skimming of the subsection summaries. If the reader's primary interest is in the analysis of control schemes, it is possible, after this skimming, to proceed directly to Chapters 3 and 4, coming back to the present chapter only as the references dictate. If the reader wishes to concentrate on the steady-state properties of (s, S) inventory policies, this chapter should be read in its entirety.

We begin in Section 2.1 with a description of the elements comprising an (s, S) inventory model; these include a specification of the demand probability distribution, of the replenishment sequence, which possibly includes a time-lag λ in delivery, and of whether or not excess demand is backlogged. We then derive the probability distribution for the amount of inventory on hand and on order, and several other related inventory statistics. The results for the case of backlogging excess demand appear in Section 2.2, and for the case of not backlogging excess demand, Section 2.3 where we concentrate mainly on a model in which the minimal order quantity D exceeds the reorder point s, implying that no more than one order is ever outstanding. In Section 2.4 we illustrate the foregoing analysis with both analytic and numerical examples.

Building upon the previous results, we study in Section 2.5 the probability distributions and associated expectations of certain fundamental statistics describing the system's operation, including inventory on hand, shortages, and order quantities; distributions of other related characteristics, including the number of periods between orders, frequency of ordering, and excess of demand over order quantity, are exhibited in Section 2.6. Both Sections 2.5 and 2.6 treat the backlog and no-backlog cases. Section 2.7 presents a method for obtaining the probability distributions of the previously considered statistics summed over several consecutive or sampled time periods. Finally, in Section 2.8 the various assumptions that lead to stationary probabilities are removed to allow, for example, the introduction of arbitrary *a priori* probabilities of the initial states, changing demand distributions, and a probabilistic specification of the system parameters.

2.1 INTRODUCTION

In this section we give a precise specification of the (s, S) inventory model. In Sections 2.1.1 and 2.1.2, we present the structure describing the operation of the stockage policy. The basic variables with which we characterize the state of the inventory system are defined in Section 2.1.3. Sections 2.1.4 and 2.1.5 are directed at establishing the mathematical framework in which the analysis is to proceed; in particular, we argue for the relevance of stationary distributions in our study. Finally, in Section 2.1.6 we review the elements of discrete Markov chain analysis, which we employ in subsequent sections, and describe the notation to be utilized.

2.1.1   The (s, S) Model

We consider the stockage of a single item, which is replenished at discrete intervals of time. We limit ourselves to policies of the (s, S) form [AHM, AKS, DKW], that is, if upon review it is discovered that stock on hand plus that on order has fallen to the level $x \leq s$, then the amount $S - x$ is ordered. In real situations the review period might be daily, weekly, monthly, etc. Demands for the item occur within each review period and diminish the amount of inventory on hand. For the purpose of analysis we make two important idealizations concerning the system's operations over time: demands from one period to the next are statistically independent [Fe, Ch. 5] and are prescribed by means of a probability distribution; and an order, when placed, is delivered after a fixed number of time periods.

Substantial investigation has been devoted to establishing the circumstances under which the adoption of an (s, S) policy is economically advantageous [AHM, AKS, DKW, Scar]. Such optimality considerations will not concern us in this chapter, but we shall concentrate on the operating characteristics of the system which are crucial to an eventual economic evaluation.

2.1.2 Timing Considerations

We further make the idealization that the sequence of demand, delivery, and opportunity for replenishment ordering is a repeating pattern over time; each recurrence of the three events comprises a time period. Although we can permute these three events in six different ways, we have freedom to choose the starting point of a period, which in effect means we only have to examine two distinct types of cycles, Sequences α and β.

	Period t		**Sequence** α		Period $t+1$	
DEMAND	DELIVERY	ORDER	DEMAND	DELIVERY	ORDER

	Period t		**Sequence** β		Period $t+1$	
DELIVERY	DEMAND	ORDER	DELIVERY	DEMAND	ORDER

We say there is a λ period delivery lag if an order placed in period t is delivered in period $t + \lambda$, where $\lambda \geq 1$. The case of "immediate" delivery (that is, when no demands occur between the placing and receiving of an order) is $\lambda = 1$ under Sequence β. Notice that between the time an order is placed and is received, demands occur in λ intervals under Sequence α and in $\lambda - 1$ intervals under Sequence β.

2.1.3 Inventory on Hand and Backlogged

In both Sequences α and β, economic analysis may reveal that inventory on hand ought to be assessed either before or after demand occurs. Consequently, we shall be interested in the following variables:

Y_t = inventory on hand after period t demand, Sequence α;

V_t = inventory on hand after period t delivery, Sequence α,

  = inventory on hand at start of period $t + 1$, Sequence α;

Z_t = inventory on hand after period t delivery, Sequence β; and

W_t = inventory on hand after period t demand, Sequence β,

  = inventory on hand at start of period $t + 1$, Sequence β.

Clearly $Y_t \leq V_t$ and $W_t \leq Z_t$.

We shall also need to define:

X_t = inventory on hand plus on order prior to placing any order in period t; and

U_t = inventory on hand plus on order subsequent to placing any order in period t,

= inventory on hand plus on order at start of period $t + 1$.

Given that an (s, S) policy is being observed, it follows that $s < U_t \leq S$.

If demand exceeds inventory on hand, then in real situations some or all of the excess demand may be lost and the remainder backlogged until an adequate replenishment order arrives. We shall consider only the two extreme situations, namely, all unfilled demand is backlogged, and all excess demand is lost. For the most part, the latter case will be investigated under the further restriction that $S - s \equiv D > s$.

In the backlog case, it is convenient to let U, V, W, X, Y, and Z encompass accumulated backlogs and (except for U) thereby encompass the domain of negative as well as positive numbers.

2.1.4 Mathematical Approach

Two aspects must be recognized in analyzing the inventory system's operational properties. One is the manner in which a problem and its solution is characterized mathematically; the other is the manner by which numerical solutions are computed for specific models. The motivation underlying the mathematical aspect is a desire for producing (i) generality of relationships; (ii) elegance, simplicity, and unity of presentation; and (iii) laxity of assumptions. With a few exceptions, we confine ourselves to discrete probability distributions of demand, and are thereby able to make considerable use of the matrix mathematics of Markov chain theory [Fe, KMST, KS]; the exceptions occur whenever the introduction of a continuous probability density results in a closed-form mathematical expression and in establishing the universality of a proposition.

The motivation underlying the computational aspect is a desire for obtaining (*a*) expediency, (*b*) speed, and (*c*) information concerning comparative accuracy. To illustrate, several of our numerical examples are computed by means of a Monte Carlo technique[1] even though we could employ a direct approach.

Our mathematical study consequently reveals those problems which do yield to ordinary calculations, and, in particular, exhibits the magnitude of

---

[1] In this monograph the terms "Monte Carlo technique" and "statistical sampling experimentation" are used synonymously.

such computations; for numerical purposes, these magnitudes need to be compared with a competing Monte Carlo approach.

2.1.5   Stationary (Steady State) Probability Analysis

The bulk of the analysis to follow is predicated on the system having reached statistical equilibrium [Fe, p. 356], or, as it is sometimes named, a steady state [AKS, Ch. 14]. Consequently, stationary probability distributions play an important role. The issue involved in applying stationary distributions is explained easily by means of an example.

Suppose that the demand distribution for an item of inventory is completely summarized by Table 2.1.1, and that the stockage policy is

TABLE 2.1.1

Number of Units Demanded in a Single Period	Probability
0	$\pi_0 > 0$
1	$\pi_1 > 0$
2	$\pi_2 > 0$
	$\Sigma \pi = 1$

(1, 3) for $\lambda = 1$ and Sequence β.[2] If the policy would operate for a very large number of periods, we would notice that the relative frequency of periods in which ending inventory on hand is 0 is closely approximated by a certain fraction, namely, the stationary probability of 0 inventory on hand [Fe, Ch. 15]; this fraction would be strictly positive, for, on repeated occasions, the ending level is 2, no order is placed, and in the following period inventory falls to the level 0. But if we know in a particular period that ending inventory is 3 units, then we know in the following period inventory on hand cannot fall below the level 1; consequently, the conditional probability of 0 units on hand at the end of the period is zero. To summarize, if precise knowledge is available about ending inventory for a given period, then the use of stationary probabilities for prediction about the ensuing period in general entails an amount of information loss.

We argue for the emphasis on stationary probabilities on the following grounds:

1. In a real and complex inventory system encompassing many items, an aggregation scheme may be imposed that involves classifying a large

---

[2] A numerical illustration is found in the last column of Table 2.4.1 on page 81 for a uniform distribution.

number (N) of items, each having the same stockage policy and demand distribution (the latter being assumed independent of each other). In this case, the stationary probabilities of inventory on hand, say, approximate the proportion of items at the associated levels. If, by utilizing these probabilities, we calculate that the expected single-item cost for one period of operation is (C), we may justifiably infer that the expected aggregate cost is (NC). In other words, an analysis based upon stationary probabilities for one item yields valid information about expected values of aggregates encompassing a large number of "identical" such items.

2. Just as an (s, S) policy is often adopted, rather than a more complicated set of rules, for reasons of convenience, a control scheme providing the same constraint period after period is likely to be imposed—assuming there is no change in the underlying structural assumptions. Therefore, statistical equilibrium analysis provides a quantification of how a control scheme operates over a long span. Management is likely to want an evaluation of a control mechanism in terms of its long-run properties.

3. To obtain determinate results such as the probability distributions of operating statistics for a given time period, we usually need to specify an *a priori* distribution expressing our probability beliefs about the initial state of the system; the stationary probabilities are distinguished in providing an appealingly plausible set.

4. The principle of aggregate control is well served by the utilization stationary probabilities. If, for example, top management were to set the following period's control constraint on the basis of the current period's item-by-item inventory status, then it would be resorting to the examination of detail data. Of course some non-stationary conditions, such as seasonal fluctuations and trend variations, can be treated analogously to stationary situations by widening the meaning of stationary to include higher order stability. We return to this topic in Section 2.8.

5. In more complicated inventory models which do not lend themselves readily to mathematical analysis, a Monte Carlo or sampling method can yield statistical data about the system's operating characteristics. In particular, estimates of stationary probabilities can be derived. By proper extension, some of our analytic techniques below can be made applicable by using the probabilities so derived.

6. Although our primary motivation for deriving the results in this chapter is to provide the means for analyzing particular control schemes and, consequently, for the reasons enumerated above, stationary distributions are important, we nevertheless point out that many of our results concerning the probabilistic behavior of a single item inventory system do extend easily when the stationary assumption is dropped. We elaborate on this point in some detail in Section 2.8.

2.1.6 Notation. Probability Distribution of Demand

In any time period, let $\xi \geq 0$ denote the amount demanded of an item. The associated demand distribution is characterized by the function $\phi(\xi)$ which, with ξ discrete, represents the probability that demand equals ξ. In a few instances we wish to consider ξ a continuous random variable possessing a density function. At such a time, we let $\phi(\xi)$ represent the density function for ξ:

$$\text{Prob}\,(\xi \leq \bar{\xi}) = \int_0^{\bar{\xi}} \phi(\xi)\,d\xi.$$

We assume that the reader is acquainted with the elementary notions for specifying a discrete Markov chain [Fe, KMST, KS]. To review these briefly, we characterize such a stochastic process by means of a transition matrix: if the process is known to be in some state i in period t, the entry at the ith row and jth column of the transition matrix gives the conditional probability of the process being in state j in period $t + 1$. An important property of the matrix is that the entry in the ith row and jth column of the λth power of the matrix yields the conditional probability that the process is in state j in period $t + \lambda$, given that the process is in state i in period t. Furthermore, if we have a row vector representing the unconditional probabilities of the process being in each state i, this row vector times the λth power of the transition matrix produces the unconditional probabilities in period $t + \lambda$. We comment that, with the exception of Section 2.8, we consider stationary processes, the transition matrices of which are identical for all periods.

We assume the existence of stationary probabilities for all the models in this chapter. The mathematical conditions which must be met [Fe, Ch. 15; KS, Ch. 15] to ensure the legitimacy of this assumption are not restrictive in our applications, although a modicum of attention to details is sometimes in order to maintain a rigorous analysis. Two examples of such details in terms of the parameters specifying the inventory process are (1) the values of s and S are finite; and (2) a potentially infinite transition matrix, such as $[T_X]$ in Section 2.2.1 below, is truncated to finite dimension if there exists a value $\bar{\xi}$ such that $\text{Prob}\,(\xi \geq \bar{\xi}) = 0$. The essence of the mathematical restrictions is that when the transition matrix in irreducible form is finite, then for any two states, there exists a number of periods such that the probability of passing from one of these states to the other is strictly positive, that is, the matrix is regular; and when the irreducible matrix is infinite, then the mean recurrence time for at least one state is finite. Whenever the transition matrix is regular [KS, Ch. 4], as it almost

always is in our models,[3] then the stationary probabilities may be characterized as follows: consider the λth power of the transition matrix and let λ
tend to infinity; the rows of the product matrix will tend to a unique
vector, namely, the stationary distribution.

Throughout we need to exhibit transition matrices containing values of
$\phi(\xi)$. For example, we may want to refer to:

$$(1) \quad \begin{bmatrix} \phi(0) & \phi(1) & \sum_{\xi=2}^{\infty} \phi(\xi) \\ & \phi(0) & \sum_{\xi=1}^{\infty} \phi(\xi) \\ & & \sum_{\xi=0}^{\infty} \phi(\xi) \end{bmatrix}.$$

(As a rule, zero-valued entries are represented by blanks in the matrix.) It
is notationally convenient to abbreviate (1) to the form:

$$(2) \quad \begin{bmatrix} 0 & 1 & \underline{2} \\ & 0 & \underline{1} \\ & & \underline{0} \end{bmatrix},$$

where we have inserted ξ for $\phi(\xi)$ and $\underline{x}$ for $\sum_{\xi=x}^{\infty} \phi(\xi)$.

Note that $\underline{0}$ has the numerical value one. In general we define the square
matrix:

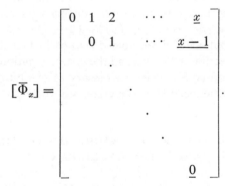

$$[\bar{\Phi}_x] = \begin{bmatrix} 0 & 1 & 2 & \cdots & \underline{x} \\ & 0 & 1 & \cdots & \underline{x-1} \\ & & \ddots & & \\ & & & & \\ & & & & \underline{0} \end{bmatrix}$$

On occasions it is necessary to emphasize the dependence of $\phi(\xi)$ on
certain of its parameters; at such points we write $\phi(\xi \mid \text{parameters})$.

---

[3] We qualify our statement to allow for the possibility that there exists a value $\bar{\xi}$ such
that $\phi(\bar{\xi}) = 1$. In this event, the drains on inventory are really deterministic, and the
corresponding transition matrix may be periodic [Fe, Ch. 15]. Nevertheless, the stationary analysis to follow is applicable, provided the "probabilities" so derived are regarded
in terms of a "law of large numbers" [KS, Ch. 5].

We repeatedly make use of the k fold convolution of $\phi(\xi)$, which represents the probability distribution of the sum of k independent values of ξ [Fe, p. 250]. We adopt the notation ϕ^k and remark if we define the square matrix (of possibly infinite dimension):

$$
(3) \qquad [\Phi] =
\begin{bmatrix}
0 & 1 & 2 & 3 & \cdots \\
  & 0 & 1 & 2 & \cdots \\
  &   & 0 & 1 & \cdots \\
  &   &   & \cdot & \\
  &   &   &   & \cdot \\
  &   &   &   &   & \cdot
\end{bmatrix},
$$

then $[\Phi]^k$ contains explicitly the k fold convolution. That is, each row of $[\Phi]^k$, starting at the main diagonal, gives the probability $\phi^k(j) = \text{Prob}\,(\xi_1 + \xi_2 + \cdots + \xi_k = j)$, for $j = 0, 1, 2, \cdots$. (In the matrix $[\Phi]^k$, j represents the number of elements to the right of a diagonal entry.) Occasionally we refer to $[\Phi]^0$ which denotes an identity matrix I with unit entries along the main diagonal and zero entries elsewhere.

We represent the stationary probabilities of the operating characteristics, for example, V, by the symbol $p_{V,\lambda}(v)$ in the backlog case and by the symbol $q_{V,\lambda}(v)$ in the no-backlog case. These expressions may be read as the stationary probability that the variable V has the value v, and acknowledge the condition that this probability depends on λ. The expression $[p_{V,\lambda}]$ represents the row vector $[p_{V,\lambda}(S)\,p_{V,\lambda}(S-1)\cdots]$. If the stationary probability distribution of a variable does not in fact depend on λ, we suppress the λ subscript. Of course, all the system's stationary probabilities depend on $\phi(\xi)$ and (s, S); if it is necessary to exhibit explicitly the dependence on such associated parameters, we write $p_{V,\lambda}(v \mid \text{parameters})$.

2.2 STATIONARY PROBABILITIES OF THE BASIC VARIABLES: BACKLOG CASE

The critical assumption in this section is that demand occurring in excess of the current amount of inventory on hand is backlogged, that is, backordered, until supply becomes available. The main task is to derive the stationary distribution $p_X(x)$ of the variable X, the amount of inventory on hand (or backlogged) and on order at the end of a period before any new order is placed. Section 2.2.1 exhibits the set of equations determining this stationary distribution; Section 2.2.2 demonstrates the relationship existing between X and the variable U, which is comprised of the same quantities as X but is measured at the start of a period. In both cases, the characterization is in terms of a discrete Markov chain. We show in Section 2.2.3 that s, the reorder point, acts as a location parameter for the distributions of X and U.

Sections 2.2.4 and 2.2.5 give algorithms for calculating the stationary probability distribution $p_X(x)$. The technique in Algorithm 2.2.4 is to compute recursively each term of the stationary distribution, where each calculation involves only the previously derived terms. The technique implied in Proposition 2.2.5(2) is also a recursive computation, where here the recursion parameter is D, the minimal order quantity ($= S - s$). In other words, the entire distribution for $D = 1$ is found first (a trivial problem), and then the distributions for $D = 2, 3, 4, \cdots$, are computed, each calculation being dependent mainly on knowing the associated term of the distribution for the previous value of D. The proposition in Section 2.2.5 also yields qualitative results on the dependence of the probability distribution of X on the value D. The equations determining the distribution of X are closely related to a renewal equation, and this resemblance is explored in Section 2.2.6, yielding an approximation technique for the values of $p_X(x)$.

Making direct use of the probability distribution of X, we show in Sections 2.2.7 and 2.2.8 how to derive the distributions for inventory on hand (or backlogged), exclusive of the amount on order, and measured either at the beginning or at the end of a period. Because of the backlog assumption, these distributions can be computed by merely convolving the distribution for X with a proper convolution of the distribution for demand, the latter being dependent on the delivery lag λ.

2.2.1 *Transition Law for X_t, Arbitrary λ, Sequences α and β*

Recalling the definition of X_t as the amount of inventory on hand and on order prior to placing any order in period t (and subsequent to any demand and delivery in period t), we may write for both Sequences α and β and any value of λ:

(1a) $$X_{t+1} = X_t - \xi \quad \text{if} \quad s + 1 \leq X_t \leq S;$$

(1b) $$X_{t+1} = S - \xi \quad \text{if} \quad X_t \leq s.$$

Note that X_{t+1} may be negative, indicating the presence of backlogged demand, that is, backorders.

Postulating ξ is discrete, we know that for $s + 1 \leq X_{t+1} \leq S$, the probability that X_{t+1} takes on the value x equals the probability that stock is replenished to the level S by an order in period t, times the probability

TABLE 2.2.1

$[T_X]$

States $(X =)$

$[T_X]$	S	$S-1$	$S-2$	$\cdots$	$s+1$	s	$s-1$	$\cdots$	0	-1	-2
S	0	1	2	$\cdots$	$D-1$	D	$D+1$	$\cdots$	S	$S+1$	$S+2$
$S-1$		0	1	$\cdots$	$D-2$	$D-1$	D	$\cdots$	$S-1$	S	$S+1$
$S-2$			0	$\cdots$	$D-3$	$D-2$	$D-1$	$\cdots$	$S-2$	$S-1$	S
$\vdots$				$\vdots$					$\vdots$		
$s+1$					0	1	2	$\cdots$	$s+1$	$s+2$	$s+3$
s	0	1	2	$\cdots$	$D-1$	D	$D+1$	$\cdots$	S	$S+1$	$S+2$
$s-1$	0	1	2	$\cdots$	$D-1$	D	$D+1$	$\cdots$	S	$S+1$	$S+2$
$\vdots$					$\vdots$				$\vdots$		
0	0	1	2	$\cdots$	$D-1$	D	$D+1$	$\cdots$	S	$S+1$	$S+2$
-1	0	1	2	$\cdots$	$D-1$	D	$D+1$	$\cdots$	S	$S+1$	$S+2$
-2	0	1	2	$\cdots$	$D-1$	D	$D+1$	$\cdots$	S	$S+1$	$S+2$

that demand in period $t + 1$ is $S - x$, plus the sum of the products of the probability that stock is at the level j, where $s + 1 \leq x \leq j \leq S$, times the probability that demand in period $t + 1$ is $j - x$, for all relevant j. (Note that $s + 1 \leq j \leq x - 1$ need not be considered, for in this instance no inventory replenishment takes place and, consequently, X_{t+1} is strictly below x.) Similarly, for $X_{t+1} \leq s$, the probability that X_{t+1} takes on the value x equals the probability that stock is replenished to the level S by an order in period t, times the probability that demand in period $t + 1$ is $S - x$, plus the sum of the products of the probability that stock is at the level j, where $s + 1 \leq j \leq S$, times the probability that demand in period $t + 1$ is $j - x$, for all relevant j. Letting $p_{X_{t+1}}(x)$ denote the probability that $X_{t+1} = x$, then:

$$(2a) \quad p_{X_{t+1}}(x) = \phi(S - x) \sum_{j=-\infty}^{s} p_{X_t}(j)$$
$$+ \sum_{j=x}^{S} \phi(j - x)p_{X_t}(j) \qquad s + 1 \leq x \leq S;$$

$$(2b) \quad p_{X_{t+1}}(x) = \phi(S - x) \sum_{j=-\infty}^{s} p_{X_t}(j) + \sum_{j=s+1}^{S} \phi(j - x)p_{X_t}(j) \qquad x \leq s.$$

The stationary probabilities are defined by dropping the time-period subscripts in (2) and thereby yielding an infinite set of linear equations in the stationary probabilities $p_X(x)$:

$$(2a') \quad p_X(x) = \phi(S - x) \sum_{j=-\infty}^{s} p_X(j)$$
$$+ \sum_{j=x}^{S} \phi(j - x)p_X(j) \qquad s + 1 \leq x \leq S;$$

$$(2b') \quad p_X(x) = \phi(S - x) \sum_{j=-\infty}^{s} p_X(j)$$
$$+ \sum_{j=s+1}^{S} \phi(j - x)p_X(j) \qquad x \leq s.$$

We exhibit this system in matrix form by constructing the (infinite) transition matrix $[T_X]$ in Table 2.2.1. Then (2) in its stationary version may be written as

$$(3) \qquad\qquad [p_X][T_X] = [p_X].$$

In Section 2.2.4 we discuss the solution of (3). But we note here that $(2a')$ agrees with the first D terms of the discrete renewal equation, which may be found in [Fe, p. 290]. This equivalence between $(2a')$ and [Fe] is seen by identifying the two sets of symbols in Table 2.2.2, where:

$$\sigma(D) = 1 - \sum_{x=s+1}^{S} p_X(x) =$$

stationary probability of placing an order, given D.

In the case of a continuous density function for demand, the stationary density equations are [AKS, Ch. 14]

$$(4a) \quad p_X(x) = \phi(S - x) \int_{-\infty}^{s} p_X(t) \, dt + \int_{x}^{S} \phi(t - x) p_X(t) \, dt \quad s < x < S;$$

and

$$(4b) \quad p_X(x) = \phi(S - x) \int_{-\infty}^{s} p_X(t) \, dt + \int_{s}^{S} \phi(t - x) p_X(t) \, dt \quad x < s.$$

TABLE 2.2.2

[Fe]	(2a′)
u_n	$p_X(S - n)$
b_n	$\phi(n)\sigma(D)$
a_n	$\phi(n)$

We shall need to refer below to a cumulative function of the $p_X(x)$ and $\phi(\xi)$. We write

$$p_X(\bar{x}) = \sum_{j=x}^{S} p_X(j)$$

$$\phi(\overline{S - x}) = \sum_{\xi=0}^{S-x} \phi(\xi).$$

Then from the stationary version of (2) it follows that:

$$(5a) \quad p_X(\bar{x}) = \phi(\overline{S - x}) \sum_{j=-\infty}^{s} p_X(j)$$

$$+ \sum_{j=x}^{S} \phi(j - x) p_X(j) \quad s + 1 \le x \le S;$$

$$(5b) \quad p_X(\bar{x}) = \phi(\overline{S - x}) \sum_{j=-\infty}^{s} p_X(j) + \phi(\overline{s - x}) \left[1 - \sum_{j=-\infty}^{s} p_X(j) \right]$$

$$+ \sum_{j=s+1}^{S} \phi(j - x) p_X(j) \quad x \le s.$$

In this notation

$$\sigma(D) \equiv 1 - p_X(\overline{s + 1}).$$

When the meaning is clear, we abbreviate the symbol $\sigma(D)$ to σ.

2.2.2 *Stationary Distribution of U_t, Arbitrary λ, Sequences α and β*

The values of U_{t+1} and X_t differ by the amount ordered at the end of period t, a quantity uniquely determined by X_t and the (s, S) policy. Consequently the stationary distributions of U and X are trivially related.

If we define the infinite matrix

(1)
$$[I^*] = \begin{bmatrix} 1 & 0 & 0 \\ 0 & I & 0 \\ 1 & & \\ 1 & 0 & 0 \\ 1 & & \\ \cdot & & \\ \cdot & & \\ \cdot & & \end{bmatrix},$$

where I is an identity matrix of order $D - 1$ and the entries 0 denote blocks of zero's,[4] then

(2) $\quad [p_U] \equiv [p_U(S) \quad p_U(S-1) \cdots p_U(s+1) \quad p_U(s) \quad p_U(s-1) \cdots]$
$\qquad = [p_X][I^*]$.

Note that $p_U(u) = 0$ for $u \leq s$, and $p_U(S) = 1$ if $S - s \equiv D = 1$.

It is convenient to record here that U in its own right may be characterized by a Markov chain. Omitting those values of $p_U(u)$ which are certainly zero, and slightly rearranging the order of the vector of $p_U(u)$, we may write the finite transition matrix as

$$[T_U] = \begin{bmatrix} 0 & 1 & \cdots & D-2 & D-1 \\ & 0 & \cdots & D-3 & D-2 \\ & & \cdot & & \cdot \\ & & & \cdot & \cdot \\ & & \cdot & & \cdot \\ & & & 0 & 1 \\ 1 & 2 & \cdots & D-1 & 0+(D) \end{bmatrix}.$$

The first row (column) is associated with $U = S - 1$, the second row (column) with $U = S - 2, \cdots$, the next to last row (column) with $U = s + 1$, and the final row (column) with $U = S$. The similarity between $[T_U]$ and $[T_X]$ is apparent; mathematically, the relationship may be referred to as a lumping of the X-process to yield the U-process [KS, p. 123].

2.2.3 Dependence of the Stationary Distributions of X and U on s

Proposition 2.2.3. (1) Let s and D be specified, and δ be any real number. Then $p_X(x \mid s, D) = p_X(x + \delta \mid s + \delta, D)$.

---

[4] Also the symbol 1 here denotes the unit integer, *not* $\phi(1)$.

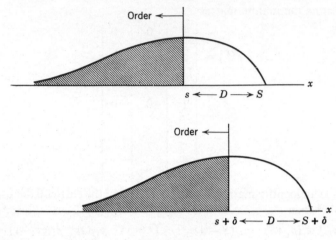

Fig. 2.2.1

(2) Given D, the stationary probability of ordering is identical for all values of s.

(3) $p_U(u \mid s, D) = p_U(u + \delta \mid s + \delta, D)$.

A diagrammatic representation of Proposition 2.2.3 clarifies the implication, Fig. 2.2.1. It is evident that the shapes of the $p_X(x)$ distribution [here exhibited for a continuous density function $\phi(\xi)$], that is, its relative frequencies, are a function of D alone, and given D, the location of the distribution depends on the value of s (or equivalently S).

Proof. We write the stationary equations as

$$[p_X(s + D \mid s, D)p_X(s + D - 1 \mid s, D) \cdots][T_X] = [p_X(s + D \mid s, D) \cdots],$$

and

$$[p_X(s + D + \delta \mid s + \delta, D)p_X(s + D + \delta - 1 \mid s + \delta, D) \cdots][T_X]$$
$$= [p_X(s + D + \delta \mid s + \delta, D) \cdots].$$

Thus both probability distributions $p_X(x \mid s, D)$ and $p_X(x + \delta \mid s + \delta, D)$ must satisfy the same stationary equations and, consequently, are equal [Fe, p. 356].

Given part (1), the definition of the probability of ordering in Section 2.2.1, and the analysis of Section 2.2.2, parts (2) and (3) follow immediately.

2.2.4 Solutions of $p_X(x)$ and $p_X\overline{(x)}$

We construct a recursive algorithm for calculating $p_X(x)$, starting at $x = S$, based on the near triangularity of the left portion of $[T_X]$.

Algorithm 2.2.4. Evaluating the stationary equation $(2a')$ in Section 2.2.1 yields for $x = S$:

$$p_X(S) = \phi(0)\sigma + \phi(0)p_X(S);$$

$$p_X(S) = \frac{\phi(0)\sigma}{1 - \phi(0)} \equiv f(0)\sigma, \qquad \text{where} \qquad f(0) = \frac{\phi(0)}{1 - \phi(0)}.$$

As a consequence of Proposition 2.2.3, $p_X(S)$ does not depend on the particular value for S, and $f(0)$ is calculable from a knowledge of $\phi(\xi)$ only. Continuing in the same fashion, we obtain:

$$p_X(S - 1) = \phi(1)\sigma + \phi(0)p_X(S - 1) + \phi(1)p_X(S);$$

$$p_X(S - 1) = \frac{1}{1 - \phi(0)} [\phi(1)\sigma + \phi(1)f(0)\sigma] \equiv f(1)\sigma.$$

In general, for $S - x \geq s + 1$, that is, $x \leq D - 1$,

$$p_X(S - x) = \frac{1}{1 - \phi(0)} \left[\phi(x) + \sum_{j=0}^{x-1} \phi(x - j)f(j) \right] \sigma \equiv f(x)\sigma.$$

Throughout, $f(j)$ depends only on $\phi(\xi)$, $\xi = 0, 1, \cdots, j$. Since

$$1 - \sigma = \sum_{x=s+1}^{S} p_X(x) = \sigma \left[\sum_{j=0}^{D-1} f(j) \right],$$

we have

$$\sigma = \left[1 + \sum_{j=0}^{D-1} f(j) \right]^{-1}.$$

As a result, we can calculate the explicit values for $p_X(x)$, $s + 1 \leq x \leq S$, once we have found $f(j)$, $0 \leq j \leq D - 1$.

It is now also possible to solve for any value of X in the stationary equation $(2b')$ in Section 2.2.1; for $S - x \leq s$, that is, $x \geq D$:

$$p_X(S - x) = \phi(x)\sigma + \sum_{j=s+1}^{S} \phi(j - S + x)p_X(j)$$

$$= \left[\phi(x) + \sum_{j=0}^{D-1} \phi(x - j)f(j) \right] \sigma \equiv f(x \mid D)\sigma.$$

The preceding is an expression in terms of $\phi(\xi)$ and the previously calculated $f(j)$, $0 \leq j \leq D - 1$. Notice that for any value of $x \leq s$, $p_X(x)$ can be calculated without having to find any other $p_X(x)$ in this domain, and that the value of $f(x \mid D)$ does depend on D. In matrix form we have

$$[p_X(s)\; p_X(s-1)\cdots]$$

$$= [p_X(S)\cdots p_X(s+1)] \begin{bmatrix} D & D+1 & D+2 & \cdots \\ D-1 & D & D+1 & \cdots \\ \cdot & & & \\ \cdot & & & \\ \cdot & & & \\ 1 & 2 & 3 & \cdots \end{bmatrix}$$

$$+ \sigma[D\; D+1\; D+2\cdots].$$

A similar recursive calculation applies to the cumulative probabilities $p_X(\bar{x})$ defined in equation (5) of Section 2.2.1:

$$p_X(\overline{S}) = \frac{\phi(0)\sigma}{1-\phi(0)} \equiv F(0)\sigma,$$

$$p_X(\overline{S-x}) = \frac{1}{1-\phi(0)}\left[\phi(\bar{x}) + \sum_{j=0}^{x-1} \phi(x-j)F(j)\right]\sigma \equiv F(x)\sigma$$

$$0 \le x \le D-1;$$

and

$$p_X(\overline{S-x}) = \phi(\bar{x})\sigma + \phi(\overline{x-D})(1-\sigma) + \sum_{j=s+1}^{S} \phi(j-S+x)p_X(j)$$

$$x \ge D;$$

or equivalently

$$p_X(\overline{S-x}) = \phi(\overline{x-D}) + \left[\phi(\bar{x}) - \phi(\overline{x-D}) + \sum_{j=0}^{D-1} \phi(x-j)F(j)\right]\sigma$$

$$x \ge D,$$

where

$$\sigma = [1 + F(D-1)]^{-1}.$$

It is of theoretical and perhaps practical interest to note that inverse computations are also implied by Algorithm 2.2.4. If we consider a hypothetical distribution $p_X(x)$ and a particular (s, S) policy, we can perform the inverse calculation for $\phi(\xi)$. It is intuitive that an arbitrary selection of $p_X(x)$ need not lead to a bona fide probability distribution $\phi(\xi)$; that is, there are some probability distributions which could never result as the stationary behavior of a chosen (s, S) policy. One such example is $p_X(x) = 1/5$ for $x = S-4, S-3, \cdots, S$, and $D = 3$. [Given a probability distribution $p_X(x)$, it is trivial to find at least one (s, S) policy which yields a legitimate $\phi(\xi)$, namely, $D = 1$ for which $p_X(S-x) = \phi(x)$.]

2.2.5 *Dependence of $p_X(x)$ on D*

Proposition 2.2.5. As usual, we let $D = S - s$. Then

(1) $\quad \dfrac{p_X(x_1 \mid D, S)}{p_X(x_2 \mid D, S)} = \dfrac{p_X(x_1 \mid D + \delta, S)}{p_X(x_2 \mid D + \delta, S)} \quad$ for $\delta > 0$ and

$s + 1 \le x_1 \le S, \quad s + 1 \le x_2 \le S.$

(2) $\quad p_X(x \mid D + 1, S) = f(S - x)\sigma' \hspace{3cm} s + 1 \le x \le S;$

$$p_X(s \mid D + 1, S) = \frac{f(D \mid D)\sigma'}{1 - \phi(0)} + f(D)\sigma';$$

and

$$p_X(x \mid D + 1, S) = \left[f(S - x \mid D) + \frac{f(D \mid D)\phi(s - x)}{1 - \phi(0)} \right]\sigma'$$

$$= f(S - x \mid D + 1)\sigma' \hspace{2cm} x \le s - 1,$$

where

$$\sigma' \equiv \sigma(D + 1) = \frac{\sigma}{1 + \dfrac{f(D \mid D)\sigma}{1 - \phi(0)}} \; (\le \sigma)$$

(3) $\quad p_X(x \mid D + 1, S) = p_X(x \mid D, S)\eta \hspace{2.5cm} s + 1 \le x \le S;$

$$p_X(s \mid D + 1, S) = \frac{p_X(s \mid D, S)}{1 - \phi(0) + p_X(s \mid D, S)};$$

and

$$p_X(x \mid D + 1, S) = p_X(x \mid D, S)\eta + \phi(s - x)p_X(s \mid D + 1, S)$$

$$x \le s - 1,$$

where

$$\eta = \frac{1 - \phi(0)}{1 - \phi(0) + p_X(s \mid D, S)} \le 1.$$

(4) $\hspace{2cm} p_X(\bar{x} \mid D, S) \ge p_X(\bar{x} \mid D + 1, S)$ for all x.

Part (1) of the proposition states that as D increases, holding S fixed, the probabilities $p_X(x)$ for $s + 1 \le x \le S$ retain a proportionality relationship; in other words, the relative shape of the right tail of the stationary distributions remains fixed. In parts (2) and (3) we give recursive methods of computing $p_X(x)$ for successively larger values of D. (Recall that when $D = 1$, $p_X(x) = \phi(S - x)$ for all x.) We would expect that increasing D would decrease the frequency of ordering and, for a fixed S, would displace the distribution toward smaller values of X; parts (2) and (4) make these

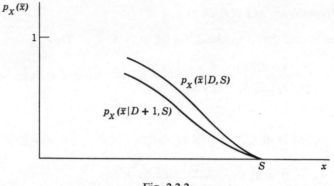

Fig. 2.2.2

effects precise. Figure 2.2.2 illustrates part (4) (in the continuous probability density case).

Proof. (1) The conclusion follows immediately, given the conditions of the proposition and noting that $p_X(x)$ may be solved as a product of $f(S-x)$ and σ as we demonstrated in Section 2.2.4.

(2) As usual, we let

$$\sigma' = \sum_{x=-\infty}^{s-1} p_X(x \mid D+1, S).$$

Then for $s+1 \le x \le S$

$$p_X(x \mid D+1, S) = \phi(S-x)\sigma' + \sum_{j=x}^{S} \phi(j-x)p_X(j \mid D+1, S) = f(S-x)\sigma',$$

which follows from Algorithm 2.2.4. In the same manner,

$$p_X(s \mid D+1, S) = \phi(D)\sigma' + \sum_{j=s}^{S} \phi(j-s)p_X(j \mid D+1, S)$$

$$p_X(s \mid D+1, S) = \frac{1}{1-\phi(0)} [f(D \mid D)]\sigma'.$$

For $x \le s-1$,

$$p_X(x \mid D+1, S) = \phi(S-x)\sigma' + \sum_{j=s}^{S} \phi(j-x)p_X(j \mid D+1, S)$$

$$= \phi(S-x)\sigma' + \phi(s-x)p_X(s \mid D+1, S)$$

$$+ \sum_{j=s+1}^{S} \phi(j-x)p_X(j \mid D+1, S)$$

$$= \left[f(S-x \mid D) + \frac{f(D \mid D)\phi(s-x)}{1-\phi(0)} \right]\sigma'.$$

As we saw in Algorithm 2.2.4,

$$\sigma' = \left[1 + \sum_{j=0}^{D} f(j)\right]^{-1}$$

$$= \left[1 + \sum_{j=0}^{D-1} f(j) + \frac{f(D \mid D)}{1 - \phi(0)}\right]^{-1}$$

$$= \left[\frac{1}{\sigma} + \frac{f(D \mid D)}{1 - \phi(0)}\right]^{-1}$$

$$= \frac{\sigma}{1 + \left[\dfrac{f(D \mid D)\sigma}{1 - \phi(0)}\right]}$$

(3) Let

$$\eta = \frac{1 - \phi(0)}{1 - \phi(0) + f(D \mid D)\sigma}$$

(where the last term in the denominator is $p_X(s \mid D, S)$ from Algorithm 2.2.4).

Then $\sigma' = \eta\sigma$. Substituting this equality into the results from part (2) gives

$$p_X(x \mid D + 1, S) = f(S - x)\sigma\eta = p_X(x \mid D, S)\eta \qquad s + 1 \le x \le S;$$

$$p_X(s \mid D + 1, S) = \frac{f(D \mid D)}{1 - \phi(0)}\left[\frac{1 - \phi(0)}{1 - \phi(0) + f(D \mid D)\sigma}\right]\sigma$$

$$= \frac{p_X(s \mid D, S)}{1 - \phi(0) + p_X(s \mid D, S)};$$

$$p_X(x \mid D + 1, S) = \left[f(S - x \mid D) + \frac{f(D \mid D)\phi(s - x)}{1 - \phi(0)}\right]$$

$$\times \left[\frac{1 - \phi(0)}{1 - \phi(0) + p_X(s \mid D, S)}\right]\sigma$$

$$= p_X(x \mid D, S)\eta + \phi(s - x)p_X(s \mid D + 1, S)$$

$$x \le s - 1.$$

(4) For $s + 1 \le x \le S$ the proposition follows immediately from part (3), $p_X(\bar{x} \mid D + 1, S) = p_X(\bar{x} \mid D, S)\eta$ where $\eta \le 1$.

Under the $(s \equiv S - D, S)$ policy, given $x \le s$, the state $t \le x$ occurs if $s + 1 \le j \le S$ and $\xi \ge j - x$, or if $j \le s$ and $\xi \ge S - x$ (where, with regard to the stationary probability analysis, we have suppressed the time period subscripts on ξ, j, and x).

(1) $\text{Prob}\,(t \leq x) = \sigma\phi(\underline{S - x}) + \sum\limits_{j=s+1}^{S} \phi(\underline{j - x})p_X(j \mid D, S)$

$$= 1 - p_X(\overline{x + 1} \mid D, S),$$

where

$$\phi(\underline{j}) = \sum\limits_{\xi = j}^{\infty} \phi(\xi) = 1 - \phi(\overline{j - 1}).$$

We may write (1) as

$$\rho = \rho_{s+1}p_X(s + 1 \mid D, S) + \rho_{s+2}p_X(s + 2 \mid D, S)$$
$$+ \cdots + \rho_S[p_X(S \mid D, S) + \sigma],$$

where

$$\rho_{s+i} = \phi(\underline{s + i - x}) \qquad i = 1, 2, \cdots, S - s.$$

Since the coefficients of the ρ_{s+i} sum to 1, ρ may be regarded as a probability weighted average of the ρ_{s+i}.

Under the $[s \equiv S - (D + 1), S]$ policy, the state $t \leq x \leq s$ occurs if $s \leq j \leq S$ and $\xi \geq j - x$, or if $j \leq s - 1$ and $\xi \geq S - x$.

(2) $\text{Prob}\,(t \leq x) = \sigma'\phi(\underline{S - x}) + \sum\limits_{j=s}^{S} \phi(\underline{j - x})p_X(j \mid D + 1, S)$

$$= 1 - p_X(\overline{x + 1} \mid D + 1, S).$$

We may write (2) as

$$\rho' = \rho_s p_X(s \mid D + 1, S) + \rho_{s+1}p_X(s + 1 \mid D + 1, S)$$
$$+ \cdots + \rho_S[p_X(S \mid D + 1, S) + \sigma']$$

$$\rho_s = \phi(\underline{s - x}) \geq 0.$$

From part (3)

$$p_X(s + i \mid D + 1, S) = p_X(s + i \mid D, S)\eta \leq p_X(s + i \mid D, S)$$
$$i = 1, 2, \cdots, S - s.$$

Since ρ' is also a probability weighted average and $\rho_s \geq \rho_{s+i}$ for $i = 1, 2, \cdots, S - s$, it follows that $\rho' \geq \rho$, or

$$p_X(\overline{x + 1} \mid D + 1, S) \leq p_X(\overline{x + 1} \mid D, S).$$

2.2.6   *Approximation of $p_X(x)$ for Large Values of D*

If we appeal to the fact noted in Section 2.2.1 relating the $p_X(x)$ for $s + 1 \leq s \leq S$ with the first D terms of the discrete renewal equation, then a proper extension[5] of the renewal theorem [Fe, p. 291] yields that, as D increases, $p_X(s + 1)$ approaches $\sigma/E(\xi)$, where the denominator represents the expected value of ξ [Fe]. Further, Proposition 2.2.5, part (1), coupled with this limiting argument, reveals that the stationary distribution $p_X(x)$ resembles a uniform distribution at the lower end of the domain $s + 1 \leq x \leq S$. For a given distribution $\phi(\xi)$, as D increases, σ decreases, so that $s + 1 \leq x \leq S$ occurs a large proportion of the time.

Supposing $\sigma/E(\xi)$ represents an adequate approximation for all $p_X(x)$, $s + 1 \leq x \leq S$, we sum these probabilities over the stated domain to obtain, as an approximation, the relation[6]

$$1 - \sigma = D\sigma/E(\xi),$$

or

$$(1) \qquad \sigma = \frac{E(\xi)}{E(\xi) + D}.$$

As we shall see in Section 2.4.2, the approximation to $p_X(x)$ and (1) are exact for the geometric distribution $\phi(\xi)$. For an intuitive explanation of (1), we suggest envisaging a deterministic situation in which exactly $E(\xi)$ items are demanded each period under the specified (s, S) policy; then the reciprocal of (1) is the total number of periods per ordering cycle,[7] and (1) is the long-run fraction of periods in which an order is placed.

Utilizing (1) and the result of the renewal theorem, we have the approximation

$$(2) \qquad p_X(x) = \frac{1}{E(\xi) + D} \qquad s + 1 \leq x \leq S.$$

Applying (2) to the stationary probability law for $x \leq s$, we obtain

$$(3) \qquad p_X(x) = \left[\frac{E(\xi)}{E(\xi) + D}\right] \phi(S - x) + \left[\frac{1}{E(\xi) + D}\right] \sum_{j=s+1}^{S} \phi(j - x).$$

We caution that whereas $\sigma/E(\xi)$ may approximate well $p_X(s + 1)$, the relations (1), (2), and (3) need not yield equally good estimates. An improved procedure would be to evaluate for some specified value $x \leq D - 1$, $f(j), j = 0, 1, \cdots, x$, and then use the estimate

$$\sigma = \left[1 + \sum_{j=0}^{x} f(j) + \frac{D - x - 1}{E(\xi)}\right]^{-1}.$$

---

[5] An extension is necessary to account for the effect that each $b_n \equiv \phi(n)\sigma(D)$, Table 2.2.2, depends on the value of D.

[6] Of course the relevant consideration is how well the right-hand side as a whole approximates the left-hand side.

[7] Fractional values are rounded upward.

As we have mentioned earlier, the $f(j)$ in this range depend only on $\phi(\xi)$, $\xi = 0, 1, \cdots, j$. Given the estimate for σ, $p_X(S - j)$ may be estimated by the product of σ and $f(j)$ for $j \leq x$, and by $\sigma/E(\xi)$ for $x + 1 \leq j \leq D - 1$. The appropriate analog to (3) may be employed to calculate the remaining $p_X(x)$.

2.2.7 Significance of $p_X(x)$ for $\lambda = 1$, Sequence β

As we mentioned above, for $\lambda = 1$ under Sequence β, an order placed in period t arrives before the following period's demand, often referred to as the case of immediate delivery. It follows that $X_t \equiv W_t$ and $U_t \equiv Z_{t+1}$. Accordingly for this case our preceding development at once yields the stationary probabilities for the fundamental variables of interest.

2.2.8 Stationary Distributions of V, W, Y, and Z

Because at present all unfilled demand is assumed to be backlogged, we are led to the fundamental observation for Sequence α,

$$U_t - \xi_{t+1} - \cdots - \xi_{t+\lambda} = V_{t+\lambda};$$

that is, if we know the total amount of the item on hand and on order at the end of period t, then the amount on hand at the end of period $t + \lambda$ (after any delivery occurs) is this value diminished by λ demands. As we saw in Section 2.2.2, $[p_U]$ is independent of λ. These remarks and their consequences are summarized by:

Proposition 2.2.8.

(1) $[p_{V,\lambda}] = [p_U][\Phi]^{\lambda}$

(2) $[p_{V,\lambda}] = [p_{V,\lambda-1}][\Phi]$

(3) $[p_{V,\lambda}] = [p_X][\Phi]^{\lambda-1}$

(4) $[p_{V,\lambda}] = [p_{Y,\lambda-1}] = [p_{W,\lambda}] = [p_{Z,\lambda+1}]$

(5) If $D = 1$, $[p_{V,\lambda}] = \phi^{\lambda}$.

The implications of Proposition 2.2.8 are: the stationary distributions of V, W, Y, and Z are essentially formed by convoluting the distributions for X and U with convolutions of $\phi(\xi)$. Because of part (3), the result of Proposition 2.2.3 demonstrating the dependence of $[p_X]$ on s holds equally well for the stationary distributions of V, W, Y, and Z. Similar extensions apply for Proposition 2.2.5, parts (1) and (4).

Proof. (1) and (2).

Part (1) follows from the discussion preceding the proposition; part (2) is an immediate consequence of separating on the right the first power of $[\Phi]$ in part (1).

$$
\begin{aligned}
(3) \qquad [p_{V,\lambda}] &= [p_U][\Phi][\Phi]^{\lambda-1} \\
&= [p_X][I^*][\Phi][\Phi]^{\lambda-1} \\
&= [p_X][T_X][\Phi]^{\lambda-1} \\
&= [p_X][\Phi]^{\lambda-1}
\end{aligned}
$$

The first equation follows from part (1); the second from relation (2) in Section 2.2.2; the third from the definition of $[I^*]$ in Section 2.2.2, and of $[T_X]$ in Table 2.2.1; and the fourth from relation (3) in Section 2.2.1. Note that $[p_{V,1}] = [p_X]$.

(4) Since $Y_{t+1} = V_t - \xi_{t+1}$,

$$
[p_{Y,\lambda-1}] = [p_{V,\lambda-1}][\Phi] = [p_{V,\lambda}].
$$

Since $Z_{t+\lambda+1} = U_t - \xi_{t+1} - \cdots - \xi_{t+\lambda}$,

$$
[p_{Z,\lambda+1}] = [p_U][\Phi]^{\lambda} = [p_{V,\lambda}].
$$

The equality $[p_{V,\lambda}] = [p_{W,\lambda}]$ is a simple consequence of the fact that if all unfilled demand is backlogged, the stationary distribution of inventory on hand at the end of a period does not depend on whether that period's demand occurs before or after that period's delivery. More formally, using the results just obtained and noting $W_t = Z_t - \xi$, we have

$$
[p_{W,\lambda}] = [p_{Z,\lambda}][\Phi] = [p_{V,\lambda-1}][\Phi] = [p_{V,\lambda}].
$$

(5) For $D = 1$, $p_U(S) = 1$, and part (1) yields the first row of $[\Phi]^{\lambda}$, which is ϕ^{λ}.

2.3 STATIONARY PROBABILITIES OF THE BASIC VARIABLES: NO-BACKLOG CASE

We now consider the case where demand in excess of inventory on hand is lost, and we wish to find the stationary probabilities of the same random variables we viewed in Section 2.2. The essential difference between the no-backlog assumption and the previous analysis is that the variable X can no longer be used to define completely a state of the system in a Markov chain characterization; the difficulty is explained in detail in Section 2.3.1. Instead, we must characterize the state in terms of inventory on hand and inventory due in at various future arrival dates (the number of which depend in part on the delivery lag). In the no-backlog case with a delivery lag greater than one period, it is not evident that an (s, S) policy ought to be employed [AKS, Ch. 10]; thus the discussion to follow must be viewed as pertaining to those situations where management has decided to restrict its inventory policies to the (s, S) type.

In the main, our analysis in this section particularizes to the model in which the minimal reorder quantity $D (=S - s)$ exceeds the reorder point s; as a consequence, no more than one order is ever outstanding at any period. Making this assumption, we demonstrate in Section 2.3.2 how the model may be viewed in terms of a finite Markov chain of dimension D. We give the full details of the characterization in Section 2.3.3, and an example in Section 2.3.4. Having derived the corresponding stationary probability distribution, we are able to compute probabilities of various related inventory-on-hand random variables, Section 2.3.5.

Several special models are examined next. In particular, the case in which the delivery lag is a single period is discussed in Section 2.3.6. Section 2.3.7 explores two versions in which an arbitrary constraint is imposed to ensure that the number of orders outstanding never exceeds one.

We show an analogy with the renewal equation in Section 2.3.8 to derive an approximation technique dependent on the value of D. Section 2.3.9 discusses the general dependence of the stationary probabilities on D, s, the delivery lag, and the expected amount of demand. For the sake of completeness, we close by exhibiting in Section 2.3.10 a model in which D is less than s, and the delivery lag is 3.

2.3.1 Complexity in the Transition Laws

The basis for the straightforward procedures and the precise qualitative results of Section 2.2 is unquestionably the simple transition law for X, the amount of inventory on hand and on order at the end of a period prior to placing any order. A knowledge of (s, S), of the previous period's X, and of the current period's demand ξ, sufficed to determine the current period's X. In the no-backlog case, additional information is needed, namely, an indication of the division between the inventory on hand and that on order. Specifically, for Sequence α the law for X_t is

$$X_{t+1} = X_t - \min(\xi, V_t) \qquad s + 1 \leq X_t \leq S$$
$$= S - \min(\xi, V_t) \qquad\qquad X_t \leq s;$$

for Sequence β, Z_{t+1} is substituted for V_t.

If we are interested in the distribution of V, say, then it is possible to characterize the states of the system at the end of a period before any new order is placed by means of a vector quantity, the components of which, for example, may indicate the current level of V and the amounts of inventory due to arrive $\lambda - 1$ periods into the future [AKS, Ch. 10], and it is easy to form the associated finite Markov chain transition matrix. Aside from solving particular numerical problems, which are seriously restricted because of the dimension of the probability vector, this approach apparently has yielded little information to date. With three exceptions, we examine the no-backlog model under the postulate that $D > s$. The impact of the assumption is that whenever an order is outstanding, $X \geq D$, and therefore no new order is placed; in other words, only one order is outstanding at any time. Loosely, we would expect to find such a policy in operation whenever the setup cost (or red tape cost) of placing an order for the item is relatively high, whereas the expected cost of its shortage is relatively low.[8] The instances when we relax the assumption are (*i*) the case $\lambda - 1$, Section 2.3.6; (*ii*) two subclasses of policies for which the (s, S) rule is modified by additional restrictions that near the end of each period only one order may be outstanding, Section 2.3.7; and (*iii*) a discussion with an illustration of the situation where $s \geq D$, Section 2.3.10. We caution the reader that in this section the postulate $D > s$ remains in force unless we make explicit mention to the contrary.

2.3.2 Stationary Distributions of V, U, and X, λ > 1, Sequence α

We find it convenient to characterize the state of the system at the end of the period *before* any order has been placed by means of three quantities: the amount of inventory on hand, the amount previously on order, and the number of periods (or opportunities for demand) until the previous order arrives.

For notation, we use the triple $(v \mid r, \tau)$; as an example, if at the end of period 1 the state is $(5 \mid 15, 2)$, then an order of 15 units of inventory will arrive toward the end of period 3, and the present inventory level of 5 will be applied to the demands in periods 2 and 3. We let $q(v \mid r, \tau)$ denote the stationary probability of the state $(v \mid r, \tau)$; for brevity we have suppressed the λ subscript. Observe that $r = 0, D, D + 1, \cdots, S$, and $\tau = 0, 1, \cdots, \lambda - 1$; we note that $r = 0$ occurs (1) if, and only if, $\tau = 0$; and (2) if $s + 1 \leq v \leq S$. Noting that, at the end of a period, (1) if no order is outstanding, $0 \leq v \leq S$; and (2) if an order is outstanding, $D \leq r \leq S$, $0 \leq v \leq S - r$, and $1 \leq \tau \leq \lambda - 1$, we calculate the total number of possible states as $(S + 1) + 0.5(\lambda - 1)(s + 1)(s + 2)$. We demonstrate in Algorithm 2.3.2 the manner in which the system can be reduced for numerical calculation to a D dimensional transition matrix, but as a first step we examine the system in its full dimension.

---

[8] A precise statement of such conditions on the economic parameters transcends the intended scope of this chapter; see [AHM, AKS, DKW, B].

Since our ultimate interest is to obtain stationary distributions of inventory on hand such as $q_{V,\lambda}(v)$, and perhaps of inventory on hand and on order $q_{X,\lambda}(x)$ and $q_{U,\lambda}(u)$, we record that[9]

$$q_{V,\lambda}(v) = \sum_r \sum_\tau q(v \mid r, \tau)$$

$$q_{X,\lambda}(x \mid \text{Sequence } \alpha) = \sum_{\substack{v \quad r \quad \tau \\ (v+r=x)}} \sum \sum q(v \mid r, \tau)$$

$$q_{U,\lambda}(u \mid \text{Sequence } \alpha) = q_{X,\lambda}(u \mid \text{Sequence } \alpha) \qquad s + 1 \leq u \leq S - 1$$

$$q_{U,\lambda}(S \mid \text{Sequence } \alpha) = q_{X,\lambda}(S \mid \text{Sequence } \alpha) + \sum_{x=0}^{s} q_{X,\lambda}(x \mid \text{Sequence } \alpha).$$

Let

(1a) $[q_V(r, \tau)] \equiv [q(S - r \mid r, \tau) \quad q(S - r - 1 \mid r, \tau) \cdots q(0 \mid r, \tau)];$

(1b) $[q_V(\tau)] \equiv [[q_V(D, \tau)][q_V(D + 1, \tau)] \cdots [q_V(S, \tau)]] \quad 0 < \tau \leq \lambda - 1;$

(1c) $[q_V(0)] \equiv [q_V(0, 0)] \equiv [[q_{V,s}(0)][q_{V,s}(0)]]$
$$= [q(S \mid 0, 0) \cdots q(s + 1 \mid 0, 0) \quad q(s \mid 0, 0) \cdots q(0 \mid 0, 0)].$$

The dimension of (1a) is $S - r + 1$, of (1b) is $.5(s + 1)(s + 2)$, and of (1c) is $S + 1$, the latter split into two parts of dimensions D and $s + 1$.

We may write the stationary equation as

(2) $[[q_V(0)][q_V(\lambda - 1)] \cdots [q_V(1)]] [T_V] = [[q_V(0)] \cdots [q_V(1)]],$

where, leaving aside details for the moment, $[T_V]$ has the block form given in Table 2.3.1.

At this point it is convenient to reduce (2) to smaller dimensions for computational purposes.

Algorithm 2.3.2. Assume, as we shall show, that $[T_{\tau,\tau-1}] = [T^*]$, for $\tau = 2, 3, \cdots, \lambda - 1$. We perform the multiplication on the left of (2) to obtain

(3a) $[q_{V,s}(0)][T_{SS}] + [q_V(1)][T_{1S}] = [q_{V,s}(0)]$

(3b) $[q_{V,s}(0)][T_{Ss}] = [q_{V,s}(0)]$

(3c) $[q_{V,s}(0)][T_{s,\lambda-1}] = [q_V(\lambda - 1)]$

(3d) $[q_V(\lambda - k)][T^*] = [q_V(\lambda - k - 1)]$ $k = 1, 2, \cdots, \lambda - 2.$

If we substitute (3b) into (3c), the result into (3d), and take account of the recursive nature of (3d), then (3d) may be written as

(3e) $[q_V(\lambda - k)] = [q_{V,s}(0)][T_{Ss}][T_{s,\lambda-1}][T^*]^{k-1} \quad k = 1, 2, \cdots, \lambda - 1,$

[9] Subsequent discussion makes it apparent that $(x \mid r, \tau)$ is an equivalent characterization of the states, i.e., since $v + r = x$, there is a one-to-one correspondence between the two definitions of states.

where $[T^*]^0 \equiv [I]$. Finally, evaluating (3e) at $k = \lambda - 1$ and combining it with (3a) yields the stationary equation

(4) $\quad [q_{V,s}(0)][[T_{SS}] + [T_{Ss}][T_{s,\lambda-1}][T^*]^{\lambda-2}[T_{1S}]] = [q_{V,s}(0)].$

It is easily demonstrated that the multiplying matrix in (4) is a Markov transition matrix: every row of the matrices $[T_{s,\lambda-1}]$, $[T^*]$, and $[T_{1S}]$

TABLE 2.3.1

$[T_V]$

$$
\begin{bmatrix}
[T_{SS}] & [T_{Ss}] & & & & \\
& & [T_{s,\lambda-1}] & & & \\
& & & [T_{\lambda-1,\lambda-2}] & & \\
& & & & \cdot & \\
& & & & & \cdot \\
& & & & [T_{2,1}] & \\
[T_{1S}] & & & & &
\end{bmatrix}
\begin{matrix}
\} \ D \\
\} \ s+1 \\
\} \ d \\
\cdot \\
\cdot \\
\} \ d \\
\} \ d
\end{matrix}
$$

$$ \underbrace{}_{D} \ \underbrace{}_{s+1} \ \underbrace{}_{d} \ \underbrace{}_{d} \cdots \underbrace{}_{d} $$

$$ \underbrace{}_{(\lambda-1)} $$

$$ d = 0.5(s + 1)(s + 2) $$

contains a set of probabilities which sum to one, Table 2.3.1, and consequently the product of these matrices in (4) has the same row-sum property. The multiplying matrix in (4) may be written as the product

(5) $\quad [[T_{SS}][T_{Ss}]] \begin{bmatrix} [I] \\ [T_{s,\lambda-1}][T^*]^{\lambda-2}[T_{1S}] \end{bmatrix},$

where again the row sum condition is fulfilled for both matrices in the product, and consequently for the product itself.

Thus our original stationary equation (2) has been reduced to (4), which is of dimension D. Subsequent to solving (4), we employ (3b) and (3e) to compute the remaining probabilities.

A word must be said about the normalizing condition for a stationary solution of (4). Because $[T_{s,\lambda-1}]$ and $[T^*]$ are transition matrices, multiplying each side of (3c) and (3d) on the right by a column vector comprised of ones, we find the resultant λ summations equal to a certain value, namely, the probability of placing an order σ. In other words,

$$ \sigma = \sum_{v=0}^{s} q(v \mid 0, 0). $$

Consequently

(6) $\quad \sum_{v=s+1}^{S} q(v \mid 0, 0) + \lambda\sigma = 1.$

TABLE 2.3.2
$$[[T_{SS}][T_{Ss}]]$$

	$(S\mid0,0)$	$(S-1\mid0,0)$	$\cdots$	$(s+1\mid0,0)$	$(s\mid0,0)$	$\cdots$	$(1\mid0,0)$	$(0\mid0,0)$
$(S\mid0,0)$	0	1	$\cdots$	$S-s-1$	$S-s$	$\cdots$	$S-1$	S
$(S-1\mid0,0)$		0	$\vdots$	$S-s-2$	$S-s-1$	$\vdots$	$S-2$	$S-1$
$\vdots$			$\ddots$	$\vdots$	$\cdot$		$\vdots$	$\vdots$
$(s+2\mid0,0)$				1	2	$\cdots$	$s+1$	$s+2$
$(s+1\mid0,0)$				0	1	$\cdots$	s	$s+1$

TABLE 2.3.3
$$[T_{s,\lambda-1}]$$

	$(s\mid D,\lambda-1)$	$(s-1\mid D,\lambda-1)$	$\cdots$	$(0\mid D,\lambda-1)$	$(s-1\mid D+1,\lambda-1)$	$(s-1\mid D+1,\lambda-1)$	$\cdots$	$(0\mid D+1,\lambda-1)$	$\cdots$	$(0\mid S,\lambda-1)$
$(s\mid0,0)$	0	1	$\cdots$	s	0	$s-1$	$\cdots$			0
$(s-1\mid0,0)$										
$\vdots$									$\cdots$	$\cdots$
$(0\mid0,0)$										

Therefore, the proper normalizing constant for (4) can be obtained by applying to (3b) a non-normalized stationary solution to (4) and adjusting so that the sum satisfies (6).

2.3.3   Components of $[T_V]$

The matrix $[[T_{SS}][T_{Ss}]]$ contains the transition probabilities associated with the communication of states $(S \mid 0, 0), \cdots, (s + 1 \mid 0, 0)$ with $(S \mid 0, 0), \cdots, (0 \mid 0, 0)$, Table 2.3.2; it closely resembles the first D rows of $[T_X]$.

In Table 2.3.3 we have $[T_{s,\lambda-1}]$, which contains the transition probabilities associated with the communication of states $(s \mid 0, 0), \cdots, (0 \mid 0, 0)$, with the states $(v \mid r, \lambda - 1)$ for $D \leq r \leq S$ and $S - r \geq v \geq 0$.

The matrices $[T_{\tau,\tau-1}]$ represent the connection between one period and the following during both of which an order is outstanding. Because an order quantity remains fixed once the order is placed, $(v \mid r, \tau)$ communicates with $(v' \mid r', \tau - 1)$ only if both $r = r'$ and $v' \leq v$. Thus the $[T_{\tau,\tau-1}]$ may be partitioned into blocks $[T_r*]$ along the main diagonal, the off-diagonal blocks containing only zero's.

$$[T_{\tau,\tau-1}] = [T^*]$$

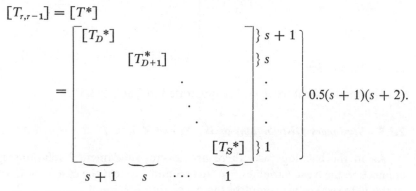

Each $[T_r*]$ is a square matrix of dimension $S - r + 1$. Note that

$$[T^*]^k = \begin{bmatrix} [T_D*]^k & & & \\ & [T_{D+1}^*]^k & & \\ & & \cdot & \\ & & & \cdot \\ & & & & [T_S*]^k \end{bmatrix}.$$

Table 2.3.4 exhibits $[T_r*]$. Observe that each $[T_r*]$ is the transition matrix of an absorbing Markov chain [Fe, Ch. 15] with the absorbing state in the lower right-hand corner.

TABLE 2.3.4
$[T_r{}^*]$

	$(S-r\,\lvert\, r,\tau-1)$	$(S-r-1\,\lvert\, r,\tau-1)$	$\cdots$	$(0\,\lvert\, r,\tau-1)$
$(S-r\,\lvert\, r,\tau)$	0	1	$\cdots$	$S-r$
$(S-r-1\,\lvert\, r,\tau)$		0	$\cdots$	$\overline{S-r-1}$
$\vdots$			$\vdots$	
$(0\,\lvert\, r,\tau)$				$\underline{0}$

$\left.\right\} S-r+1$

Since we are assuming Sequence α, a delivery occurs subsequent to a period's demand. Consequently, for a period in which a delivery occurs, we have $D \le v \le S$, and the state $(v \mid r, 1)$ communicates only with the states $(v' \mid 0, 0)$ for $r \le v' \le r + v$. If we let

$$[T_r{}^{**}] = [[T_r{}^*][0_r]],$$

where $[0_r]$ is a matrix of zero's having $S - r + 1$ rows and $r - s - 1$ columns, then

$$[T_{1S}] = \begin{bmatrix} [T_D{}^{**}] \\ [T_{D+1}^{**}] \\ \cdot \\ \cdot \\ \cdot \\ [T_S{}^{**}] \end{bmatrix}$$

2.3.4   Illustration

The model $(2, 6)$ for $\lambda = 3$ is illustrated in Table 2.3.5.

2.3.5   Stationary Distributions of W, Y, and Z, $\lambda > 1$

As in the backlog case, there are several fundamental relationships connecting the basic variables. In this section we treat the case $\lambda > 1$, and in the next section we complete the discussion for $\lambda = 1$.

Proposition 2.3.5. (1) For $\lambda \ge 1$, $[q_{V,\lambda}] = [q_{Z,\lambda+1}]$.
(2) For $\lambda > 1$, $[q_{Y,\lambda-1}] = [q_{W,\lambda}] = [q_{V,\lambda-1}][\overline{\Phi}_S]$.

Proof. (1) Analogous to the definition of the state $(v \mid r, \tau)$ in Sequence α, we may define the state $(z \mid r, \tau)$ in Sequence β as denoting (z) the units of inventory on hand after any delivery but before current demand, (r) the amount of any outstanding order, and (τ) the number of periods until delivery. As an example, if, after the opportunity for delivery has occurred in period 1, the state is $(5 \mid 15, 2)$, then an order of 15 units of inventory will arrive at the start of period 3, and the present level of 5 will be applied to the demands in periods 1 and 2.

TABLE 2.3.5
$[T_V]$ for $(2, 6)$, $\lambda = 3$

	1	2	3	4	5	6	7	8	9	10	11	12	13	14	15	16	17	18	19
1. $(6\mid0,0)$	0	1	2	3	4	5	6												
2. $(5\mid0,0)$		0	1	2	3	4	5												
3. $(4\mid0,0)$			0	1	2	3	4												
4. $(3\mid0,0)$				0	1	2	3												
5. $(2\mid0,0)$								0	1	2									
6. $(1\mid0,0)$											0	1							
7. $(0\mid0,0)$													0						
8. $(2\mid4,2)$														0	1	2			
9. $(1\mid4,2)$															0	1			
10. $(0\mid4,2)$																0			
11. $(1\mid5,2)$																	0	1	
12. $(0\mid5,2)$																		0	
13. $(0\mid6,2)$																			0
14. $(2\mid4,1)$	0	1	2																
15. $(1\mid4,1)$		0	1																
16. $(0\mid4,1)$			0																
17. $(1\mid5,1)$	0	1																	
18. $(0\mid5,1)$		0																	
19. $(0\mid6,1)$	0																		

TABLE 2.3.6
Proposition 2.3.5 (1)

V, λ	$Z, \lambda + 1$
$q_V(S \mid 0, 0)$	$q_Z(S \mid 0, 0)$
$\cdot$	$\cdot$
$\cdot$	$\cdot$
$\cdot$	$\cdot$
$q_V(s + 1 \mid 0, 0)$	$q_Z(s + 1 \mid 0, 0)$
$q_V(s \mid 0, 0)$	$q_Z(s \mid D, \lambda)$
$\cdot$	$\cdot$
$\cdot$	$\cdot$
$q_V(0 \mid 0, 0)$	$q_Z(0 \mid S, \lambda)$
$q_V(S - r \mid r, \tau)$	$q_Z(S - r \mid r, \tau)$
$\cdot$	$\cdot$
$\cdot$	$\cdot$
$q_V(0 \mid r, \tau)$	$q_Z(0 \mid r, \tau)$

$$\tau = 1, 2, \cdots, \lambda - 1$$

61

The correspondence between V in a λ model and Z in a $\lambda + 1$ model is seen in Table 2.3.6; note that we have added subscripts to the stationary probabilities to distinguish the appropriate random variables.

(2) Establishing the relationship between V and Y parallels the discussion for the backlog case, with the modification required by $[\overline{\Phi}_S]$, defined in Section 2.1.6, and therefore is not repeated here.

Utilizing part (1) we have

$$[q_{W,\lambda}] = [q_{Z,\lambda}][\overline{\Phi}_S] = [q_{V,\lambda-1}][\overline{\Phi}_S].$$

The principal implication of the proposition is that the stationary distributions of Y, W, and Z can be obtained from the stationary distribution of V, in certain cases, after applying a convolution operator. Consequently much of our attention is turned toward an analysis of $[q_{V,\lambda}]$. We mention that in a straightforward manner it is possible to analyze these systems in states such as $(w \mid r, \tau)$ and $(y \mid r, \tau)$, but since we shall have no need for these particular quantities, we do not pursue the idea further. We also point out that we postpone a discussion of the probability distribution of shortages until Section 2.5.2.

2.3.6 Stationary Distributions when $\lambda = 1$—No Restriction on D and s

For $\lambda = 1$ under Sequence α, at the time V is valued, there is never an order outstanding. Thus in this situation we may characterize the problem in terms of $[q_{V,1}]$ directly.[10] Further there is no need to restrict $D > s$.

TABLE 2.3.7
$D > s, \lambda = 1$

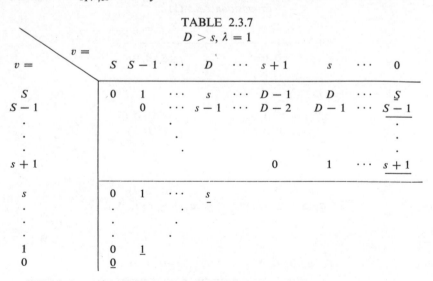

[10] Precisely, $q(v \mid 0, 0) = q_{V,1}(v)$ for $0 \le v \le S$.

Tables 2.3.7 and 2.3.8 illustrate the transition matrices for $D > s$ and $D \leq s$. Because of Proposition 2.3.5 (1), a similar analysis can be made for $\lambda = 2$ under Sequence β.

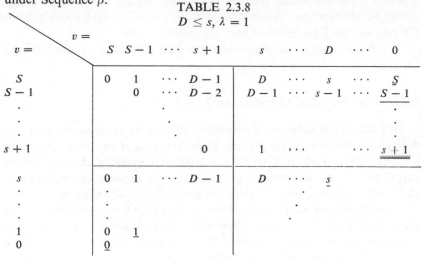

TABLE 2.3.8
$D \leq s, \lambda = 1$

$v =$ $v =$	S	$S-1$	$\cdots$	$s+1$	s	$\cdots$	D	$\cdots$	0
S	0	1	$\cdots$	$D-1$	D	$\cdots$	s	$\cdots$	S
$S-1$		0	$\cdots$	$D-2$	$D-1$	$\cdots$	$s-1$	$\cdots$	$S-1$
.			.						.
.			.						.
.			.						
$s+1$				0	1	$\cdots$		$\cdots$	$s+1$
s	0	1	$\cdots$	$D-1$	D	$\cdots$	s		
.		.					.		
.		.					.		
1	0	1							
0	0	0							

For $\lambda = 1$ under Sequence β, where again we make no restriction on the relationship between D and s, there is a simple correspondence between the variables in the backlog and no-backlog cases.

Proposition 2.3.6.

(1)
$$q_{W,1}(w) = p_{W,1}(w) \qquad\qquad 0 < w \leq S$$
$$q_{W,1}(0) = \sum_{w=-\infty}^{0} p_{W,1}(w);$$

(2)
$$q_{Z,1}(z) = p_{Z,1}(z) \qquad\qquad s+1 \leq z \leq S.$$

It follows from part (1) that in this situation, the backlog and no-backlog cases agree in the probability of ordering, of amounts of shortage, as well as of amounts of inventory on hand. Noting in Section 2.2.7 the equivalence between X and W, and between U and Z, we have already seen a recursive procedure for computing $[q_{W,1}]$ and $[q_{Z,1}]$. Furthermore, parts (1) and (3) of Proposition 2.2.3 are applicable for positive values of x and $x + \delta$.

Proof. (1) The appropriate stationary equations for $q_{W,1}(w)$ are

(1a) $\quad q'_{W,1}(w) = \phi(S - w) \sum_{j=0}^{s} q_{W,1}(j) + \sum_{j=w}^{S} \phi(j - w) q_{W,1}(j) \quad s+1 \leq w \leq S$

(1b) $\quad q_{W,1}(w) = \phi(S - w) \sum_{j=0}^{s} q_{W,1}(j) + \sum_{j=s+1}^{S} \phi(j - w) q_{W,1}(j) \qquad 0 < w \leq s$

(1c) $\quad q_{W,1}(0) = \phi(S) \sum_{j=0}^{s} q_{W,1}(j) + \sum_{j=s+1}^{S} \phi(j) q_{W,1}(j).$

Substituting into (1a) and (1b) the hypothesized equivalence between $q_{W,1}(w)$ and $p_{W,1}(w)$, and recalling that $p_{W,1}(w) = p_X(w)$, we obtain the stationary version of the relation (2) in Section 2.2.1, which the $p_X(x)$ satisfy by construction. A similar substitution into (1c) agrees with relation (2b') in Section 2.2.1 summed over the domain $-\infty \le x \le 0$.

(2) A matching of the equivalence in part (1) with that between $[p_X]$, $[p_U]$, and $[p_{Z,1}]$ produces the result.

2.3.7 Constrained (s, S) Policies for λ > 1

We define one subclass of inventory policies by constraining an (s, S) policy such that only one order may be outstanding at any time. We define a second subclass which relaxes the restriction to allow, at the end of every period before any new order is placed, only one order to be outstanding; this version imposes no constraint for $\lambda = 2$ under Sequence α.

The first type of model is illustrated in Table 2.3.9 under Sequence α for the policy (2, 3), $\lambda = 3$; as in Section 2.3.2, the states are $(v \mid r, \tau)$. The second type is exhibited in Table 2.3.10 also under Sequence α for (2, 3), $\lambda = 3$. The essential difference between the two schemes is that the less restrictive model permits an order to be placed immediately prior to the period in which an outstanding order is to be delivered.

TABLE 2.3.9

(2, 3), $\lambda = 3$ Only One Order Outstanding at Any Time

	1	2	3	4	5	6	7	8	9	10	11	12	13	14	15	16
1. (3 | 0, 0)	0	1	2	<u>3</u>												
2. (2 | 0, 0)					0	1	<u>2</u>									
3. (1 | 0, 0)								0	<u>1</u>							
4. (0 | 0, 0)										<u>0</u>						
5. (2 | 1, 2)											0	1	<u>2</u>			
6. (1 | 1, 2)												0	<u>1</u>			
7. (0 | 1, 2)													<u>0</u>			
8. (1 | 2, 2)														0	<u>1</u>	
9. (0 | 2, 2)															<u>0</u>	
10. (0 | 3, 2)																<u>0</u>
11. (2 | 1, 1)	0		1	<u>2</u>												
12. (1 | 1, 1)			0	<u>1</u>												
13. (0 | 1, 1)				<u>0</u>												
14. (1 | 2, 1)	0		<u>1</u>													
15. (0 | 2, 1)			<u>0</u>													
16. (0 | 3, 1)	<u>0</u>															

TABLE 2.3.10

(2, 3), $\lambda = 3$ Only One Order Outstanding Prior to Any New Order

	1	2	3	4	5	6	7	8	9	10	11	12	13	14	15	16
1. (3 | 0, 0)	0	1	2	3												
2. (2 | 0, 0)					0	1	2									
3. (1 | 0, 0)							0	1								
4. (0 | 0, 0)									0							
5. (2 | 1, 2)											0	1	2			
6. (1 | 1, 2)												0	1			
7. (0 | 1, 2)													0			
8. (1 | 2, 2)														0	1	
9. (0 | 2, 2)															0	
10. (0 | 3, 2)																0
11. (2 | 1, 1)	0	1	2													
12. (1 | 1, 1)					0	1										
13. (0 | 1, 1)						0										
14. (1 | 2, 1)	0	1														
15. (0 | 2, 1)					0											
16. (0 | 3, 1)	0															

It is useful to reduce the size of the first model, which in its full form has the same dimension as $[T_V]$, in a manner analogous to Algorithm 2.3.2. The transition matrix for an (s, S) policy constrained to allow only one order outstanding at a time (and $D \leq s$) is nearly identical to $[T_V]$ in Table 2.3.1. The alteration which must be made is to define the dimensions of $[0_r]$ as $S - r + 1$ rows and r columns so that $[T_r^{**}]$ has $S + 1$ columns; in other words, non-zero entries now may appear in the block on the immediate right of $[T_{1S}]$. It is convenient to adopt the notation $[[T_{1S}][T_{1s}]]$ for the lower left corner of the transformation matrix, where, as previously, the first partition contains D columns, and the second $s + 1$ columns.

Algorithm 2.3.7. Multiplying the stationary probabilities times the transition matrix for an (s, S) policy constrained to allow only one order outstanding at a time yields the component equations

(1a) $$[q_{V,s}(0)][T_{SS}] + [q_V(1)][T_{1S}] = [q_{V,s}(0)]$$

(1b) $$[q_{V,s}(0)][T_{Ss}] + [q_V(1)][T_{1s}] = [q_{V,s}(0)]$$

(1c) $$[q_{V,s}(0)][T_{s,\lambda-1}] = [q_V(\lambda - 1)]$$

(1d) $$[q_V(\lambda - k)][T^*] = [q_V(\lambda - k - 1)] \quad k = 1, 2, \cdots, \lambda - 2.$$

Notice the similarity of (1a), (1c), and (1d) to (3a), (3c), and (3d) in Section 2.3.2. By similar substitutions we derive

(1e) $[q_V(\lambda - k)] = [q_{V,s}(0)][T_{s,\lambda-1}][T^*]^{k-1}$ $k = 1, 2, \cdots, \lambda - 1.$

Thus

(2a) $[q_{V,S}(0)][T_{SS}] + [q_{V,s}(0)][T_{s,\lambda-1}][T^*]^{\lambda-2}[T_{1S}] = [q_{V,S}(0)];$

and

(2b) $[q_{V,S}(0)][T_{Ss}] + [q_{V,s}(0)][T_{s,\lambda-1}][T^*]^{\lambda-2}[T_{1s}] = [q_{V,s}(0)].$

Equation (2) is of dimension $S + 1$.

2.3.8 Approximation of $q_{V,\lambda}(v)$ for Large Values of D

In this section we return to systems satisfying $D > s$. The relationships between s, S and D are illustrated in Fig. 2.3.1. Unless mention is made to the contrary, our approximations proceed under the assumption that s is held constant. Our method will be to characterize $[q_{V,\lambda}]$ with respect to the first D terms of a discrete renewal equation and then to apply an analysis parallel to that in Section 2.2.6.

Let

(1) $[\sigma_S \quad \sigma_{S-1} \cdots \sigma_D] \equiv [q_V(1)][T_{1S}].$

Then, summing both sides of (1),

(2) $$\sum_{v=D}^{S} \sigma_v = \sigma.$$

Using the notation in (1), we observe that (3a) in Section 2.3.2 agrees with the first D terms of a renewal equation for $q_{V,\lambda}(v)$

(3) $$q_{V,\lambda}(v) = \sigma_v + \sum_{j=v}^{S} \phi(j - v)q_{V,\lambda}(j) \qquad s + 1 \leq v \leq S.$$

Because at the outset of studying a model we do not know σ_v, (3) cannot be used in as straightforward a manner as can its counterpart for the distribution of $p_X(x)$.[11] But by letting D grow large, we can employ a simple extension of the basic renewal theorem [Fe, p. 290] to derive that $\sigma/E(\xi)$

Fig. 2.3.1

[11] An exception occurs for $s = 0$; then $\sigma_S = \sigma$ and Algorithm 2.2.4, slightly revised, along with (5) of Section 2.3.2, may be employed for recursive calculations of $q_{V,\lambda}(v)$.

approximates $q_{V,\lambda}(v)$ for values of $v \geq s + 1$. In the domain of $s + 1 \leq v < D$, the approximation is enhanced by the fact that the entire contribution of σ_v has taken place in the preceding domain $D \leq v \leq S$; a similar improvement is engendered by a decrease in s, which causes the entire contribution of σ_v to occur for a few high values of V.

If s is small relative to $\lambda E(\xi)$ and D is large, then we might use as an approximation

(4a)
$$\sum_{v=s+1}^{S} q_{V,\lambda}(v) = \frac{D\sigma}{E(\xi)}.$$

Combining (4a) with (5) of Section 2.3.2, we obtain the further approximations

(4b)
$$\sigma = \frac{E(\xi)}{\lambda E(\xi) + D}$$

(4c)
$$q_{V,\lambda}(s + 1) = [\lambda E(\xi) + D]^{-1}.$$

For an intuitive explanation of (4b), we suggest envisaging a deterministic situation in which exactly $E(\xi)$ items are demanded each period under a $(s = 0, S = D)$ policy. The reciprocal of (4b) is then the total number of periods per ordering cycle.

We caution that, as in the backlog case, the renewal approximation in terms of σ may be excellent whereas (4) may not. In particular, if s is large relative to $\lambda E(\xi)$, the system's behavior resembles that of the backlog case; in such circumstances, (1) of Section 2.2.6 may provide a better estimate for σ.

Equation (3) may be extended to values $0 < v \leq s$. The manipulation involved is to sum the $q(v \mid r, \tau)$, as defined by (2) of Section 2.3.2, to form $q_{V,\lambda}(v)$:

(5) $q_{V,\lambda}(v) = \sum_{j=v}^{S} \phi(j - v) q_{V,\lambda}(j) - \sum_{j=v}^{s} \phi(j - v) \sum_{r} q(j \mid r, 1)$ $0 < v \leq s$.

Let
$$\sigma_v{}^* = \left[\sum_{r} q(s \mid r, 1) \sum_{r} q(s - 1 \mid r, 1) \cdots \sum_{r} q(v \mid r, 1) \right] \begin{bmatrix} \phi(\overline{s - v}) \\ \phi(\overline{s - v - 1}) \\ \cdot \\ \cdot \\ \cdot \\ \phi(\overline{1}) \\ \phi(\overline{0}) \end{bmatrix}.$$

Then a renewal theorem, applicable to (5), yields for large values of D the approximation

(6)
$$q_{V,\lambda}(v) = \frac{\sigma - \sigma_v{}^*}{E(\xi)}$$ $0 < v \leq s$.

Since $\sigma_v{}^*$ is not ordinarily known at the outset of the analysis, the approximation (6) is useful when $\sigma_v{}^*$ is small enough to be ignored. As D increases, $\sigma_v{}^* \leq \sigma$ decreases. Needless to say, $\sigma_v{}^*$ is negligible if the bulk of its components are of small magnitude; this occurs for example when $\lambda E(\xi)$ is large relative to s, for then $\sum_r q(0 \mid r, 1)$, the probability of being out of stock is likely to be large during the period before a delivery.[12]

The implication of the above analysis is that as D increases, the distribution of $[q_{V,\lambda}]$ resembles a uniform distribution, especially in the domain $s + 1 \leq v < D$; and if s is sufficiently small, the domain may be extended (for approximation purposes) to $v > 0$. These tendencies are to be compared with the backlog model in which it is the distribution $p_X(x)$ which resembles a uniform distribution for $x \geq s + 1$.

2.3.9   *Dependence of* $q_{V,\lambda}(v)$ *on* D, s, λ, *and* $E(\xi)$

The generalizations to follow stem from a combination of plausible reasoning and the approximations in Section 2.3.8; they are not meant to be rigorous formulations, and consequently they should be interpreted with leniency. We give empirical evidence of their validity in Section 2.4.9.

In examining the dependence of $[q_{V,\lambda}]$ on the system's parameters, we find no results analogous to the backlog case which facilitate recursive numerical computations. But a combination of heuristic reasoning and the approximations in Section 2.3.8 yield certain relevant generalizations. We consider the four parameters D, s, λ, and $E(\xi)$, and vary each, one at a time.

An increase in D, with s fixed, implies an increase in S. As a result we may expect σ to diminish and the distribution $[q_{V,\lambda}]$ to resemble a uniform distribution at a lower level.

An increase in s brings about an increase in σ. We have already seen an indication of this: as s increases, the behavior of the no-backlog case approaches that of the backlog case, and an estimate for σ shifts from (4b) in Section 2.3.8 to (1) in Section 2.2.6, the latter giving a larger value. An intuitive argument may be framed through a comparison of two possible cases $s = 0$ and $s > 0$. In the former case, whenever a delivery occurs, $S = D$ items are on hand and this figure must be reduced to zero before another order takes place. When s is positive, demand during the delivery lag period may reduce inventory on hand so that, when the delivery occurs, the total amount on hand is less than S; thus less than D demands are required to reduce the amount on hand to the level s.

---

[12] A more precise estimate of the magnitude of $\sum_r q(0 \mid r, 1)$ can be obtained from the probability that the sum of the demands during $\lambda - 1$ periods is at least equal to s.

As the time lag λ increases, the likelihood decreases that any inventory will be on hand when the delivery takes place; consequently, as λ gets large, demands for at least $D - s$ items will eventually intervene between a delivery and the next order. Further increases in λ lengthen the replenishment cycle, a tendency which in turn implies a lowering of the stationary value for σ. This effect is, of course, seen in the approximation (1) in Section 2.3.8.

Finally, substantially increasing $E(\xi)$ causes inventory to be drawn down to the reorder level s more rapidly, and therefore increases σ. But since σ is bounded by one, the result of the renewal theorem states that as $E(\xi)$ increases, the distribution $[q_{V,\lambda}]$ for positive values of V flattens at a lower level.

2.3.10   A General (s, S) Policy

In principle, the stationary probabilities for a general (s, S) policy with no-backlogging may be characterized by means of a finite Markov chain; the accompanying difficulty is that the dimension of the transition matrix grows large, even after making reductions of the sort we have seen for the case $D > s$. Our previous representation of a state as $(v \mid r, \tau)$ can be extended in an obvious manner. For example, if $2D > s$, then no more than two orders can be outstanding at any time. Accordingly, we may define a state as $(v \mid r_1, \tau_1; r_2, \tau_2)$ to represent the current value of V, and the quantities of at most two outstanding orders, each with an indication of its delivery date. In general, we must observe in constructing the list of possible states that (1) the total amount on hand and on order cannot exceed S, (2) whenever an order is outstanding, the amount on hand cannot exceed s, and (3) each outstanding order must be at least D.

An alternative mode of representation has been suggested in [AKS, Ch. 10]. We illustrate this view by assuming $\lambda = 3$ under Sequence α; a state at the end of a period before any new order is placed is characterized by a triple (v, amount to be delivered next period, and amount to be delivered after next). As an example, if at the end of period 1 the state is (5, 10, 15), then 5 units are applied to period 2 demand, the leftover amount is combined with the delivered amount 10 to meet period 3 demand, and the amount left over at that point is combined with 15 to meet period 4 demand. Further, if demand in period 2 is 3, and an order of 20 is placed at the end of period 1, then the state at the end of period 2 is (12, 15, 20).

Of course there is a one-to-one correspondence between the possible states defined by our notational scheme and the one in the previous paragraph. Thus there is no reason to prefer one system over the other in regard to the size of the associated transition matrix. But, loosely, if s/D is not too large as compared to λ, there is an economy of notation in our

TABLE 2.3.11
$(3, 5), \lambda = 3$

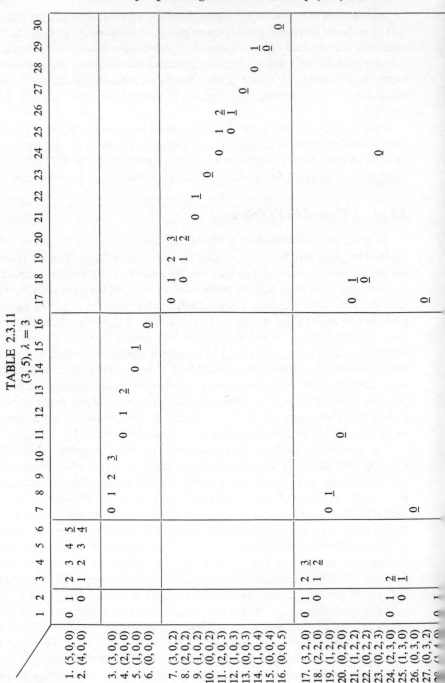

Row labels:

1. (5,0,0)
2. (4,0,0)
3. (3,0,0)
4. (2,0,0)
5. (1,0,0)
6. (0,0,0)
7. (3,0,2)
8. (2,0,2)
9. (1,0,2)
10. (0,0,2)
11. (2,0,3)
12. (1,0,3)
13. (0,0,3)
14. (1,0,4)
15. (0,0,4)
16. (0,0,5)
17. (3,2,0)
18. (2,2,0)
19. (1,2,0)
20. (1,2,2)
21. (1,2,2)
22. (0,2,2)
23. (0,2,3)
24. (2,3,0)
25. (1,3,0)
26. (0,3,0)
27. (0,3,2)

presentation. Furthermore, this convention may make more apparent the type of reductions suggested in Algorithms 2.3.2 and 2.3.7.

For the sake of completeness, we illustrate in Table 2.3.11 the transition matrix for the policy $(3, 5)$, $\lambda = 3$ under Sequence α in the notation of [AKS, Ch. 10].

2.4 EXAMPLES

A general assessment of the available analytic results and the merits of various computing techniques appears in Section 2.4.1. The remaining sections illustrate the several methods by a number of specific examples. The analytic derivations of closed-form expressions for the probability distribution of X in the backlog case are contained in Section 2.4.2, for the negative binomial demand distribution; in Section 2.4.3, for the gamma distribution; and in Section 2.4.4, for the uniform distribution. Analogous numerical examples computed from Algorithm 2.2.4 for uniform, binomial, and Poisson distributions appear in Section 2.4.5. In this section we also compare estimates of the probabilities obtained through a Monte Carlo simulation with the values obtained from the algorithm, the underlying demand distribution employed being Poisson. Making use of a previous Poisson example and Proposition 2.2.8, we show in Section 2.4.6 a calculation for the random variable inventory on hand (exclusive of inventory on order). The approximations for the probability distribution of X derived from an extended application of the renewal theorem in Section 2.2.6 are examined in Section 2.4.7 for all the examples in the immediately preceding sections.

The calculations in a no-backlog model are illustrated in Section 2.4.8. Here the probability distribution of inventory on hand is obtained by raising the associated finite Markov chain matrix to sufficiently high powers. A sensitivity analysis of the variation in these probabilities as changes are made in the system's parameters (namely, s, D, time-lag, mean value of demand) appears in Section 2.4.9; an analysis of the renewal type approximations is given in Section 2.4.10.

At the close, Sections 2.4.11 and 2.4.12, we provide illustrations of constrained (s, S) policies, defined in Section 2.3.7, and an unconstrained policy where D is less than s, given in Section 2.3.10; here again we compare probabilities obtained by algorithmic calculations with those obtained by Monte Carlo simulation.

2.4.1 Scope and Method

We now illustrate the principal results of the preceding sections by means of examples. Only for relatively few probability distributions $\phi(\xi)$

is it possible to derive closed-form mathematical expressions for the stationary distributions; two such classes are the discrete and continuous uniform distributions, and the negative binomial along with its continuous analog, the gamma distribution. All these analyses are under the backlog assumption.

The remainder of the examples are numerical calculations for specific inventory systems. As we mentioned in Section 2.1.4, several avenues of approach are often available in the computation of the probability distributions. Specifically, depending to some extent on the model, the choices we have utilized are recursive calculations like those in Section 2.2.4, iteration of the Markov chains [KS, Ch. 4], and Monte Carlo simulation. In several instances we present a comparison of the methods. Each computing technique has certain immediate advantages of its own. The recursive calculations, when possible, are simple and very accurate. Raising the Markov chain matrices to successively higher powers yields information about the rapidity of the system's reaching statistical equilibrium [Fe, p. 356]. Monte Carlo simulation exhibits the random fluctuations over time which are to be anticipated, and the method can provide simultaneously estimates of several probability distributions of the system's operating characteristics;[13] all the Monte Carlo studies in this chapter are based on 10,000 periods of operation.

2.4.2 Negative Binomial Distribution

Consider the negative binomial (or Pascal) distribution

$$\phi(\xi) = \binom{r-1+\xi}{r-1} p^r q^\xi, \quad p+q=1, \quad 0 < p < 1, \quad \xi = 0, 1, 2, \cdots$$

which has $E(\xi) = rq/p$ and variance rq/p^2. We shall derive the form of $p_X(x)$. As a preliminary, we need the results of a mathematical lemma concerning the application of differencing operators to the stationary equations for this distribution.

Let E, Δ, and $(qE - 1)$ denote the forward and difference operators [Go]

$$Eg(x) = g(x + 1)$$

$$\Delta g(x) = g(x + 1) - g(x)$$

$$(qE - 1)g(x) = qg(x + 1) - g(x),$$

---

[13] In models with no backlogging, $\lambda > 1$ and $D \leq s$, methods other than Monte Carlo do not appear generally feasible.

obeying the usual rules such as

$$(E - \alpha)g(x) = g(x + 1) - \alpha g(x)$$

$$(qE - 1)^{r+1}g(x) \equiv (qE - 1)^r(qE - 1)g(x) \equiv (qE - 1)(qE - 1)^r g(x).$$

Lemma 2.4.2. Let $g(x)$ be any function.

(1) For all values of x, $(qE - 1)^r q^{-x} g(x) = q^{-x}(E - 1)^r g(x) \equiv q^{-x}\Delta^r g(x)$.

(2) For $x \leq t$, $(qE - 1)^r q^{-x} \left(\dfrac{r - 1 + t - x}{r - 1} \right) = 0$.

(3) For $x \leq S - r$, $(qE - 1)^r \displaystyle\sum_{t=x}^{S} q^{t-x} \left(\dfrac{r - 1 + t - x}{r - 1} \right) g(t) = (-1)^r g(x)$.

Proof. (1) For $r = 1$

$$(qE - 1)q^{-x}g(x) = q[q^{-x-1}g(x + 1)] - q^{-x}g(x)$$
$$= q^{-x}\Delta g(x).$$

Suppose the lemma is true for r. We show it is then true for $r + 1$

$$(qE - 1)^{r+1}q^{-x}g(x) = (qE - 1)(qE - 1)^r q^{-x}g(x)$$
$$= (qE - 1)q^{-x}\Delta^r g(x)$$
$$= q[q^{-x-1}\Delta^r g(x + 1)] - q^{-x}\Delta^r g(x)$$
$$= q^{-x}\Delta^{r+1}g(x).$$

(2) We have by part (1)

$$(qE - 1)^r q^{-x} \left(\frac{r - 1 + t - x}{r - 1} \right) = q^{-x}\Delta^r \left[\frac{(r - 1 + t - x)!}{(r - 1)!\,(t - x)!} \right].$$

Simplifying the right-hand side:

(1) $\quad \dfrac{q^{-x}}{(r - 1)!} \Delta^r[(r - 1 + t - x)(r - 2 + t - x) \cdots (t + 1 - x)].$

Let $K_i = r - 1 + t - i$, $i = 0, 1, \cdots, r - 2$. Then the term in brackets in (1) is

$$(K_0 - x)(K_1 - x) \cdots (K_{r-2} - x) = P^{r-1}(x),$$

a polynomial of degree $r - 1$ in x. Consequently [Go, p. 47] $\Delta^r P^{r-1}(x) = 0$.

(3) For $r = 1$

$$(qE - 1)\sum_{t=x}^{S} q^{t-x} \left(\frac{t - x}{0} \right) g(t) = q \sum_{t=x+1}^{S} q^{t-x-1}g(t) - \sum_{t=x}^{S} q^{t-x}g(t) = -g(x).$$

Suppose the lemma is true for r. We show it is then true for $r + 1$. Let

$$G = (qE - 1)^{r+1} \sum_{t=x}^{S} q^{t-x} \frac{(r + t - x)!}{(r)!\,(t - x)!} g(t).$$

Let

$$G^* = (qE - 1)^r \sum_{t=x}^{S} q^{t-x} \frac{(r+t-x)!}{(r)!\,(t-x)!}\, g(t)$$

$$= (qE - 1)^r \sum_{t=x}^{S} q^{t-x} \left(1 + \frac{t-x}{r}\right) \frac{(r+t-x-1)!}{(r-1)!\,(t-x)!}\, g(t)$$

$$= (qE - 1)^r \sum_{t=x}^{S} q^{t-x} \frac{(r-1+t-x)!}{(r-1)!\,(t-x)!}\, g(t)$$

$$+ q(qE - 1)^r \sum_{t=x+1}^{S} q^{t-x-1} \frac{(r+t-x-1)!}{(r)!\,(t-x-1)!}\, g(t)$$

$$= (-1)^r g(x) + qEG^*,$$

by hypothesis. Rewriting the result:

$$(qE - 1)G^* = (-1)^{r+1} g(x)$$
$$G = (-1)^{r+1} g(x).$$

Having proved Lemma 2.4.2, we are ready to state the form of $p_X(x)$ when $\phi(\xi)$ is a negative binomial distribution.

Proposition 2.4.2. For the stationary probability distribution $p_X(x)$ associated with $\phi(\xi) = \binom{r-1+\xi}{r+1} p^r q^\xi,\ \xi = 0, 1, 2, \cdots,$

(1) for $x \geq s - r,\quad (qE - 1)^r p_X(x) = 0;$

(2) for $x \leq s,\quad p_X(x) = C_0 \left(\frac{1}{q}\right)^x + C_1 x \left(\frac{1}{q}\right)^x + C_2 x^2 \left(\frac{1}{q}\right)^x$

$$+ \cdots + C_{r-1} x^{r-1} \left(\frac{1}{q}\right)^x;$$

(3) for $s + 1 \geq x \leq S - r,\quad [(qE - 1)^r - (-p)^r] p_X(x) = 0;$

(4) for $s + 1 \geq x \leq S,$

$$p_X(x) = \sum_{j=r}^{2r-1} C_j \left[\frac{1}{q} - \frac{p}{q} \left(\cos \frac{2\pi j}{r} + i \sin \frac{2\pi j}{r}\right)\right]^x.$$

Proof. (1) The stationary equation is

(2) $p_X(x) = \binom{r-1+S-x}{r-1} p^r q^{S-x} \sum_{j=-\infty}^{s} p_X(j)$

$$+ \sum_{j=s+1}^{S} \binom{r-1+j-x}{r-1} p^r q^{j-x} p_X(j).$$

Then

$$(3) \quad (qE - 1)^r p_X(x) = \left[p^r q^S \sum_{j=-\infty}^{s} p_X(j) \right] (qE - 1)^r q^{-x} \binom{r - 1 + S - x}{r - 1}$$

$$+ p^r \sum_{j=s+1}^{S} q^j p_X(j)(qE - 1)^r q^{-x} \binom{r - 1 + j - x}{r - 1}$$

$$= 0,$$

by Lemma 2.4.2, part (2).

(2) Equation (3) is a homogeneous linear difference equation with constant coefficients. The associated characteristic equation in the variable t is

$$(4) \quad\quad\quad\quad\quad\quad (qt - 1)^r = 0.$$

The unique root of (4) is $t = 1/q$, which has multiplicity r. The coefficients C_j are constants of summation.

(3) The stationary equation is

$$p_X(x) = \binom{r - 1 + S - x}{r - x} p^r q^{S-x} \sum_{j=-\infty}^{s} p_X(j)$$

$$+ \sum_{j=x}^{S} \binom{r - 1 + j - x}{r - 1} p^r q^{j-x} p_X(j)$$

Then

$$(qE - 1)^r p_X(x) = \left[p^r q^S \sum_{j=-\infty}^{s} p_X(j) \right] (qE - 1)^r \binom{r - 1 + S - x}{r - 1} q^{-x}$$

$$+ p^r (qE - 1)^r \sum_{j=x}^{S} \binom{r - 1 + j - x}{r - 1} q^{j-x} p_X(j)$$

$$= 0 + p^r (-1)^r p_X(x),$$

by Lemma 2.4.2, parts (2) and (3).

Thus

$$(5) \quad\quad\quad\quad [(qE - 1)^r - (-p)^r] p_X(x) = 0.$$

The characteristic equation associated with (5) has roots

$$\left[\frac{1}{q} - \frac{p}{q} \left(\cos \frac{2\pi j}{r} + i \sin \frac{2\pi j}{r} \right) \right]$$

where the complex trigonometric expression is introduced to account for the r roots of unity. For $r = 1$, the single root equals 1; for $r = 2$, the pair of roots equal 1 and $\left(\dfrac{2 - q}{q} \right)$. Once again, the C_j are constants of summation.

As we shall see momentarily, certain analytic properties may be invoked to determine the constants of summation. But in the computation of particular numerical examples, it seems easier to combine the above analysis with that of Algorithm 2.2.4 to identify the values of these constants.

We illustrate Proposition 2.4.2 with two special cases. Consider the geometric distribution for which $r = 1$ and $E(\xi) = \dfrac{q}{1-q}$. Then we have

$$p_X(x) = C_0 \left(\frac{1}{q}\right)^x \qquad\qquad x \leq s$$

$$p_X(x) = C_1 \qquad\qquad s + 1 \leq x \leq S.$$

Examination of the stationary equations $(2a')$ and $(2b')$ in Section 2.2.1 reveals that the two relations are identical when we let $x = s + 1$. Consequently

$$C_0 \left(\frac{1}{q}\right)^{s+1} = C_1,$$

and

$$p_X(x) = C_1 q^{s+1-x} \qquad\qquad x \leq s.$$

Since $p_X(x)$ is a probability distribution

$$\sum_{x=-\infty}^{S} p_X(x) = C_1 \left[(S - s) + \frac{q}{1-q} \right] = 1$$

$$C_1 = \frac{1}{E(\xi) + D}.$$

Thus when $\phi(\xi)$ is a geometric distribution

$$p_X(x) = \frac{1}{E(\xi) + D} \qquad\qquad s + 1 \leq x \leq S$$

$$= \frac{1}{E(\xi) + D} q^{s+1-x} \qquad\qquad x \leq s;$$

$$\sigma = \frac{1}{E(\xi) + D}.$$

Note that relations (1) and (2) of Section 2.2.6 hold exactly for the geometric distribution.

Next consider the negative binomial distribution when $r = 2$, for which $E(\xi) = \dfrac{2q}{1-q}$. By properly interpreting the coefficients in Proposition 2.4.2, we may write

$$p_X(x) = C_0 q^{s+1-x} + C_1(s - x)q^{s+1-x}, \qquad x \leq s,$$

$$p_X(x) = C_2 + C_3 \rho^{x-s-1}, \qquad s + 1 \leq x \leq S,$$

where $\rho = \dfrac{2-q}{q}$.

We may solve for C_0, C_1, C_2, and C_3 by using the following set of relations which are linear in the unknown parameters:

(6a) $\quad \sum\limits_{x=-\infty}^{S} p_X(x) = 1$

(6b) $\quad C_0 q^{s+1-(s+1)} + C_1[s - (s+1)]q^{s+1-(s+1)} = C_2 + C_3 \rho^{s+1-(s+1)}$

(6c) $\quad q^2 p_X(s+2) - 2q p_X(s+1) + p_X(s) = 0$

(6d) $\quad p_X(S) = \dfrac{\phi(0)}{1-\phi(0)} \sum\limits_{x=-\infty}^{s} p_X(x).$

Relation (6a) expresses that $p_X(x)$ is a probability distribution, and (6b) that the stationary equations (2a') and (2b') in Section 2.2.1 are identical at $s+1$. Relation (6c) can be proved by applying the operator $(qE-1)^2$ to (2a') and (2b') in Section 2.2.1 at $s+1$ and s, respectively. Relation (6d) was derived in Algorithm 2.2.4.

The result of solving (6) is

$$p_X(x) = C\{-\rho^D + \rho^{x-s-1}\}, \qquad s+1 \le x \le S$$
$$p_X(x) = C\{[1-\rho^D]q^{s+1-x} + [q-1][1+\rho^D][s+1-x]q^{s+1-x}\},$$
$$x \le s,$$

where

$$C = \left[\frac{-2q}{1-q}\rho^D - \rho^D D + \frac{\rho^D-1}{\rho-1} \right]^{-1} \le 0.$$

It may be shown that

$$\sigma = C\left[\frac{-2q}{1-q}\rho^D \right]$$

$$p_X(x) = \frac{[-\rho^D + \rho^{x-s-1}]\sigma}{\dfrac{-2q}{1-q}\rho^D}, \qquad s+1 \le x \le S.$$

At $x = s+1$, if we let D increase indefinitely, as in Section 2.2.6,

$$p_X(x) \to \frac{\sigma}{E(\xi)} = \frac{1}{0.75E(\xi) + D}.$$

It is well known that the λ-fold convolution of a negative binomial distribution with parameters p and r is itself a negative binomial distribution [Fe, p. 252]:

$$\phi^\lambda(\xi) = \binom{\lambda r - 1 + \xi}{\lambda r - 1} p^{\lambda r} q^\xi, \qquad \xi = 0, 1, 2, \cdots.$$

From Proposition 2.2.8, part (3),

$$p_{V,\lambda}(v) = \sum_{j=v}^{S} \phi^{\lambda-1}(j-v)p_X(j).$$

Consider $r = 1$ and $\lambda = 2$. Then

$$\begin{aligned} p_{V,2}(v) &= \frac{1}{E(\xi) + D} - \frac{q^D q^{s+1-v}}{E(\xi) + D}, \qquad s+1 \le v \le S \\ &= \frac{(1-q)q^{s+1-v}}{E(\xi) + D}\left[s + 1 - v + \frac{1-q^D}{1-q}\right], \qquad v \le s. \end{aligned}$$

2.4.3   Gamma Distribution

Analysis of the density function $p_X(x)$ for the gamma distribution

$$\phi(\xi) = \frac{\tau(\tau\xi)^{k-1}e^{-\tau\xi}}{(k-1)!} \qquad \xi \ge 0$$

$$E(\xi) = k/\tau, \qquad \text{Variance }(\xi) = k/\tau^2,$$

may be found in [AKS, Ch. 14], and consequently only a brief summary is given here. Differentiating equation (4) in Section 2.2.1 k times with respect to x yields a pair of homogeneous linear differential equations with constant coefficients, and these may be solved in a standard fashion [KB, p. 37]. Since the gamma distribution is the continuous analog of the negative binomial, the results of the two cases are similar.

For $k = 1$, the resulting stationary density is

$$p_X(x) = \frac{1}{\mu + D}, \qquad s \le x \le S$$

$$p_X(x) = \frac{1}{\mu + D}e^{-\tau(s-x)}, \qquad x \le s$$

where $E(\xi) \equiv \mu = 1/\tau$.

The λ-fold convolution of the gamma distribution is a gamma distribution:

$$\phi^\lambda(\xi) = \frac{\tau(\tau\xi)^{\lambda k-1}e^{-\tau\xi}}{(\lambda k - 1)!}.$$

Consider $k = 1$ and $\lambda = 2$. Then

$$\begin{aligned} p_{V,2}(v) &= \frac{1}{\mu + D} - \frac{e^{-\tau D}e^{-\tau(s-v)}}{\mu + D}, \qquad s \le v \le S \\ &= \frac{e^{-\tau(s-v)}}{\mu + D}[s - v + 1 - e^{-\tau D}], \qquad v \le s, \end{aligned}$$

where again $\mu = 1/\tau$.

2.4.4   Uniform Distribution

Consider the discrete uniform distribution

$$\phi(\xi) = \mu \qquad \xi = 0, 1, \cdots, \frac{1}{\mu} - 1 \ (= \text{integer}), \quad E(\xi) = \frac{\mu^{-1} - 1}{2}.$$

Let $\tau = 1/\mu$. We assume throughout that $D < \tau - 1$.

Proposition 2.4.4. For $\phi(\xi)$ a discrete uniform distribution

(1) $p_X(x) = \mu(1 - \mu)^{x-s-1}$ for $s + 1 \le x \le S$

(2) $p_X(x) = \mu$ for $S - \tau + 1 < x < s$

(3) $p_X(x) = \mu - \mu(1 - \mu)^{\tau-1-s+x}$ for $s - \tau + 1 \le x \le S - \tau$

(4) $p_X(x) = 0$ for $x \le s - \tau$

(5) $\sigma = (1 - \mu)^D$.

Proof.   (1) For $s + 1 \le x \le S$ the stationary equation is

$$p_X(x) = \mu \sum_{j=-\infty}^{s} p_X(j) + \mu \sum_{j=x}^{S} p_X(j) = \mu\sigma + \mu \sum_{j=x}^{S} p_X(j).$$

Then, using the Δ and E operators of Section 2.4.2,

(1a) $\Delta p_X(x) = -\mu p_X(x)$

(1b) $[E - (1 - \mu)]p_X(x) = 0.$

The general solution of (1) is

$$p_X(x) = C(1 - \mu)^x,$$

where C is a constant of summation. Now

$$p_X(s + 1) = \mu\sigma + \mu \sum_{j=s+1}^{S} p_X(j) = \mu,$$

and

$$p_X(s + 1) = C(1 - \mu)^{s+1}.$$

Therefore,

$$C = \mu(1 - \mu)^{-s-1}.$$

(2) For $x \le s$, the stationary equation is

$$p_X(x) = \phi(S - x)\sigma + \sum_{j=s+1}^{S} \phi(j - x)p_X(j).$$

In particular, for $S - \tau + 1 \leq x \leq s$,

$$p_X(x) = \mu\sigma + \mu(1 - \sigma) = \mu.$$

(3) For $s - \tau + 1 \leq x \leq S - \tau$,

$$p_X(x) = 0 + \mu \sum_{j=s+1}^{\tau-1+x} p_X(j) = \mu \sum_{j=s+1}^{\tau-1+x} \mu(1 - \mu)^{j-1-s} = \mu^2 \sum_{i=0}^{\tau-2+x-s} (1 - \mu)^i$$

$$= \mu - \mu(1 - \mu)^{\tau-1-s+x}.$$

(4) For $x \leq s - \tau$, the value of the right-hand side of the stationary equation is zero.

(5) Since

$$\sum_{j=s+1}^{S} \mu(1 - \mu)^{j-s-1} = 1 - (1 - \mu)^D, \quad \text{then} \quad \sigma = (1 - \mu)^D.$$

For the continuous uniform distribution

$$\phi(\xi) = \mu \qquad 0 \leq \xi \leq 1/\mu \equiv \tau,$$

where $D < \tau$, we state without proof the stationary density $p_X(x)$. The derivation of the results proceeds parallel to the proof of Proposition 2.4.4, where the differential operator replaces the difference operator.

$$p_X(x) = \mu e^{-\mu(x-s)} \qquad s \leq x \leq S$$
$$= \mu \qquad S - \tau \leq x \leq s$$
$$= \mu - \mu e^{-1-\mu(x-s)} \qquad s - \tau \leq x \leq S - \tau$$
$$= 0 \qquad x \leq s - \tau$$
$$\sigma = e^{-\mu D}$$

2.4.5   Numerical Examples of $p_X(x)$

In Table 2.4.1 for three distributions we exhibit $p_X(x \mid D = 3)$, computed according to Algorithm 2.2.4. We also show the stationary probabilities for the uniform distribution with $D = 2$ and 4; if we use Proposition 2.2.5, part (3), to pass from $D = 2$ to $D = 3$ to $D = 4$, then $\eta = 2/3$ followed by $\eta = 18/23$. In Tables 2.4.1 and 2.4.2 we have underlined the values of $p_X(s + 1)$ as a visual aid in the discussion of Section 2.4.7.

We analyze $p_X(x)$ for the Poisson distribution, $E(\xi) = 1$, $D = 3, 4, 5$, in Tables 2.4.2[14] and 2.4.3. Algorithm 2.2.4 and Proposition 2.2.5 are employed to obtain the stationary distributions accurate to four decimal places; to pass from $D = 3$ to $D = 4$, $\eta = 0.7776$, and from $D = 4$ to

[14] In Table 2.4.2, the case $D = 6$ is computed from Algorithm 2.2.4.

TABLE 2.4.1

		Uniform $E(\xi) = 1$			
		$D = 3$		$D = 4$	$D = 2$
j	$\phi(j)$	$f(j)$	$p_X(S - j)$	$p_X(S - j)$	$p_X(S - j)$
0	1/3	1/2	4/27	8/69	2/9
1	1/3	3/4	6/27	12/69	3/9
2	1/3	9/8	9/27	18/69	3/9
3		5/8	5/27	15/69	1/9
4		3/8	3/27	11/69	
5				5/69	
σ			8/27	16/69	4/9

	Binomial $N = 5$ $p = .2$ $E(\xi) = 1$			Poisson $E(\xi) = 2$		
		$D = 3$			$D = 3$	
j	$\phi(j)$	$f(j)$	$p_X(S - j)$	$\phi(j)$	$f(j)$	$p_X(S - j)$
0	.3277	.4874	.1434	.1353	.1565	.0785
1	.4096	.9062	.2666	.2707	.3620	.1816
2	.2048	1.0052	.2957	.2707	.4754	.2384
3	.0512	.6735	.1981	.1804	.4353	.2183
4	.0064	.2618	.0770	.0902	.2983	.1496
5	.0003	.0577	.0170	.0361	.1602	.0803
6		.0067	.0020	.0120	.0699	.0350
7		.0003	.0001	.0034	.0255	.0128
8				.0008	.0079	.0040
9				.0002	.0022	.0011
10					.0005	.0003
11					.0001	
σ			.2943			.5015

$D = 5$, $\eta = 0.8181$. We compare these probability figures with their estimates derived from a Monte Carlo simulation of 10,000 periods. The example is also used to test the speed with which statistical equilibrium is approached. The transition matrix $[T_X]$, truncated to the dimension 15, and having six-decimal-place probability entries, is raised to successively higher powers. As a result, the entries in each column j, $j = 0, 1, 2, \cdots, 14$,

TABLE 2.4.2

Poisson $E(\xi) = 1$

j	$\phi(j)$	$f(j)$	D = 3 $p_X(S-j)$ Algorithm	D = 3 $p_X(S-j)$ Monte Carlo	D = 4 $p_X(S-j)$ Algorithm	D = 4 $p_X(S-j)$ Monte Carlo	D = 5 $p_X(S-j)$ Algorithm	D = 5 $p_X(S-j)$ Monte Carlo	D = 6 $p_X(S-j)$ Algorithm
0	.3679	.5820	.1663	.1698	.1293	.1337	.1058	.1053	.0895
1	.3679	.9207	.2631	.2603	.2046	.2054	.1674	.1694	.1416
2	.1839	.9961	.2847	.2818	.2214	.2150	.1811	.1785	.1532
3	.0613	.6328	.1809	.1861	.2225	.2268	.1820	.1879	.1540
4	.0153	.2639	.0754	.0717	.1405	.1365	.1818	.1752	.1539
5	.0031	.0800	.0229	.0233	.0587	.0607	.1149	.1185	.1538
6	.0005	.0189	.0054	.0056	.0178	.0165	.0480	.0493	.0973
7	.0001	.0036	.0010	.0011	.0042	.0045	.0146	.0116	.0407
8		.0006	.0002	.0002	.0008	.0009	.0035	.0033	.0124
9		.0001		.0001	.0001		.0007	.0008	.0029
10							.0001	.0002	.0006
11									.0001
σ			.2859	.2881	.2222	.2191	.1819	.1837	.1540

TABLE 2.4.3

DIFFERENCE BETWEEN MAXIMAL AND MINIMAL ELEMENTS IN COLUMN j OF $[T_X]^k$

Poisson $E(\xi) = 1$

j	$D = 3$			$D = 4$				$D = 5$			
	$k=1$	$k=4$	$k=10$	$k=1$	$k=4$	$k=10$	$k=14$	$k=1$	$k=4$	$k=10$	$k=14$
0	.3679	.0069	.0000	.3679	.0339	.0002	.0000	.3679	.0654	.0021	.0002
1	.3679	.0069	.0000	.3679	.0339	.0002	.0000	.3679	.0779	.0029	.0003
2	.1839	.0034	.0000	.3679	.0321	.0002	.0000	.3679	.0771	.0024	.0003
3	.3066	.0042	.0000	.3066	.0272	.0002	.0000	.3679	.0624	.0023	.0002
4	.1686	.0026	.0000	.3526	.0231	.0001	.0000	.3526	.0655	.0024	.0002
5	.0582	.0009	.0000	.1809	.0123	.0001	.0000	.3648	.0580	.0018	.0002
9	.0001	.0000		.0005	.0000			.0031	.0004	.0000	
14	.0000			.0000				.0000			

converge to $p_X(S - j)$. Loosely, the speedier the convergence, the less the time dependence in the model, that is, the less useful is information about the state of the system in period t for predicting the state after several periods hence.[15] We measure in Table 2.4.3 how rapidly the convergence takes place by the difference between the largest and smallest element in each column of $[T_X]^k$.

We may summarize the results by noting that the Monte Carlo simulation for 10,000 periods gives approximately two-decimal-place accuracy. This conclusion is corroborated by further examples below.[16] As to the speed toward statistical equilibrium, convergence is slower for larger values of D, as we might suppose.

TABLE 2.4.4*a*

			Poisson $E(\xi) = 1$	
			$p_{V,3}(S - j)$	$p_{V,4}(S - j)$
j	$p_U(S - j)$	$\phi^3(j)$	$D = 3$	$D = 3$
			Algorithm	Algorithm
0	.4522	.0498	.0225	.0083
1	.2631	.1494	.0806	.0380
2	.2847	.2240	.1548	.0907
3		.2240	.2028	.1478
4		.1680	.1987	.1815
5		.1008	.1536	.1770
6		.0504	.0972	.1439
7		.0216	.0517	.0988
8		.0081	.0237	.0588
9		.0027	.0095	.0308
10		.0008	.0034	.0144
11		.0002	.0011	.0060
12		.0001	.0003	.0023
13			.0001	.0008
14				.0003
15				.0001
σ			.2859	.2859

[15] The reader may wish to review the discussion in Section 2.1.6.

[16] In Section 2.7.1 we discuss briefly the probability distribution of such Monte Carlo estimates; in anticipation, we mention that the estimates are unbiased and approximately normally distributed.

2.4.6 Examples of $p_{V,\lambda}(v)$

For $\phi(\xi)$ a Poisson distribution with mean 1, we present several distributions $[p_{V,\lambda}]$, Tables 2.4.4a–e. The values for

$$p_{V,3}(v \mid D = 3) \text{ and } p_{V,4} (v \mid D = 3)$$

in Table 2.4.4a are calculated according to Proposition 2.2.8, part (1), and utilize the data in Table 2.4.2. The values for $p_{V,4}(v \mid D = 5)$ in Table 2.4.4b are calculated both from Proposition 2.2.8 with the data in Table 2.4.2, and from a Monte Carlo simulation. The examples in Tables

TABLE 2.4.4b

			Poisson $E(\xi) = 1$				
	$D = 5$		$p_{V,4}(S - j)$				
j		$\phi^4(j)$	$D = 5$		$D = 6$	$D = 7$	$D = 9$
	$p_U(S - j)$		Algorithm	Monte Carlo	Monte Carlo	Monte Carlo	Monte Carlo
0	.2876	.0183	.0053	.0071	.0059	.0040	.0037
1	.1674	.0733	.0241	.0257	.0189	.0185	.0132
2	.1811	.1465	.0577	.0537	.0462	.0425	.0338
3	.1820	.1954	.0973	.0960	.0863	.0722	.0548
4	.1818	.1954	.1321	.1308	.1160	.0974	.0816
5		.1563	.1530	.1534	.1323	.1077	.0937
6		.1042	.1537	.1479	.1327	.1326	.0981
7		.0595	.1340	.1301	.1330	.1297	.1010
8		.0298	.1014	.1059	.1140	.1213	.0997
9		.0132	.0670	.0696	.0910	.0999	.1073
10		.0053	.0389	.0410	.0597	.0737	.0931
11		.0019	.0201	.0225	.0339	.0479	.0778
12		.0006	.0093	.0094	.0159	.0281	.0619
13		.0002	.0039	.0038	.0079	.0136	.0374
14		.0001	.0015	.0019	.0033	.0069	.0215
15		.0000	.0005	.0011	.0019	.0030	.0122
16			.0002	.0000	.0006	.0008	.0057
17			.0001	.0001	.0003	.0001	.0025
18			.0000	.0000	.0002	.0000	.0008
19				.0000	.0000	.0001	.0002
σ			.1819	.1839	.1527	.1323	.1052

2.4.4*c* and 2.4.4*d* are derived from Monte Carlo calculations, and those in Table 2.4.4*e* from Proposition 2.2.8. Recall that σ depends on D but not on λ; the exhibited variation in Tables 2.4.4*c* and 2.4.4*d* is due to sampling fluctuation, and the actual values for $D = 5$ and 6 are found in Table 2.4.4*e*.

TABLE 2.4.4c

Poisson $E(\xi) = 1$

j	$\phi^6(j)$	$p_{V,6}(S - j)$			
		$D = 5$	$D = 6$	$D = 7$	$D = 9$
		Monte Carlo	Monte Carlo	Monte Carlo	Monte Carlo
0	.0025	.0015	.0006	.0005	.0008
1	.0149	.0051	.0034	.0042	.0026
2	.0446	.0145	.0126	.0146	.0082
3	.0892	.0407	.0310	.0245	.0230
4	.1339	.0647	.0538	.0495	.0357
5	.1606	.0977	.0798	.0660	.0555
6	.1606	.1227	.1047	.0960	.0739
7	.1377	.1350	.1227	.1089	.0790
8	.1033	.1280	.1289	.1107	.0961
9	.0688	.1202	.1209	.1180	.1009
10	.0413	.0981	.1055	.1102	.1024
11	.0225	.0677	.0845	.0898	.0943
12	.0113	.0445	.0588	.0731	.0873
13	.0052	.0316	.0407	.0547	.0773
14	.0022	.0148	.0228	.0354	.0605
15	.0009	.0079	.0145	.0232	.0393
16	.0003	.0033	.0071	.0106	.0267
17	.0001	.0010	.0040	.0048	.0175
18	.0000	.0009	.0019	.0023	.0099
19		.0000	.0012	.0008	.0046
20		.0001	.0004	.0012	.0023
21		.0000	.0002	.0005	.0011
22		.0000	.0000	.0002	.0007
23		.0000	.0000	.0003	.0003
24		.0000	.0000	.0000	.0000
25		.0000	.0000	.0000	.0001
σ		.1807	.1555	.1333	.1061

TABLE 2.4.4*d*

Poisson $E(\xi) = 1$

j	$\phi^8(j)$	$p_{V,8}(S-j)$			
		$D = 5$	$D = 6$	$D = 7$	$D = 9$
		Monte Carlo	Monte Carlo	Monte Carlo	Monte Carlo
0	.0003	.0001	.0004	.0002	.0004
1	.0027	.0001	.0004	.0010	.0008
2	.0107	.0025	.0022	.0021	.0022
3	.0286	.0084	.0090	.0063	.0064
4	.0573	.0193	.0159	.0144	.0097
5	.0916	.0397	.0344	.0307	.0263
6	.1221	.0595	.0562	.0516	.0381
7	.1396	.0895	.0832	.0709	.0521
8	.1396	.1072	.1013	.0873	.0696
9	.1241	.1292	.1135	.0958	.0818
10	.0993	.1217	.1188	.1126	.0907
11	.0722	.1120	.1164	.1085	.0980
12	.0481	.0953	.1024	.1087	.1014
13	.0296	.0813	.0803	.0892	.0930
14	.0169	.0543	.0611	.0734	.0851
15	.0090	.0336	.0445	.0533	.0756
16	.0045	.0232	.0266	.0374	.0553
17	.0021	.0118	.0151	.0256	.0399
18	.0009	.0061	.0097	.0141	.0300
19	.0004	.0029	.0044	.0084	.0204
20	.0002	.0018	.0021	.0049	.0100
21	.0001	.0004	.0013	.0021	.0071
22	.0000	.0001	.0007	.0006	.0033
23		.0000	.0001	.0007	.0017
24		.0000	.0000	.0002	.0006
25		.0000	.0000	.0000	.0004
26		.0000	.0000	.0000	.0001
σ		.1861	.1546	.1339	.1057

In Tables 2.4.4*f*–*h* information about the right tails of $[p_{V,\lambda}]$ appears; specifically the largest k such that

$$\sum_{j=0}^{k} p_{V,\lambda}(S - j) \geq \omega$$

is given for several values of $E(\xi)$, λ, D, and ω. Notice in these tables that

TABLE 2.4.4e

	Poisson $E(\xi) = 1$					
	$p_{V,5}(S-j)$		$p_{V,7}(S-j)$		$p_{V,9}(S-j)$	
j	$D = 5$	$D = 6$	$D = 5$	$D = 6$	$D = 5$	$D = 6$
	Algorithm	Algorithm	Algorithm.	Algorithm	Algorithm	Algorithm
0	.0019	.0016	.0003	.0002	.0000	.0000
1	.0108	.0091	.0020	.0017	.0003	.0003
2	.0311	.0263	.0077	.0065	.0016	.0014
3	.0618	.0523	.0201	.0170	.0054	.0045
4	.0966	.0817	.0403	.0341	.0133	.0113
5	.1267	.1083	.0667	.0566	.0269	.0228
6	.1441	.1271	.0943	.0808	.0461	.0392
7	.1438	.1346	.1170	.1024	.0688	.0590
8	.1266	.1287	.1293	.1174	.0912	.0795
9	.0988	.1106	.1283	.1226	.1088	.0972
10	.0687	.0851	.1152	.1171	.1179	.1091
11	.0429	.0587	.0941	.1025	.1169	.1129
12	.0241	.0365	.0702	.0823	.1066	.1082
13	.0123	.0205	.0480	.0607	.0898	.0962
14	.0058	.0105	.0303	.0412	.0701	.0796
15	.0025	.0049	.0177	.0295	.0510	.0614
16	.0010	.0021	.0096	.0151	.0347	.0443
17	.0004	.0008	.0049	.0082	.1221	.0299
18	.0001	.0003	.0023	.0041	.0132	.0189
19		.0001	.0010	.0020	.0074	.0113
20			.0004	.0009	.0040	.0063
21			.0002	.0004	.0020	.0034
22			.0001	.0002	.0010	.0017
23				.0001	.0004	.0008
24					.0002	.0004
25					.0001	.0002
26						.0001
σ	.1819	.1548	.1819	.1548	.1819	.1548

for a given D and ω, k seems to depend mainly on the value of $\lambda E(\xi)$. These tables are based on calculations of $[p_{V,\lambda}]$ according to Proposition 2.2.8.

We point out that for a specified (s, S) policy, the probabilities such as those in Table 2.4.4 may be used to compute the stationary probability of no inventory on hand at the end of a period (when V is valued). For example, if the policy is $(2, 5)$, $\lambda = 3$ (first case in Table 2.4.4a), then the stationary probability of having no inventory on hand is $(0.1536 + 0.0972 + \cdots + 0.0001) = 0.3406$.

TABLE 2.4.4f

Largest k such that $\sum_{j=0}^{k} P_{V,\lambda}(S - j) \geq .80$

Poisson $E(\xi) = \mu$

$\lambda = 1$

					μ			
D	.25	.50	.75	1.00	3.00	5.00	7.00	10.00
1	1	1	1	2	6	8	9	13
2	1	2	2	2	9	11	12	14
4	3	3	3	4	15	17	19	21
8	6	6	7	7	28	30	31	34
16	13	13	13	13	53	55	57	60
32								
64								

$\lambda = 5$

D	.25	.50	.75	1.00	3.00	5.00	7.00	10.00
1	2	4	5	7	19	30	40	56
2	3	4	6	7	22	32	43	57
4	4	6	7	8	27	38	48	63
8	7	8	10	11	40	50	60	75
16	14	15	16	17	65	75	85	100
32								
64								

$\lambda = 9$

D	.25	.50	.75	1.00	3.00	5.00	7.00	10.00
1	3	6	9	11	32	51	70	98
2	4	7	9	12	35	54	72	99
4	5	8	10	13	40	59	77	105
8	8	11	13	16	52	70	88	116
16	15	17	19	21	77	95	113	140
32								
64								

$\lambda = 3$

					μ			
D	.25	.50	.75	1.00	3.00	5.00	7.00	10.00
1	1	2	3	4	13	19	25	35
2	2	3	4	5	15	21	28	36
4	3	4	5	6	21	27	33	42
8	7	7	8	9	34	40	45	54
16	13	14	14	15	59	65	71	80

$\lambda = 7$

D	.25	.50	.75	1.00	3.00	5.00	7.00	10.00
1	3	5	7	9	26	41	55	77
2	3	5	8	10	28	43	57	78
4	5	7	9	11	34	48	62	84
8	8	10	11	13	46	60	74	95
16	14	16	18	19	71	85	99	120

TABLE 2.4.4g

Largest k such that $\displaystyle\sum_{j=0}^{k} p_{V,\lambda}(S-j) \geq .90$

Poisson $E(\xi) = \mu$

Column group A — μ

D	.25	.50	.75	1.00	3.00	5.00	7.00	10.00
$\lambda = 1$								
1								
2								
4	1	1	2	2	7	9	11	14
8	2	2	2	3	10	12	14	16
16	3	4	4	4	17	19	21	24
32	7	7	7	8	31	33	35	38
64	14	14	15	15	60	62	64	67
$\lambda = 5$								
4	3	5	6	8	21	32	43	59
8	3	5	7	8	24	35	46	61
16	5	6	8	10	30	41	51	67
32	8	10	11	13	44	54	64	80
64	15	16	18	19	72	82	92	107
$\lambda = 9$								
4	4	7	10	13	35	54	74	102
8	5	8	11	13	37	57	76	104
16	6	9	12	15	43	62	81	110
32	9	12	15	17	56	75	94	122
64	16	19	21	24	84	102	121	148

Column group B — μ

D	.25	.50	.75	1.00	3.00	5.00	7.00	10.00
$\lambda = 3$								
1								
2								
4	2	3	4	5	14	21	27	37
8	3	4	5	6	17	24	30	39
16	4	5	6	7	23	30	36	46
32	7	8	9	10	37	43	50	59
64	15	15	16	17	66	72	78	87
$\lambda = 7$								
4	4	6	8	10	27	43	58	81
8	4	6	9	11	31	46	61	82
16	5	8	10	12	37	52	66	88
32	9	11	13	15	50	65	79	101
64	16	18	19	21	78	92	106	128

TABLE 2.4.4h

Largest k such that $\displaystyle\sum_{j=0}^{k} p_{V,\lambda}(S - j) \geq .99$

Poisson $E(\xi) = \mu$

$\lambda = 1$

D	μ = .25	.50	.75	1.00	3.00	5.00	7.00	10.00
1	2	3	3	4	9	12	14	18
2	3	3	4	4	13	16	18	22
4	4	5	6	6	20	23	26	29
8	7	9	9	10	35	38	41	44
16	16	16	17	17	67	69	71	75
32								
64								

$\lambda = 5$

D	μ = .25	.50	.75	1.00	3.00	5.00	7.00	10.00
1	4	7	9	11	26	38	50	67
2	5	7	9	11	29	41	53	69
4	7	9	11	13	36	48	59	77
8	10	12	14	16	51	62	74	91
16	18	20	21	23	81	92	104	120
32								
64								

$\lambda = 9$

D	μ = .25	.50	.75	1.00	3.00	5.00	7.00	10.00
1	6	10	13	17	41	62	82	111
2	7	11	14	17	44	65	85	114
4	8	12	15	18	50	71	92	121
8	12	15	18	21	65	85	105	135
16	19	22	25	28	95	115	135	164
32								
64								

$\lambda = 3$

D	μ = .25	.50	.75	1.00	3.00	5.00	7.00	10.00
1	3	5	6	8	18	26	33	43
2	4	6	7	8	21	29	36	46
4	6	7	8	10	28	36	43	53
8	9	11	12	13	43	50	57	68
16	17	18	19	20	74	81	88	98

$\lambda = 7$

D	μ = .25	.50	.75	1.00	3.00	5.00	7.00	10.00
1	5	8	11	14	34	50	66	90
2	6	9	12	14	37	53	69	92
4	8	10	13	16	43	60	76	99
8	11	14	16	19	58	74	90	113
16	18	21	23	26	88	104	119	142

2.4.7   Approximations for the Backlog Case

We examine the goodness of the approximations for $p_X(s + 1)$ and σ given in Section 2.2.6. In Table 2.4.5*a* we analyze the distributions previously discussed in Table 2.4.1. In Tables 2.4.5*b* and 2.4.6 we consider the

TABLE 2.4.5*a*
EXAMINATION OF BACKLOG APPROXIMATIONS

	$p_X(s + 1)$			σ	
	Actual Value	$\sigma/E(\xi)$	$\dfrac{1}{E(\xi) + D}$	Actual Value	$\dfrac{E(\xi)}{E(\xi) + D}$
Table 2.4.1					
Uniform $E(\xi) = 1$					
$D = 2$	.3333	.4444	.3333	.4444	.3333
$D = 3$	.3333	.2963	.2500	.2963	.2500
$D = 4$	.2174	.2319	.2000	.2319	.2000
Binomial $E(\xi) = 1$	.2957	.2943	.2500	.2943	.2500
Poisson $E(\xi) = 2$	.2384	.2507	.2000	.5015	.4000

TABLE 2.4.5*b*
EXAMINATION OF BACKLOG APPROXIMATIONS
Poisson Distribution with Parameter $E(\xi)$

$E(\xi)$	D	$P_X(s + 1)$			σ	
		Actual Value	$\sigma/E(\xi)$	$\dfrac{1}{E(\xi) + D}$	Actual Value	$\dfrac{E(\xi)}{E(\xi) + D}$
.25	1	.7788	.8848	.8000	.2212	.2000
	2	.4681	.4708	.4444	.1177	.1111
	4	.2424	.2424	.2353	.0606	.0588
	8	.1231	.1232	.1212	.0308	.0303
	16	.0620	.0620	.0615	.0155	.0154
.50	1	.6065	.7870	.6667	.3935	.3333
	2	.4353	.4444	.4000	.2222	.2000
	4	.2353	.2354	.2222	.1177	.1111
	8	.1212	.1212	.1176	.0606	.0588
	16	.0615	.0616	.0606	.0308	.0303

TABLE 2.4.5b (cont.)

$E(\xi)$	D	$p_X(s + 1)$			σ	
		Actual Value	$\sigma/E(\xi)$	$\dfrac{1}{E(\xi) + D}$	Actual Value	$\dfrac{E(\xi)}{E(\xi) + D}$
.75	1	.4724	.7017	.5714	.5276	.4286
	2	.4017	.4199	.3636	.3157	.2727
	4	.2287	.2280	.2105	.1714	.1579
	8	.1194	.1190	.1143	.0895	.0857
	16	.0611	.0609	.0597	.0458	.0448
1	1	.3679	.6321	.5000	.6321	.5000
	2	.3679	.3996	.3333	.3996	.3333
	3	.2847	.2859	.2500	.2859	.2500
	4	.2225	.2222	.2000	.2222	.2000
	5	.1818	.1819	.1667	.1819	.1667
	6	.1538	.1540	.1429	.1548	.1429
	8	.1176	.1177	.1111	.1177	.1111
	16	.0606	.0606	.0588	.0606	.0588
3	4	.1812	.1828	.1429	.5488	.4286
	8	.1050	.1052	.0909	.3158	.2727
	16	.0571	.0571	.0526	.1714	.1579
	32	.0299	.0298	.0286	.0896	.0857
	64	.0153	.0153	.0149	.0458	.0448
5	4	.1161	.1568	.1111	.7840	.5555
	8	.0976	.0950	.0769	.4749	.3846
	16	.0540	.0541	.0476	.2703	.2381
	32	.0290	.0290	.0270	.1449	.1351
	64	.0150	.0150	.0145	.0752	.0725
7	4	.0485	.1319	.0909	.9240	.6364
	8	.1022	.0876	.0667	.6132	.4667
	16	.0519	.0513	.0435	.3593	.3043
	32	.0282	.0282	.0256	.1972	.1795
	64	.0148	.0148	.0141	.1037	.0986
10	4	.0075	.0990	.0714	.9898	.7142
	8	.0742	.0819	.0556	.8190	.5556
	16	.0414	.0474	.0385	.4740	.3846
	32	.0272	.0270	.0238	.2704	.2381
	64	.0145	.0145	.0135	.1449	.1351

TABLE 2.4.6

Poisson $E(\xi) = 4$

j	$\phi(j)$	$p_X(S - j)$			
		$D = 2$	$D = 4$	$D = 8$	$D = 16$
0	.0183	.0170	.0126	.0075	.0041
1	.0733	.0694	.0514	.0304	.0169
2	.1465	.1414	.1067	.0630	.0351
3	.1954	.1920	.1528	.0903	.0502
4	.1954	.1954	.1715	.1032	.0574
5	.1563	.1590	.1610	.1046	.0581
6	.1042	.1078	.1305	.1018	.0565
7	.0595	.0626	.0929	.0997	.0554
8	.0298	.0318	.0586	.0974	.0552
9	.0132	.0144	.0329	.0905	.0554
10	.0053	.0058	.0166	.0763	.0555
11	.0019	.0022	.0076	.0569	.0556
12	.0006	.0007	.0031	.0373	.0556
13	.0002	.0002	.0012	.0216	.0556
14	.0001	.0001	.0004	.0111	.0556
15	.0000	.0000	.0001	.0051	.0556
16			.0000	.0021	.0546
17				.0008	.0505
18				.0003	.0424
19				.0001	.0315
20				.0000	.0206
21					.0120
22					.0062
23					.0028
24					.0012
25					.0005
26					.0002
27					.0001
σ		.9135	.6765	.3997	.2226
$E(\xi)/E(\xi) + D$		.6667	.5000	.3333	.2000
$p_X(s + 1)$		.0694	.1528	.0997	.0556
$\sigma/E(\xi)$		.2284	.1691	.0999	.0556
$1/E(\xi) + D$		.1667	.1250	.0833	.0500

94

TABLE 2.4.7
DIFFERENCE BETWEEN MAXIMAL AND MINIMAL ELEMENTS
IN COLUMN j OF $[T_X]^k$
Poisson $E(\xi) = 4$

j	$D = 8$	$D = 16$		
	$k = 8$	$k = 8$	$k = 16$	$k = 24$
0	.0002	.0031	.0005	.0001
1	.0007	.0125	.0021	.0003
2	.0012	.0255	.0043	.0006
3	.0012	.0352	.0060	.0009
4	.0010	.0381	.0066	.0010
5	.0010	.0352	.0062	.0009
6	.0015	.0328	.0056	.0008
7	.0017	.0332	.0049	.0008
8	.0013	.0367	.0054	.0009
9	.0008	.0386	.0055	.0010

Four place accuracy is obtained at the 8th power for $D = 2, 4$, at the 16th power for $D = 8$, and at the 40th power for $D = 16$. Intermediate powers were not calculated.

manner in which the approximations improve for increasing values of D when we use a Poisson distribution. We also present in Table 2.4.7 information regarding the speed of convergence for $\phi(\xi)$ a Poisson distribution with mean 4.[17] The conclusion given in Section 2.4.5 concerning the effect of increasing D is noticed again, and further the speed seems to be decreased by a higher value for $E(\xi)$.

2.4.8 Calculations with $[T_V]$

In Tables 2.4.8a–c we exhibit $q(v \mid r, \tau)$ for the policy (3, 8), $\lambda = 8$, with Poisson distributions having mean .5, 1, and 2; these figures are calculated by raising $[T_V]$, containing six-decimal-place probability entries, to high powers.[18] We also show the associated distributions $[q_{V,\lambda}]$ and $[q_{X,\lambda}]$, computed according to Section 2.3.2; for the sake of comparison, a set of

[17] In the calculation of matrix powers, we use truncated matrices for $[T_X]$ of dimension 19, 21, 25, and 33, for $D= 2, 4, 8$, and 16, respectively; the entries are six-decimal-place probabilities.

[18] The first value of k such that the regular Markov chain $[T_V]$ has all positive elements when raised to this power is 2λ. For mean .5, three-decimal-place accuracy in

estimates for $[q_{V,\lambda}]$ found by means of a Monte Carlo simulation is exhibited in Table 2.4.12.

We apply Algorithm 2.3.2 to the model (0, 5), $\lambda = 3$, with a Poisson distribution having mean 1, the results appearing in Table 2.4.9; these may serve for comparison with estimates from a Monte Carlo simulation. Referring to Section 2.3.2, in solving for relation (4) we employ the suggestion contained in the first footnote in Section 2.3.8. The probabilities $q(v \mid 0, 0)$, $v > 0$, are first obtained in terms of $q(5 \mid 0, 0)$; then $q(0 \mid 0, 0)$ is calculated in terms of $q(5 \mid 0, 0)$ according to relation (3*b*), and the normalization suggested in (6) follows.

2.4.9   *Effects of Variation in System Parameters on* $[q_{V,2}]$ (*Monte Carlo Simulation*)

Letting $\phi(\xi)$ be a Poisson distribution having mean 1 and $\lambda = 8$, we exhibit in Table 2.4.10 the effects of changes in the (*s, S*) policy. We can discern that holding D fixed and letting s increase causes $q_{V,8}(0)$ and $q_{V,8}(S)$ to decrease, and $q_{V,8}(s + 1)$ and σ to increase, where $D > s$. Holding s fixed and letting D increase causes σ to decrease. These increases in D also bring about a decrease in $q_{V,8}(0)$ if $D > s$. If $D \leq s$, $q_{V,8}(0)$ also decreases, but there is a discontinuity when the assumption that no more than one order may be outstanding comes into force, having the result that $q_{V,8}(0)$ jumps upward. For a fixed value of $S(=7, 8, 9)$, letting s increase seems to cause $q_{V,8}(0)$, $q_{V,8}(S)$, and $q_{V,8}(S - 1)$ to decrease, $q_{V,8}(s + 1)$ to increase for $D > s$, and σ to increase.

In Tables 2.4.11*a*, *b* we let $\phi(\xi)$ be a Poisson distribution having mean 1 and $D = 5$, and examine $\lambda = 4, 6, 8$, and $s = 1, 2, 4, 6, 8$.[19] Holding λ fixed and increasing s causes movements in the same direction noted in Table 2.4.10 for $D > s$. For $D \leq s$, $q_{V,\lambda}(s + 1)$ seems to decrease and σ to increase. Observe that $D < s$ for $s = 6, 8$; consequently, more than one order may be outstanding at a time. This option coupled with the effect of increasing s causes $q_{V,\lambda}(0)$ to decrease sharply, especially for larger λ. Keeping s fixed, as λ increases, $q_{V,\lambda}(0)$ increases, $q_{V,\lambda}(S)$, $q_{V,\lambda}(s + 1)$, and σ decrease.

---

the stationary probabilities is obtained by going from the 32nd to the 64th power (intermediate powers in this instance and to follow were not calculated), and four-decimal-place accuracy from the 64th to the 128th power. For mean 1, four-decimal-place accuracy is obtained by going from the 64th to the 128th power; three-decimal-place accuracy is not present in the 64th power. For mean 2, four-decimal place accuracy in practically all instances is obtained by going from the 192nd to the 256th power; three-decimal-place accuracy is not present in the 128th power.

[19] Note that the case $s = 0$ is in Table 2.4.9; it is repeated in Table 2.4.11*a* for convenience.

TABLE 2.4.8*a*
(3, 8), $\lambda = 8$
Poisson $E(\xi) = .5$

v, r	$q(v \mid r, \tau)$							
	$\tau = 7$	$\tau = 6$	$\tau = 5$	$\tau = 4$	$\tau = 3$	$\tau = 2$	$\tau = 1$	$\sum_\tau$
3, 5	.0351	.0213	.0129	.0078	.0048	.0029	.0017	.0866
2, 5	.0176	.0213	.0194	.0157	.0119	.0086	.0061	.1006
1, 5	.0044	.0107	.0145	.0157	.0149	.0130	.0107	.0838
0, 5	.0000	.0047	.0111	.0187	.0264	.0334	.0393	.1344
2, 6	.0081	.0049	.0030	.0018	.0011	.0007	.0004	.0199
1, 6	.0040	.0049	.0044	.0036	.0027	.0020	.0014	.0231
0, 6	.0012	.0035	.0059	.0079	.0095	.0106	.0115	.0501
1, 7	.0013	.0008	.0005	.0003	.0002	.0001	.0001	.0032
0, 7	.0008	.0013	.0016	.0018	.0019	.0020	.0021	.0117
0, 8	.0003	.0003	.0003	.0003	.0003	.0003	.0003	.0020

v	$\phi(8 - v)$	$q(v \mid 0, 0)$	$q_{V,8}(v)$	$\dfrac{\sigma - \sigma_v^*}{E(\xi)}$	σ_v^*	$q_{X,8}(v)$
8	.6065	.0041	.0041			.1157
7	.3033	.0217	.0217			.1570
6	.0758	.0698	.0698			.2036
5	.0126	.1702	.1702			.3046
4	.0016	.1454	.1454			.1454
3	.0002	.0579	.1445	.1451	.0011	.0579
2	.0000	.0133	.1337	.1361	.0055	.0133
1	.0000	.0021	.1121	.1171	.0150	.0021
0	.0000	.0003	.1984			.0003

σ	.0736
$E(\xi)/\lambda E(\xi) + D$	.0556
$q_{V,8}(4)$	.1453
$\sigma/E(\xi)$	.1472
$1/\lambda E(\xi) + D$	.1111

TABLE 2.4.8*b*
(3, 8), $\lambda = 8$
Poisson $E(\xi) = 1$

v, r	$q(v \mid r, \tau)$							
	$\tau = 7$	$\tau = 6$	$\tau = 5$	$\tau = 4$	$\tau = 3$	$\tau = 2$	$\tau = 1$	$\sum_{\tau}$
3, 5	.0211	.0078	.0029	.0011	.0004	.0001	.0001	.0333
2, 5	.0211	.0155	.0086	.0042	.0019	.0009	.0004	.0525
1, 5	.0105	.0155	.0128	.0084	.0048	.0026	.0013	.0559
0, 5	.0046	.0185	.0330	.0436	.0501	.0537	.0556	.2592
2, 6	.0089	.0033	.0012	.0004	.0002	.0001	.0000	.0140
1, 6	.0089	.0065	.0036	.0018	.0008	.0004	.0002	.0221
0, 6	.0064	.0143	.0193	.0219	.0231	.0237	.0239	.1326
1, 7	.0027	.0010	.0004	.0001	.0001	.0000	.0000	.0043
0, 7	.0046	.0063	.0069	.0072	.0073	.0073	.0073	.0469
0, 8	.0021	.0021	.0021	.0021	.0021	.0021	.0021	.0148

v	$\phi(8 - v)$	$q(v \mid 0, 0)$	$q_{V,8}(v)$	$\dfrac{\sigma - \sigma_v{}^*}{E(\xi)}$	$\sigma_v{}^*$	$q_{X,8}(v)$
8	.3679	.0034	.0034			.0697
7	.3679	.0139	.0139			.1354
6	.1839	.0481	.0481			.2366
5	.0613	.1218	.1218			.3810
4	.0153	.0863	.0863			.0863
3	.0031	.0573	.0906	.0908	.0000	.0573
2	.0005	.0241	.0906	.0906	.0003	.0241
1	.0001	.0073	.0896	.0898	.0010	.0073
0	.0000	.0021	.4557			.0021

σ	.0909
$E(\xi)/\lambda E(\xi) + D$	.0769
$q_{V,8}(4)$	.0863
$\sigma/E(\xi)$	.0909
$1/\lambda E(\xi) + D$	.0769

TABLE 2.4.8c
(3, 8), $\lambda = 8$
Poisson $E(\xi) = 2$

v, r	$q(v \mid r, \tau)$							
	$\tau = 7$	$\tau = 6$	$\tau = 5$	$\tau = 4$	$\tau = 3$	$\tau = 2$	$\tau = 1$	$\sum_{\tau}$
3, 5	.0058	.0008	.0001	.0000	.0000	.0000	.0000	.0067
2, 5	.0115	.0031	.0006	.0001	.0000	.0000	.0000	.0154
1, 5	.0115	.0062	.0019	.0005	.0001	.0000	.0000	.0202
0, 5	.0137	.0324	.0399	.0419	.0424	.0425	.0425	.2553
2, 6	.0041	.0006	.0001	.0000	.0000	.0000	.0000	.0047
1, 6	.0082	.0022	.0004	.0001	.0000	.0000	.0000	.0109
0, 6	.0179	.0274	.0296	.0301	.0302	.0302	.0302	.1956
1, 7	.0022	.0003	.0004	.0000	.0000	.0000	.0000	.0026
0, 7	.0142	.0162	.0164	.0165	.0165	.0165	.0165	.1127
0, 8	.0110	.0110	.0110	.0110	.0110	.0110	.0110	.0768

v	$\phi(8 - v)$	$q(v \mid 0, 0)$	$q_{V,8}(v)$	$\dfrac{\sigma - \sigma_v{}^*}{E(\xi)}$	$\sigma_v{}^*$	$q_{X,8}(v)$
8	.1353	.0127	.0127			.1034
7	.2707	.0230	.0230			.1620
6	.2707	.0461	.0461			.2618
5	.1804	.0734	.0734			.3287
4	.0902	.0435	.0435			.0435
3	.0361	.0425	.0492	.0501	.0000	.0425
2	.0120	.0302	.0503	.0501	.0000	.0302
1	.0034	.0165	.0502	.0501	.0000	.0165
0	.0009	.0110	.6513			.0110

σ	.1001
$E(\xi)/\lambda E(\xi) + D$	.0952
$q_{V,8}(4)$	.0435
$\sigma/E(\xi)$	.0501
$1/\lambda E(\xi) + D$	.0476

TABLE 2.4.9

(0, 5)

Poisson $E(\xi) = 1$

v	$\dfrac{q(v\mid 0,0)}{q(5\mid 0,0)}$	$q_{V,1}(v)$		$q_{V,4}(v)$		$q_{V,6}(v)$		$q_{V,8}(v)$	
		Algorithm	Monte Carlo	Algorithm	Monte Carlo	Algorithm	Monte Carlo	Algorithm	Monte Carlo
5	1.0000	.2434	.2369	.1666	.1665	.1376	.1389	.1172	.1162
4	.5820	.1417	.1439	.0969	.0896	.0801	.0834	.0682	.0698
3	.6296	.1533	.1484	.1049	.1079	.0866	.0840	.0738	.0722
2	.6327	.1540	.1544	.1054	.1077	.0871	.0861	.0742	.0779
1	.6320	.1538	.1606	.1053	.1063	.0870	.0868	.0741	.0757
0	.6319	.1538	.1558	.4209	.4220	.5217	.5202	.5925	.5882
σ		.1538	.1558	.1052	.1055	.0869	.0869	.0741	.0736
$E(\xi)/\lambda E(\xi) + D$		.1667	.1667	.1111	.11i1	.0999	.0999	.0769	.0769

$$\frac{\Sigma}{q(5\mid 0,0)} = \sum_{v=1}^{5} \frac{q(v\mid 0,0)}{q(5\mid 0,0)} = 3.4763$$

$q(5\mid 0,0)[(2)] = 1$

$q(5\mid 0,0) = [(2)]^{-1}$,

$q(5\mid 0,0)[(1)] = \lambda q_{V,8}(0)$

$[(1)]/[(2)] = \lambda q_{V,8}(0) = q_{V,\lambda}(0)$

$q_{V,8}(0) = \sigma$

λ	(1) $\dfrac{\lambda q_{V,8}(0)}{q(5\mid 0,0)}$	(2) $\dfrac{\Sigma + \lambda q_{V,8}(0)}{q(5\mid 0,0)}$
1	.6319	4.1082
4	2.5236	6.0039
6	3.7914	7.2677
8	5.0552	8.5315

TABLE 2.4.10
Poisson $E(\xi) = 1$
$\lambda = 8$
(Monte Carlo Simulation)

v	$q_{V,8}(v)$					
	(2, 5)	(2, 6)	(3, 6)	(2, 7)	(3, 7)	(4, 7)
7				.0154	.0036	.0042
6		.0137	.0070	.0427	.0167	.0158
5	.0155	.0468	.0272	.1129	.0581	.0384
4	.0551	.1237	.0519	.0750	.1304	.1074
3	.1363	.0895	.2191	.0859	.0905	.2123
2	.0977	.0933	.1378	.0840	.0970	.1314
1	.0986	.0933	.1228	.0814	.0982	.1227
0	.5968	.5397	.4342	.5027	.5055	.3678
σ	.0992	.0908	.1565	.0836	.0990	.1711
$E(\xi)/\lambda E(\xi) + D$	.0909	.0833	.0909	.0769	.0833	.0909

v	$q_{V,8}(v)$						
	(2, 8)	(3, 8)	(4, 8)	(2, 9)	(3, 9)	(4, 9)	(4, 10)
10							.0008
9				.0127	.0039	.0007	.0061
8	.0124	.0047	.0040	.0376	.0150	.0050	.0171
7	.0372	.0145	.0114	.1005	.0435	.0170	.0493
6	.1051	.0531	.0279	.0605	.1087	.0619	.1226
5	.0717	.1193	.0616	.0710	.0777	.1314	.0833
4	.0750	.0855	.1939	.0724	.0816	.0901	.0918
3	.0819	.0859	.1219	.0735	.0852	.0995	.0829
2	.0793	.0883	.1176	.0731	.0801	.0962	.0896
1	.0767	.0868	.1125	.0699	.0803	.0957	.0820
0	.4607	.4619	.3492	.4288	.4240	.4025	.3745
σ	.0771	.0904	.1436	.0715	.0837	.0980	.0901
$E(\xi)/\lambda E(\xi) + D$	.0714	.0769	.0833	.0667	.0714	.0769	.0833

TABLE 2.4.11*a*
Poisson $E(\xi) = 1$, $D = 5$
(Monte Carlo Simulation)

v	$q_{V,\lambda}(v)$					
	(0, 5)			(1, 6)		
	$\lambda = 4$	$\lambda = 6$	$\lambda = 8$	$\lambda = 4$	$\lambda = 6$	$\lambda = 8$
6				.0647	.0563	.0504
5	.1665	.1389	.1162	.1523	.1232	.1028
4	.0896	.0834	.0698	.1066	.0858	.0714
3	.1079	.0840	.0722	.1163	.0879	.0773
2	.1077	.0861	.0779	.1105	.0912	.0805
1	.1063	.0868	.0757	.1158	.0910	.0763
0	.4220	.5208	.5882	.3338	.4646	.5413
σ	.1055	.0869	.0736	.1124	.0926	.0772
$E(\xi)/\lambda E(\xi) + D$	.1111	.0999	.0769	.1111	.0999	.0769

v	$q_{V,\lambda}(v)$					
	(2, 7)			(4, 9)		
	$\lambda = 4$	$\lambda = 6$	$\lambda = 8$	$\lambda = 4$	$\lambda = 6$	$\lambda = 8$
9				.0046	.0019	.0007
8				.0241	.0059	.0050
7	.0257	.0175	.0154	.0657	.0275	.0170
6	.0693	.0528	.0427	.1223	.0798	.0619
5	.1653	.1304	.1129	.1753	.1517	.1314
4	.1190	.0935	.0750	.1439	.1126	.0901
3	.1248	.1026	.0859	.1373	.1181	.0995
2	.1198	.0997	.0840	.1222	.1195	.0962
1	.1090	.0973	.0814	.0865	.1062	.0957
0	.2671	.4062	.5027	.1181	.2768	.4025
σ	.1240	.1006	.0836	.1520	.1223	.0980
$E(\xi)/\lambda E(\xi) + D$	.1111	.0999	.0769	.1111	.0999	.0769

TABLE 2.4.11*b*
Poisson $E(\xi) = 1$, $D = 5$
(Monte Carlo Simulation)

v	$q_{V,\lambda}(v)$					
	(6, 11)			(8, 13)		
	$\lambda = 4$	$\lambda = 6$	$\lambda = 8$	$\lambda = 4$	$\lambda = 6$	$\lambda = 8$
13				.0051	.0005	.0006
12				.0303	.0061	.0018
11	.0065	.0017	.0016	.0576	.0233	.0060
10	.0264	.0074	.0057	.0976	.0434	.0188
9	.0620	.0264	.0145	.1347	.0721	.0381
8	.1033	.0519	.0304	.1473	.0939	.0574
7	.1418	.0807	.0512	.1582	.1310	.0952
6	.1588	.1366	.1050	.1283	.1498	.1262
5	.1682	.1799	.1681	.1036	.1478	.1709
4	.1241	.1321	.1222	.0669	.1166	.1203
3	.0922	.1230	.1146	.0376	.0859	.1037
2	.0566	.0911	.1077	.0192	.0548	.0895
1	.0306	.0717	.0821	.0074	.0337	.0645
0	.0295	.0975	.1969	.0062	.0411	.1070
σ	.1733	.1599	.1416	.1787	.1694	.1551
$E(\xi)/\lambda E(\xi) + D$	.1111	.0999	.0769	.1111	.0999	.0769

The effect of changing the mean [of a Poisson $\phi(\xi)$] is illustrated in Table 2.4.12 for the policy (3, 8), $\lambda = 8$. Increasing the Poisson expectation increases $q_{V,8}(0)$ and σ, and decreases $q_{V,8}(s + 1 = 4)$.

2.4.10 Approximations for the No-backlog Case

Tables 2.4.8 through 2.4.12 contain values for the approximations suggested in Section 2.3.8. The approximations directly based on an extended renewal theorem, that is, those in terms of σ, agree well with the actual figures for values of V around $s + 1$. As D increases, the approximations improve and, furthermore, the distribution $[q_{V,\lambda}]$ resembles a uniform distribution sufficiently fast so that the renewal approximation is good for a domain of values above $s + 1$.

The behavior of approximations (4*b*) and (4*c*) in Section 2.3.8 is as predicted, namely, there is an improvement, *ceteris paribus*, with increases

TABLE 2.4.12
Poisson, (3, 8), $\lambda = 8$
(Monte Carlo Simulation)

v	$q_{V,8}(v)$						
	$E(\xi) = .25$	$E(\xi) = .50$	$E(\xi) = .75$	$E(\xi) = 1$	$E(\xi) = 2$	$E(\xi) = 4$	$E(\xi) = 8$
8	.0211	.0041	.0035	.0047	.0141	.0390	.0765
7	.0818	.0283	.0144	.0145	.0245	.0245	.0142
6	.1388	.0734	.0586	.0531	.0409	.0322	.0120
5	.2002	.1672	.1384	.1193	.0763	.0367	.0113
4	.1781	.1382	.1139	.0855	.0441	.0216	.0046
3	.1564	.1435	.1109	.0859	.0497	.0240	.0081
2	.1147	.1325	.1054	.0883	.0464	.0260	.0118
1	.0659	.1111	.1101	.0868	.0474	.0259	.0140
0	.0430	.2017	.3448	.4619	.6566	.7701	.8475
σ	.0475	.0736	.0840	.0904	.1001	.1058	.1102
$E(\xi)/\lambda E(\xi) + D$	.0357	.0556	.1071	.0769	.0952	.1081	.1159
$E(\xi)/E(\xi) + D$	.0476	.0999	.1304	.1667	.2857	.4444	.6154
$q_{V,8}(4)$	.1781	.1382	.1139	.0855	.0441	.0216	.0046
$\sigma/E(\xi)$	.1900	.1472	.1120	.0904	.0501	.0265	.0138
$1/\lambda E(\xi) + D$	.1429	.1111	.0999	.0769	.0476	.0270	.0145

TABLE 2.4.13
Poisson $E(\xi) = .25$, $D = 10$, $\lambda = 8$
(Monte Carlo Simulation)

v	$q_{V,8}(v)$	
	(3, 13)	(5, 15)
15		.0128
14		.0410
13	.0132	.0793
12	.0436	.0897
11	.0698	.0953
10	.1087	.0916
9	.0876	.0990
8	.0904	.0936
7	.0941	.0976
6	.1037	.1065
5	.0937	.0851
4	.1032	.0604
3	.0843	.0312
2	.0493	.0122
1	.0334	.0033
0	.0250	.0014
σ	.0240	.0242
$E(\xi)/\lambda E(\xi) + D$	.0208	.0208
$E(\xi)/E(\xi) + D$	.0244	.0244
$q_{V,8}(s + 1)$	.1032	.1065
$\sigma/E(\xi)$	.0960	.0968
$1/E(\xi) + D$	.0976	.0976

in D, λ, and $E(\xi)$, and with decreases in s. The notable failures[20] are found in Table 2.4.12 for small values of $E(\xi)$. In these instances the likelihood of inventory falling to zero during a delivery lag period is not large, and therefore as s increases the backlog approximations provide better estimates. To illustrate the effects of increasing D and s for such situations, we present in Table 2.4.13 the results of the policies (3, 13) and (5, 15) for $\phi(\xi)$ a Poisson distribution having mean .25. The increase in D over that in Table 2.4.12 causes the distribution $[q_{V,\lambda}]$ to flatten at a value well predicted by the renewal theorem in terms of σ; because the values of s

---

[20] That is, failures occurring when the underlying assumption $D > s$ is valid. Several cases of $D \leq s$ appear in Tables 2.4.10 and 2.4.11, and the approximation values are poor.

are large relative to $\lambda E(\xi)$, the backlog approximations serve well for estimating σ.

2.4.11 Constrained (s, S) Policies

We discussed in Section 2.3.7 two types of constraints on (s, S) policies, namely, only one order may be outstanding at any time, and only one order may be outstanding at the end of every period before any new order is

TABLE 2.4.14
Poisson $E(\xi) = 1$
$(2, 3)$, $\lambda = 3$

$(v \mid r, \tau)$	One Order Any Time	One Order at End
$(3 \mid 0, 0)$	.0290	.0203
$(2 \mid 0, 0)$	.1754	.0191
$(1 \mid 0, 0)$	.1458	.0114
$(0 \mid 0, 0)$	.0023	.0016
$(2 \mid 1, 2)$	.0646	.0785
$(1 \mid 1, 2)$	.0646	.3772
$(0 \mid 1, 2)$	.0464	.0050
$(1 \mid 2, 2)$	.0537	.0042
$(0 \mid 2, 2)$	.0922	.0072
$(0 \mid 3, 2)$	.0023	.0016
$(2 \mid 1, 1)$	.0237	.0289
$(1 \mid 1, 1)$	.0475	.1677
$(0 \mid 1, 1)$	.1042	.2642
$(1 \mid 2, 1)$	.0197	.0015
$(0 \mid 2, 1)$	.1261	.0098
$(0 \mid 3, 1)$	.0023	.0016

v	$q_{V,3}(v)$		
	One Order Any Time	One Order at End	General (Monte Carlo)
3	.0290	.0203	.0927
2	.2637	.1265	.2742
1	.3313	.5620	.3995
0	.3759	.2912	.2336
σ	.3236	.4738	.4859

placed. As we mentioned, the second restriction is less severe than the first, in that the second permits an order to be placed in a period immediately prior to one in which a delivery occurs. In Table 2.4.14 we tabulate the stationary probabilities under the two restrictions for the policy (2, 3), $\lambda = 3$, and $\phi(\xi)$, a Poisson distribution having mean 1; for the sake of

TABLE 2.4.15
Poisson $E(\xi) = 1$
(3, 5), $\lambda = 3$

State	Stationary Probability	v	$q_{V,3}(v)$ Algorithm	Monte Carlo
(5, 0, 0)	.0495	5	.0495	.0532
(4, 0, 0)	.1468	4	.1468	.1445
(3, 0, 0)	.1231	3	.2577	.2531
(2, 0, 0)	.0545	2	.2767	.2754
(1, 0, 0)	.0098	1	.1322	.1359
(0, 0, 0)	.0030	0	.1371	.1379
(3, 0, 2)	.0856			
(2, 0, 2)	.0720	σ	.3301	.3306
(1, 0, 2)	.0226			
(0, 0, 2)	.0099			
(2, 0, 3)	.0459			
(1, 0, 3)	.0200			
(0, 0, 3)	.0144			
(1, 0, 4)	.0036			
(0, 0, 4)	.0062			
(0, 0, 5)	.0030			
(3, 2, 0)	.0490			
(2, 2, 0)	.0775			
(1, 2, 0)	.0422			
(0, 2, 0)	.0259			
(1, 2, 2)	.0083			
(0, 2, 2)	.0143			
(0, 2, 3)	.0099			
(2, 3, 0)	.0268			
(1, 3, 0)	.0243			
(0, 3, 0)	.0248			
(0, 3, 2)	.0144			
(1, 4, 0)	.0013			
(0, 4, 0)	.0084			
(0, 5, 0)	.0030			

Four-decimal-place accuracy is obtained between the 18th and 21st power of the transition matrix.

comparison we also show Monte Carlo estimates of the stationary probabilities for the unconstrained policy. We summarize the results by noting
that the more restrictive the constraints, the higher the probability of no
inventory on hand and the lower the value of σ; in the lesser of the two
constrained situations, ordering takes place most often in periods immediately preceding a delivery.

2.4.12   General (*s, S*) Policy

We utilize the illustration in Section 2.3.10 for an example of an (*s, S*)
policy with $D < s$. Table 2.4.15 contains the stationary probabilities for
the policy (3, 5), $\lambda = 3$, assuming a Poisson distribution $\phi(\xi)$ having mean 1
and computed from the transition matrix Table 2.3.11. We also exhibit a
Monte Carlo simulation of the model for the sake of comparison.

2.5   EXPECTATIONS OF PRIMARY OPERATING CHARACTERISTICS

The probability analysis in Sections 2.2 and 2.3 can be employed in a
direct manner to evaluate expectations of various system operating characteristics, that is, if we have any real valued function defined on the states of
the system, then the expected value of the function with respect to the
stationary probabilities can be calculated in a straightforward fashion by
computing the particular probability weighted average. Certain functions
in particular, such as the amount of items purchased, Section 2.5.1, the
number of items on hand, and the number of shortages, Section 2.5.2, are
important in evaluating one inventory system versus another, and in understanding the operational behavior of statistical control schemes. We
presently investigate these expectations. Throughout we restrict our
attention to a system that has attained statistical equilibrium, that is, a
system for which stationary probabilities may be applied legitimately.

In Section 2.5.3 we study an expectation of a function which might
reflect management's over-all economic evaluation of the system's operation; it contains terms representing purchase expenditures, set-up ordering
costs, inventory holding charges, and outage penalties. Supposing management desires to select an (*s, S*) policy which minimizes the expectation, we
devise a simple condition to determine the value of *s* in the backlog case.
In Section 2.5.4 we particularize this analysis to the special case of the
delivery lag being one period, and solve for *s* when the demand distribution
is either geometric or exponential.

2.5.1 Purchases

Let $r_t \geq 0$ be the amount of inventory purchased in period t, where

$$r_t = 0, \qquad s + 1 \leq X_t \leq S$$
$$= S - X_t, \qquad X_t \leq s,$$

and let $r_t^* > 0$ be the order size, given that a purchase is made. It follows that the probability distribution of r can be stated easily in terms of the probability distribution of X. We suppress the subscript t whenever we deal with the random variables in a situation of statistical equilibrium. As before we adopt the notation $E(T)$ for the expected value of T [Fe].

Proposition 2.5.1. (1) If unfilled demand is backlogged, $E(r) = E(\xi)$.
(2) If unfilled demand is not backlogged, $E(r) - E(\xi) - E(\text{shortage})$.
(3) $E(r^*) = E(r)/\sigma$.

The implication of Proposition 2.5.1 is that in the backlog case, the expected amount purchased equals the expected demand regardless of the particular (s, S) policy, the value of λ, and the ordering Sequence α or β, whereas in the no-backlog case, there is a dependence on these parameters through the value of expected shortage; a further implication is that in any case, the expected order size is the expected amount purchased normalized by the probability of ordering. *A fortiori*, if purchase costs are proportional to r, say, $C_{\text{pur}}r$, then $E(\text{purchase cost})$ is independent of (s, S), λ, Sequence α or β, in the backlog case.

Proof. (1) For Sequence α,

$$y_t + r_{t-\lambda} - \xi_{t+1} \equiv y_{t+1},$$

and for Sequence β,

$$w_{t-1} + r_{t-\lambda} - \xi_t \equiv w_t.$$

Taking expectations on both sides of these equations with respect to the stationary probabilities [Fe, Ch. 9] and, consequently, suppressing the period subscripts, followed by rearranging terms, yields the desired result.

(2) For Sequence α, let

$$f_{t+1}(\alpha) \equiv \max(0, \xi_{t+1} - y_t - r_{t-\lambda}) = \text{shortage in period } t+1,$$

and for Sequence β, let

$$f_t(\beta) \equiv \max(0, \xi_t - w_{t-1} - r_{t-\lambda}) = \text{shortage in period } t.$$

Then for the two sequences we have:

$$y_t + r_{t-\lambda} - \xi_{t+1} + f_{t+1}(\alpha) \equiv y_{t+1}$$
$$w_{t-1} + r_{t-\lambda} - \xi_t + f_t(\beta) \equiv w_t.$$

Taking expectations, as in part (1), yields the desired result. Note that our conclusion is valid for a general (s, S) policy.

(3) We may view $E(r)$ as a probability weighted average of conditional expectations:

$$E(r) = E(r^*)\sigma + 0(1 - \sigma).$$

2.5.2 *Inventory Holdings and Demand Shortages*

Depending on the real situation which the model (perhaps approximately) represents, inventory on hand may be valued either subsequent to delivery, when it is relatively high, or subsequent to demand, when it is relatively low. Thus the stationary probabilities of Y, V, Z, or W, whichever is applicable, are used directly to calculate the average amount of inventory on hand, or if desired, the average inventory holding cost.

The probability distribution of the amount of a shortage $0, 1, 2, \cdots$, may be found by multiplying $[p_{V,\lambda}]$ or $[p_{Z,\lambda}]$ times the probability matrix

$$
\begin{bmatrix}
\underline{0} - (S+1) & S+1 & S+2 & \cdots \\
\underline{0} - (S) & S & S+1 & \\
\underline{0} - (S-1) & S-1 & S & \\
\cdot & \cdot & \cdot & \\
\cdot & \cdot & \cdot & \\
\cdot & \cdot & \cdot & \\
0 & 1 & 2 & \cdots \\
\hline
0 & 1 & 2 & \cdots \\
0 & 1 & 2 & \cdots \\
\cdot & \cdot & \cdot & \\
\cdot & \cdot & \cdot & \\
\cdot & \cdot & \cdot & \\
\end{bmatrix}
$$

and $[q_{V,\lambda}]$ or $[q_{Z,\lambda}]$ times

$$
\begin{bmatrix}
\underline{0} - (S+1) & S+1 & S+2 & \cdots \\
\underline{0} - (S) & S & S+1 & \\
\cdot & \cdot & \cdot & \\
\cdot & \cdot & \cdot & \\
\cdot & \cdot & \cdot & \\
0 & 1 & 2 & \cdots \\
\end{bmatrix}
$$

Having these probabilities, we may calculate the average shortage cost directly.

For Sequence α the expected number of shortages conditional on the value of V is

$$(1a) \qquad \sum_{\xi=v}^{\infty} (\xi - v)\phi(\xi) = \sum_{\xi=v}^{\infty} \xi\phi(\xi) - v\sum_{\xi=v}^{\infty} \phi(\xi) \qquad 0 \le v \le S$$

$$(1b) \qquad E(\xi) \qquad\qquad\qquad\qquad\qquad\qquad v \le 0.$$

In the case of Sequence β, $\lambda > 1$, we substitute values of Z for those of V in (1); we discuss $\lambda = 1$ in Section 2.5.4. The unconditional expected number of shortages is the average of (1) with respect to $p_{V,\lambda}(v)$, $p_{Z,\lambda}(z)$, $q_{V,\lambda}(v)$, or $q_{Z,\lambda}(z)$, whichever is appropriate.

2.5.3 *Minimization of a Cost Function*

A particular (s, S) inventory scheme is often rated with respect to the model's performance as measured by a specified "expected cost function." Consider the backlog model and suppose, for example, the "expected cost function" is:

$$(1) \quad L(s, S \,|\, \text{backlog}) \equiv C_{\text{pur}}E(r) + C_{\text{fix}}\sigma$$

$$+ C_{\text{in}} \sum_{v=1}^{S} vp_{V,\lambda}(v) - C_{\text{out}} \sum_{v=-\infty}^{0} vp_{V,\lambda}(v),$$

where C_{pur} is a constant representing a unit purchase cost, C_{fix} is a fixed setup cost incurred whenever an order is placed, C_{in} is a unit inventory holding charge, and C_{out} is a unit outage charge levied on the current number of items backlogged. Some possible alternative representations involve substitutions of Y, W, or Z for V; furthermore, certain mixtures of these status variables are conceivable, such as V and Y. We explore the dependence of (1) on the value of s. For the sake of notational convenience, we continue to make sole reference to V rather than to a complete set of alternatives as suggested above, except to mention that the proposition to follow is valid in terms of these variables because of Proposition 2.2.8.

Proposition 2.5.3. If D is held constant, $L(s, S \,|\, \text{backlog})$ is minimized with respect to s for that value of s satisfying both

$$C_{\text{out}} \sum_{v=-\infty}^{-1} p_{V,\lambda}(v) \le C_{\text{in}} \sum_{v=0}^{s+D} p_{V,\lambda}(v)$$

and

$$C_{\text{out}} \sum_{v=-\infty}^{0} p_{V,\lambda}(v) \ge C_{\text{in}} \sum_{v=1}^{s+D} p_{V,\lambda}(v).$$

A rearrangement of the relations in the proposition yields[21]

$$\sum_{v=-\infty}^{-1} p_{V,\lambda}(v) \leq \frac{C_{in}}{C_{in} + C_{out}}$$

$$\sum_{v=-\infty}^{0} p_{V,\lambda}(v) \geq \frac{C_{in}}{C_{in} + C_{out}}$$

Proof. We first note that from Proposition 2.2.3, part (2), and Proposition 2.5.1, part (1), the values of the first two terms of $L(s, S \mid \text{backlog})$ are independent of s; therefore we may ignore their presence here. Suppose s minimizes $L(s, S \mid \text{backlog})$; then

$$C_{in} \sum_{v=1}^{s+D} v p_{V,\lambda}(v \mid s, D) - C_{out} \sum_{v=-\infty}^{0} v p_{V,\lambda}(v \mid s, D)$$

$$\leq C_{in} \sum_{v=1}^{s+1+D} v p_{V,\lambda}(v \mid s+1, D) - C_{out} \sum_{v=-\infty}^{0} v p_{V,\lambda}(v \mid s+1, D).$$

Rearranging terms and invoking Proposition 2.2 3, part (1), along with Proposition 2.2.8, part (3), give

$$C_{out}\left[\sum_{v=-\infty}^{0} v p_{V,\lambda}(v-1 \mid s, D) - \sum_{v=-\infty}^{0} v p_{V,\lambda}(v \mid s, D)\right]$$

$$\leq C_{in}\left[\sum_{v=1}^{s+1+D} v p_{V,\lambda}(v-1 \mid s, D) - \sum_{v=1}^{s+D} v p_{V,\lambda}(v \mid s, D)\right],$$

which, when simplified, yields the first condition for s. The second condition is derived analogously by a comparison using $p_{V,\lambda}(v \mid s-1, D)$.

The significance of Proposition 2.5.3 is that once D is given, then s, which is a location parameter for the backlog stationary distributions of V, W, Y, and Z, is easily determined so as to minimize $L(s, S \mid \text{backlog})$: we select s so that the probability of the status variable being non-positive "equals" the proportion $\dfrac{C_{in}}{C_{in} + C_{out}}$. Because s is not a location parameter for the stationary distributions in the no-backlog case, no analog to Proposition 2.5.3 is applicable in this situation.

---

[21] If $p_{V,\lambda}(v)$ is a stationary density function, the two relations for s collapse into a corresponding single equality:

$$\int_{v=-\infty}^{0} p_{V,\lambda}(v)\, dv = \frac{C_{in}}{C_{in} + C_{out}}.$$

2.5.4   Special Results for Sequence β, λ = 1

We turn attention to the special properties of $L(s, S)$ in the case of immediate delivery.[22] In the backlog situation, for $\lambda > 1$, we kept as distinct variables the amount of shortages in a period and the number of items backlogged. For $\lambda = 1$ under Sequence β, the two random variables, and therefore their expectations, are identical; that is,

$$- \sum_{w=-\infty}^{0} w p_{W,1}(w) = E(\text{shortage}).$$

In the no-backlog case, we let

$$L(s, S \mid \text{no-backlog}) =$$
$$C_{\text{pur}}E(r) + C_{\text{fix}}\sigma + C_{\text{in}} \sum_{w=1}^{S} w q_{W,\lambda}(w) + C_{\text{out}}E(\text{shortage}).$$

Recalling the equivalence relations in Proposition 2.3.6 and the result of Proposition 2.5.1, part (2), we have

$$L(s, S \mid \text{no-backlog}, \lambda = 1)$$
$$= C_{\text{pur}}E(\xi) + C_{\text{fix}}\sigma + C_{\text{in}} \sum_{w=1}^{S} w p_{W,1}(w) - (C_{\text{out}} - C_{\text{pur}}) \sum_{w=-\infty}^{0} w p_{W,1}(w).$$

Observe that for $\lambda = 1$ the only difference between $L(s, S \mid \text{backlog})$ and $L(s, S \mid \text{no-backlog})$ is $-C_{\text{pur}}E(\text{shortage})$.

Utilizing the implications of Proposition 2.3.6 and a proof which parallels that for Proposition 2.5.3 we have:

Proposition 2.5.4.   If D is held constant, $L(s, S \mid \text{no-backlog}, \lambda = 1)$ is minimized with respect to s for that value of s satisfying both

$$(C_{\text{out}} - C_{\text{pur}}) \sum_{w=-\infty}^{-1} p_{W,1}(w) \leq C_{\text{in}} \sum_{w=0}^{S} p_{W,1}(w),$$

and

$$(C_{\text{out}} - C_{\text{pur}}) \sum_{w=-\infty}^{0} p_{W,1}(w) \geq C_{\text{in}} \sum_{w=1}^{S} p_{W,1}(w).$$

To illustrate the results of this and the previous section, suppose $\phi(\xi) = pq^{\xi}$, $\xi = 0, 1, \cdots$, which we investigated in Section 2.4.2. Then

(1) $L(s, S \mid \text{backlog}, \lambda = 1) = C_{\text{pur}}\mu + C_{\text{fix}} \dfrac{\mu}{\mu + D}$

$$+ \frac{C_{\text{in}}}{\mu + D} \left[\mu s - \mu^2 + \mu^2 q^s + Ds + \frac{D^2 + D}{2} \right] - \frac{C_{\text{out}}}{\mu + D} [-\mu^2 q^s],$$

where $\mu \equiv E(\xi) = q/p$.

---

[22] Recall the discussion in Sections 2.2.7 and 2.3.6.

Holding D fixed and minimizing (1) with respect to s by taking first differences yields

$$\frac{\mu q^s}{\mu + D} \geq \frac{C_{in}}{C_{in} + C_{out}}$$

$$\frac{\mu q^{s+1}}{\mu + D} \leq \frac{C_{in}}{C_{in} + C_{out}},$$

which agrees with the result of Proposition 2.5.3. In Section 3.2.4, we exhibit minimum cost (s, S) policies for a selected set of economic parameter values. In the no-backlog case, $\lambda = 1$, Sequence β, C_{pur} would be subtracted from the denominators.

If $\phi(\xi) = \tau e^{-\tau \xi}$, a density function which we viewed in Section 2.4.3, then

$$L(s, S \mid \text{backlog}, \lambda = 1) = C_{pur}\mu + C_{fix}\frac{\mu}{\mu + D}$$

$$+ \frac{C_{in}}{\mu + D}\left[\mu s - \mu^2 + \mu^2 e^{-\tau s} + \frac{D(2s + D)}{2}\right]$$

$$- \frac{C_{out}}{\mu + D}[-\mu^2 e^{-\tau s}],$$

where $\mu = 1/\tau$.

The minimizing s is

$$\frac{\mu e^{-\tau s}}{\mu + D} = \frac{C_{in}}{C_{in} + C_{out}}.$$

2.6   DERIVATIVE OPERATING CHARACTERISTICS

The operating characteristics of interest here are values of net demand, which is roughly the amount demanded corrected by the amount replenished, and the occurrences of reorders. We study the probability distribution and expectation of net demand in Section 2.6.1 for both the backlog and no-backlog models, illustrating the calculations with several Poisson examples.

The analysis of occurrences of reorders is contained in Sections 2.6.2 and 2.6.3. Since we assume that a delivery occurs a fixed number of time periods after an order is placed, the distributions derived apply equally well to replenishment shipments of inventory. The two problems posed are to find the probability distribution and expectation of (*a*) the number of periods between successive orders and (*b*) the number of orders within a given time span. The derivation begins by adding the condition that an order has been placed in the preceding period; having found these conditional probabilities, we extend the analysis to the general case. We study both the backlog and no-backlog models.

2.6.1 Net Demand

We define the random variable "net demand" n_t, in any period t, as the difference between the amount of demand filled and backlogged and the amount purchased; specifically

$$n_t \equiv \xi_t - r_t \qquad \text{backlog assumption,}$$

and

$$n_t \equiv \xi_t - f_t - r_t \qquad \text{no-backlog assumption,}$$

where r and f are as defined in Section 2.5.1. A direct consequence of Proposition 2.5.1, parts (1) and (2), is that when statistical equilibrium is attained,

Proposition 2.6.1.

$$E(n) = 0.$$

As we explain, we may find the probability distribution for n by considering the probability of any value of n conditional on the value of U in the backlog model and on the value of V or Z in the no-backlog model, and then by averaging with respect to $[p_U]$, $[q_{V,\lambda}]$, or $[q_{Z,\lambda}]$. Thus in the backlog model the distribution of n does not depend on the parameters s, λ, or the Sequence α or β, but only on the value D.

Table 2.6.1 contains the conditional probabilities of n, given u for the backlog situation. Notice that $D - 1 \geq n \geq 1 - D$. The value of n is

TABLE 2.6.1

CONDITIONAL PROBABILITIES OF n GIVEN u

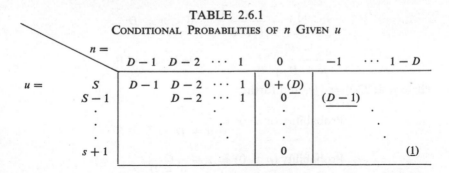

$u =$	$n =$	$D-1$	$D-2$	$\cdots$	1	0	-1	$\cdots$	$1-D$
	S	$D-1$	$D-2$	$\cdots$	1	$0+(D)$			
	$S-1$		$D-2$	$\cdots$	1	0^-	$(D-1)$		
	.			.		.		.	
	.			.		.		.	
	.			.		.		.	
	$s+1$					0			(1)

zero either if no demand occurs or if the amount U of inventory on hand and on order is S and demand is at least D, in which case the amount purchased is identical to the amount demanded. A positive n occurs whenever the value of U is drawn down toward $s + 1$; a non-positive n occurs whenever demand is at least the value of U minus the value s. Multiplying the entries in Table 2.6.1 by $[p_U]$ we obtain as the unconditional probabilities:

$$\phi(n)\left[\sum_{u=n+s+1}^{S} p_U(u)\right] \qquad 0 < n \leq D - 1$$

$$\phi(0) + \phi(\underline{D})p_U(S) \qquad n = 0$$

$$\phi(\underline{n + D})p_U(n + S) \qquad 1 - D \leq n < 0.$$

If $\phi(\xi)$ is a density function, the unconditional density function for $n \neq 0$ is

$$\phi(n)[\sigma + p_U(\overline{S}) - p_U(\overline{n + s})] \qquad 0 < n < D$$

$$\phi(\underline{n + D})p_U(n + S) \qquad -D < n < 0,$$

and the probability that $n = 0$ is

$$\phi(\underline{D})\dot{\sigma}.$$

As examples, if $\phi(\xi) = pq^\xi$, $\xi = 0, 1, \cdots$, which we examined in Section 2.4.2, then

$$pq^n\left[1 - \frac{n}{\mu + D}\right] \qquad 0 < n \leq D - 1$$

$$p + \frac{(\mu + 1)q^D}{\mu + D} \qquad n = 0$$

$$\frac{q^{n+D}}{\mu + D} \qquad 1 - D \leq n < 0,$$

where $\mu \equiv E(\xi) = q/p$. If $\phi(\xi) = \tau e^{-\tau\xi}$, which we examined in Section 2.4.3, then the density function for n is

$$\tau e^{-\tau n}\left[1 - \frac{n}{\mu + D}\right] \qquad 0 < n < D$$

$$\frac{e^{-\tau(n+D)}}{\mu + D} \qquad -D < n < 0,$$

where $\mu \equiv E(\xi) = 1/\tau$, and further

$$\text{Probability } (n = 0) = \frac{\mu e^{-\tau D}}{\mu + D}$$

$$\text{Probability } (n > 0) = 1 - \frac{\mu}{\mu + D}$$

$$\text{Probability } (n < 0) = \frac{\mu}{\mu + D}[1 - e^{-\tau D}].$$

In Table 2.6.2 we give the numerical distribution of n for two of the examples in Section 2.4.5.

For the no-backlog model, we assume $D > s$. The conditional probabilities of n given the value of V (Sequence α) appear in Table 2.6.3; here we interpret V as the amount of inventory on hand at the start of a period.

TABLE 2.6.2

EXAMPLES OF DISTRIBUTION OF n USING $\phi(\xi)$ IN TABLE 2.4.1

n	$D = 3$	
	Uniform	Binomial
2	4/27	.0896
1	6/27	.2885
0	9/27	.3530
−1	2/27	.0700
−2	6/27	.1988

If $s + 1 \leq v \leq S$, then no order is currently outstanding; consequently the conditional probabilities are analogous to the backlog model. If $0 \leq v \leq s$, then an order is outstanding and will not be delivered at least until after the current demand; since $D > s$, a new order will not be placed currently. Thus n is non-negative and is equal to the amount of filled demand. We obtain the unconditional distribution of n by multiplying the entries in Table 2.6.3 by $[q_{V,\lambda}]$:

$$\phi(n)\left[\sum_{v=n+s+1}^{S} q_{V,\lambda}(v)\right] \qquad s+1 \leq n \leq D-1$$

$$\phi(n)\left[\sum_{v=n+s+1}^{S} q_{V,\lambda}(v) + \sum_{v=n}^{s} q_{V,\lambda}(v)\right] + \phi(n+1)q_{V,\lambda}(n) \qquad 0 < n \leq s$$

$$\phi(0) + \phi(1)q_{V,\lambda}(0) + \phi(D)q_{V,\lambda}(S) \qquad n = 0$$

$$\phi(n+D)q_{V,\lambda}(n+S) \qquad 1-D \leq n < 0.$$

If in the no-backlog model the situation is described by Sequence β, then we refer to the variable Z. Given that $s + 1 \leq z \leq S$, there is no order outstanding, and therefore an analysis parallel to the same situation for V applies. Given that $0 \leq z \leq s$, there must be an order outstanding for the following reason: since $D > s$, a delivery has not just been made, and Z must have the same value as the previous W. Because this value of W does not exceed s, either an order has just been placed or a previous

TABLE 2.6.3

CONDITIONAL PROBABILITIES OF n GIVEN v

$v =$ / $n =$	$D-1$	$D-2$	$\cdots$	$s+1$	s	$s-1$	$\cdots$	1	0	-1	$\cdots$	$1-D$
S	$D-1$	$D-2$	$\cdots$	$s+1$	s	$s-1$	$\cdots$	1	$\underline{\overline{0}+\overline{(D)}}$	$\underline{(D-1)}$	$\cdots$	$\underline{(1)}$
$S-1$		$D-2$	$\cdots$	$s+1$	s	$s-1$	$\cdots$	1	0			
$\vdots$				$s+1$	s	$s-1$	$\cdots$	1	0			
$s+2$				$s+1$	s	$s-1$	$\cdots$	1	0			
$s+1$				$s+1$	s	$s-1$	$\cdots$	1	0			
$s-1$						$s-1$	$\cdots$	1	0			
$\vdots$							$\cdots$	1	0			
1								1	0			
0					$\underline{(s)}$	$\underline{(s-1)}$	$\cdots$	$\underline{(1)}$	$\underline{(0)}$	$\underline{(1)}$	$\cdots$	$\underline{(D-1)}$

order remains outstanding (it could not have just been delivered for $z \leq s$). Consequently an analysis parallel to the same situation for V applies. In summary, the conditional probabilities of n given z for Sequence β are the same as those in Table 2.6.3 and are combined with $[q_{Z,\lambda}]$ to obtain the unconditional distribution of n.

We exhibit in Table 2.6.4 the distribution of n for the examples in Section 2.4.8.

TABLE 2.6.4

EXAMPLES OF DISTRIBUTION OF n WITH POISSON, $(3, 8)$, $\lambda = 8$

n	$F(\xi) = .5$	$F(\xi) = 1$	$E(\xi) - 2$
4	.0000	.0001	.0011
3	.0024	.0083	.0223
2	.0303	.0526	.0653
1	.2091	.1921	.1123
0	.6846	.6559	.6991
−1	.0000	.0003	.0033
−2	.0010	.0039	.0149
−3	.0154	.0322	.0436
−4	.0572	.0545	.0376

2.6.2 The Number of and Time Intervals Between Orders (Deliveries): Conditional Distributions

In this section and the next we discuss the exact probability distributions of the number and spacing of orders over time, once the model has reached statistical equilibrium.[23] Since deliveries follow orders exactly λ periods later, the distributions to be derived pertain to deliveries as well, and where appropriate, we interchange the words "order" and "delivery." In our inventory models the probability of a state occurring in one period is not independent of the existing state in the previous period. Therefore, a difficulty to be overcome in the analysis below is to find a characterization of the process that enables us to deal with recurrent events [Fe, Ch. 13]. Paraphrasing [Fe], we say an event in a sequence of trials is recurrent if, after each of its occurrences, the trials following form a replica of the whole experiment.

---

[23] Asymptotic results are referred to in Section 2.7. In anticipation, if ρ and τ in relation (1a) below are large, the central limit theorem may be invoked to yield a normal distribution approximation.

We begin our analysis by considering the system immediately after an order has been placed, that is, the value of U_t is S, and we determine the number of periods elapsing until placing the next order. We define T as the number of periods between orders, where $T = 1, 2, \cdots$. For example, in the backlog model, if demand in period t is at least D, an order is placed at the end of the period and we say that $T = 1$. Note that in the no-backlog model with $D > s$, $\text{Prob}(T = \tau) = 0$ for $\tau \leq \lambda$ in Sequence α and $\tau \leq \lambda - 1$ in Sequence β.

Proposition 2.6.2. Assume an order is placed in the preceding period.
(1) In the backlog model,

$$\text{Prob}(T = \tau \mid \text{order just occurred}) = \phi^\tau(\underline{D}) + \phi^{\tau-1}(\underline{D}).$$

(2) In the no-backlog model,

$$\text{Prob}(T = \tau \mid \text{order just occurred}) = \sum_{v=D}^{S} q_{V,\lambda}^*(v)[\phi^{\tau-\lambda}(\underline{v-s}) - \phi^{\tau-\lambda-1}(\underline{v-s})]$$

$$\text{for Sequence } \alpha,$$

$$= \sum_{z=D}^{S} q_{Z,\lambda}^*(z)[\phi^{\tau-\lambda+1}(\underline{z-s}) - \phi^{\tau-\lambda}(\underline{z-s})]$$

$$\text{for Sequence } \beta,$$

where

$$q_{V,\lambda}^*(v) = q_{V,\lambda}(v) \Big/ \sum_{v=D}^{S} q_{V,\lambda}(v)$$

$$q_{Z,\lambda}^*(z) = q_{Z,\lambda}(z) \Big/ \sum_{z=D}^{S} q_{Z,\lambda}(z)$$

$$\phi^j(\underline{\xi}) = 0 \quad \text{for} \quad j \leq 0.$$

Proof. (1)[24] Since we assume the value of U is S, no order is placed after τ periods have elapsed, if accumulated demand is less than D; thus

$$\text{Prob}(T > \tau) = 1 - \phi^\tau(\underline{D}),$$

where, for notational convenience, we have suppressed the assumed condition in the expression on the left. Consequently,

$$\text{Prob}(T \leq \tau) = \phi^\tau(\underline{D}).$$

$$\text{Prob}(T = \tau) = \text{Prob}(T \leq \tau) - \text{Prob}(T \leq \tau - 1) = \phi^\tau(\underline{D}) - \phi^{\tau-1}(\underline{D}).$$

As usual in this case, the probability distribution depends only on the system parameter D.

[24] This result appears in [AKS, Ch. 15].

(2) Because an order has just been placed, λ periods must elapse until the delivery is made. At that time, the amount of inventory on hand, which is between the values S and D, is given by the variable V or Z in Sequence α or β, respectively. Consequently $q^*_{V,\lambda}(v)$ or $q^*_{Z,\lambda}(z)$ is the conditional stationary probability of inventory on hand given that a delivery has just arrived. As in the proof of (1), the bracketed term multiplying the stationary probability and containing the difference between convolutions represents the probability of $T - \lambda$ or $T - \lambda - 1$ periods in addition to λ elapsing in Sequence α or β, respectively, thereby completing the demonstration.

The general problem of this sort is to determine the probability that T^ρ periods elapse between ρ orders.[25] Whenever the value of U equals S, we witness a recurrent event in our above analysis. Hence the probability that $T^\rho = \tau$ can be found from the ρ-fold convolution of the distribution in Proposition 2.6.2 evaluated at τ. The probability that no order occurs in τ periods is the same as the probability that the first order does not occur in τ periods

$$\text{Prob}(T^0 = \tau \mid \text{order just occurred}) = 1 - \text{Prob}(T \leq \tau \mid \text{order just occurred}).$$

We turn attention to the conditional probability distribution of the quantity of orders during a specified number of periods. Previously we have observed that the probability of an order occurring in one period is σ once the system has reached stationary equilibrium. If an order has just been placed, then we can use the analysis above to find the probability that in the next $\tau \geq 1$ periods, the number of orders N^τ is at least ρ [Fe, p. 297]:

(1a) $\text{Prob}(N^\tau \geq \rho \mid \text{order just occurred})$
$$= \text{Prob}(T^\rho \leq \tau \mid \text{order just occurred})$$

(1b) $\text{Prob}(N^\tau \geq 0 \mid \text{order just occurred})$
$$= \text{Prob}(N^\tau \leq \tau \mid \text{order just occurred}) = 1.$$

We may read (1a) as the probability that ρ or more orders occur in a span of τ periods is the same as the probability that ρ orders occur when $1, 2, \cdots,$ or τ periods elapse.

2.6.3 *Unconditional Distributions*

To obtain the unconditional probability that $T^\rho = \tau$ periods elapse between ρ orders or deliveries, we first determine the unconditional probability that t periods elapse until the first order or delivery and then utilize

---

[25] Note that ρ is to be interpreted as a superscript and not as a multiplicative exponent of T.

this value as a weight for the conditional probability that $\rho - 1$ orders or deliveries occur in $\tau - t$ periods, numbers which we found in the preceding section.

In the backlog model, the probability that the first order occurs at the end of t periods is

$$\sum_{u=s+1}^{S} p_U(u)[\phi^t(\underline{u - s}) - \phi^{t-1}(\underline{u - s})].$$

In the no-backlog model with $D > s$, it is convenient to frame the discussion in terms of deliveries. If the current period is t^* and the first delivery arrives in period $t^* + \lambda^*$, we say that the first delivery occurs within $\lambda^* + 1$ periods, where $\lambda^* = 0, 1, \cdots$.

For Sequence α,

$$\text{Prob(first delivery within } t \text{ periods)} = \sum_{v=0}^{s} \sum_{r=D}^{S-v} q(v\,|\,r, t) \qquad 1 \le t \le \lambda - 1$$

$$= \sum_{v=0}^{s} q(v\,|\,0, 0) \qquad t = \lambda$$

$$= \sum_{v=s+1}^{S} q(v\,|\,0,0)[\phi^{t-\lambda}(\underline{v - s}) - \phi^{t-\lambda-1}(\underline{v - s})] \qquad \lambda + 1 \le t;$$

and for Sequence β,

$$\text{Prob(first delivery within } t \text{ periods)} = \sum_{z=0}^{s} \sum_{r=D}^{S-z} q(z\,|\,r, t) \qquad 1 \le t \le \lambda - 1$$

$$= \sum_{z=s+1}^{S} q(z\,|\,0, 0)[\phi^{t+1-\lambda}(\underline{z - s}) - \phi^{t-\lambda}(\underline{z - s})] \qquad \lambda \le t.$$

Having determined the above probabilities, we may state *Proposition 2.6.3.*

$$\text{Prob}(T^\rho = \tau) = \sum_{t=1}^{\tau} \text{Prob(first order within } t \text{ periods)}$$

and $\qquad \times \text{Prob}(T^{\rho-1} = \tau - t \,|\, \text{order just occurred})$

(1) in the backlog model,

$$\text{Prob}(T^0 = \tau) = \sum_{u=s+1}^{S} p_U(u)[1 - \phi^\tau(\underline{u - s})];$$

(2) in the no-backlog model under Sequence α,

$$\text{Prob}(T^0 = \tau) = \sum_{v=s+1}^{S} q(v\,|\,0, 0)[1 - \phi^{\tau-\lambda}(\underline{v - s})] \qquad \tau \ge \lambda$$

$$= \sum_{v=0}^{S} q(v\,|\,0, 0) \qquad \tau = \lambda - 1$$

$$= \sum_{v=0}^{S} q(v\,|\,0, 0) + \sum_{t=\tau+1}^{\lambda-1} \sum_{v=0}^{s} \sum_{r=D}^{S-v} q(v\,|\,r, t) \qquad \tau < \lambda - 1;$$

(3) in the no-backlog model under Sequence β,

$$\text{Prob}\,(T^0 = \tau) = \sum_{z=s+1}^{S} q(z \mid 0, 0)[1 - \phi^{\tau - \lambda + 1}(z - s)] \qquad \tau \geq \lambda - 1$$

$$= \sum_{z=s+1}^{S} q(z \mid 0, 0) + \sum_{t=\tau+1}^{\lambda-1} \sum_{z=0}^{s} \sum_{r=D}^{S-z} q(z \mid r, t) \qquad \tau < \lambda - 1.$$

Observe that $\text{Prob}\,(T^{\rho-1} = \tau - t \mid \text{order just occurred}) = 0$ if $\tau - t < \rho - 1$ in the backlog model; if $\tau - t < (\rho - 1)(\lambda + 1)$ in the no-backlog model under Sequence α; and if $\tau - t < (\rho - 1)\lambda$ in the no-backlog model under Sequence β. As we mentioned above, the word "delivery" may be substituted for "order" in Proposition 2.6.3.

The relation (1a) in Section 2 6.2 with the condition removed can now be invoked to obtain the unconditional probability distribution of the quantity of orders or deliveries during a specified number of periods.

We mention that elementary manipulation of expectations with respect to the stationary probabilities yields

(1a) $E(T^\rho) = \rho/\sigma$

(1b) $E(N^\tau) = \tau\sigma.$

2.7   RANDOM SUMS INDUCED BY A MARKOV PROCESS

Some index number control schemes require a sum or average of operating variables as observed during several time periods. Consequently, we need a method of determining the probability distribution, for example, of the total quantity of purchases during a specified number of consecutive periods, or, as another illustration, of the average amount of inventory on hand and on order when the model is observed or sampled every fourth period for a set number of times. In this section we give a mathematical representation of such problems with several illustrative applications. We caution that the practicability of the method varies considerably with the application and the parameter values of the inventory model.

The general theory yielding the probability distribution of a sum for T consecutive periods of a function defined on the states of a Markov chain is given in Section 2.7.1; we also exhibit the expectation and variance of the sum. We summarize the asymptotic theory in which the central limit theory applies. Specific examples of the method are given next: shortages in Section 2.7.2, inventory on hand in Section 2.7.3, purchase and number of orders in Section 2.7.4, and net demand in Section 2.7.5. The method for handling sampled sums is explained in Section 2.7.6.

2.7.1   Mathematical Representation

We view our model in terms of a Markov process which is characterized by the (perhaps infinite) transition matrix $[M]$. Let j_t denote the process as being in state j at period t, and $p_{j_t j_{t+1}}$ the transition probability of the system moving from state j_t to the state j_{t+1}. For notational convenience, let the first period of interest be designated $t = 1$, and define π_{j_1} as the *a priori* probability of state j_1. Assume further that $h_t(j_t)$ is a real valued function defined for each state j_t. We want to investigate the probability distribution of the sum[26]

$$h_1(j_1) + h_2(j_2) + \cdots + h_T(j_T) = h,$$

which we denote by Prob (h, T). Let Prob $(h, T \mid j_T)$ be the *joint* probability that both (h, T) and j_T occur.[27]

Proposition 2.7.1.

(1) $\text{Prob}\,(h, T \mid j_T) = \displaystyle\sum_{j_{T-1}} p_{j_{T-1} j_T} \text{Prob}\,(h - h_T(j_T), T - 1 \mid j_{T-1})$

(2) $\text{Prob}\,(h, T) = \displaystyle\sum_{j_T} \text{Prob}\,(h, T \mid j_T).$

The significance of the proposition is that the Prob (h, T) may be calculated by computing recursively the joint probabilities Prob $(h^*, t \mid j_t)$ for $t = 2, 3, \cdots, T$, and then summing these values over all possible j_T; if $h_t(j_t) \geq 0$, then only $0 \leq h^* \leq h$ need be considered in the recursive calculations. We illustrate the procedure in the next section. Under this non-negativity assumption we may employ the idea expressed in relation $(1a)$, Section 2.6.2, to derive from Prob (h, T) the probability distribution that the cumulative sum of $h(j)$ equals h for the first time in period t, where $t = 1, 2, \cdots$.

Proof.   (1)

$$\text{Prob}\,[h_1(j_1) + \cdots + h_T(j_T) = h \mid j_T] = \underbrace{\sum_{j_{T-1}} \cdots \sum_{j_1}}_{h_1(j_1) + \cdots + h_{T-1}(j_{T-1}) = h - h_T(j_T)} \pi_{j_1} p_{j_1 j_2} \cdots p_{j_{T-1} j_T}$$

$$= \sum_{j_{T-1}} p_{j_{T-1} j_T} \underbrace{\sum_{j_{T-2}} \cdots \sum_{j_1}}_{h_1(j_1) + \cdots + h_{T-2}(j_{T-2}) = h - h_T(j_T) - h_{T-1}(j_{T-1})} \pi_{j_1} p_{j_1 j_2} \cdots p_{j_{T-2} j_{T-1}}$$

$$= \sum_{j_{T-1}} p_{j_{T-1} j_T} \text{Prob}\,(h - h_T(j_T), T - 1 \mid j_{T-1}).$$

---

[26] Observe that if we are interested in averaging $h_t(j_t)$ over T periods, then the above probability of h also yields the probability of h/T after averaging.

[27] Note that this symbol is *not* to be construed as a conditional probability.

(2) The second conclusion follows from the set of j_T being mutually exclusive and completely exhaustive.

If the model has reached statistical equilibrium and $h_t(j_t)$ for $t = 1$, $2, \cdots, T$ are identical functions $h(j)$, the stationary expectation of the sum is

$$E[h_1(j_1) + h_2(j_2) + \cdots + h_T(j_T)] = TE[h(j)],$$

where $E[h(j)]$ is the single-period stationary expectation of $h(j)$.

Furthermore, if we consider the functions $h_t'(j_t')$ which are identically $h'(j')$ for $t = 1, 2, \cdots, T$, then the stationary covariance between consecutive sums of $h(j)$ and $h'(j')$ is [KS, Ch. 4]

$$(1) \quad \text{Cov}\left[\sum_{t=1}^{T} h_t(j_t), \sum_{t=1}^{T} h_t'(j_t')\right]$$

$$= \sum_{j}\sum_{j'} p_j^* h(j)h'(j') \sum_{t=1}^{T-1} (T-t)(p_{jj'}^t - p_{j'}^*)$$

$$+ \sum_{j}\sum_{j'} p_{j'}^* h(j)h'(j') \sum_{t=1}^{T-1} (T-t)(p_{j'j}^t - p_j^*)$$

$$+ T\sum_{j}\sum_{j'} (p_j^* \delta_{jj'} - p_j^* p_{j'}^*) h(j)h'(j'),$$

where

$p_j^* = $ stationary probability of state j for $[M]$;

$\delta_{jj'} = 1$ if $j = j'$

$\quad\quad = 0$ if $j \neq j'$; and

$p_{jj'}^t = $ the element in row j and column j' of $[M]^t$.

By letting $h(j) = h'(j')$ for $j = j'$, expression (1) becomes the variance of the probability distribution of the sum of the $h(j)$, or, if multiplied by $1/T^2$, the variance of sample means of the observed T values of $h(j)$. A special case of interest is when $[M] = [T_X]$ and $D = 1$, that is, when the policy is $(S - 1, S)$ with backlogging. Then the covariance from (1) is identical to T times the single-period covariance computed by utilizing the stationary probabilities $p_j^* = p_X(x)$; this fact follows from the observation that for all t, $p_{jj'}^t - p_j^* = 0$.

As T grows large, the probability distribution of the sample means of T values of $h(j)$ is given by an application of the central limit theorem [Fe, p. 374; D, p. 221], that is, the distribution is approximately normal[28] [BL, CM, Sch] with mean $E(h)$ and variance derived from the limiting value of relation (1). Specifically, the limiting variance[29] is [KS, Ch. 4]

$$(2) \quad \lim_{T \to \infty} \text{Var}\left(\frac{\sum_{t} h(j)}{T}\right) = \frac{1}{T}\sum_{j}\sum_{j'} h(j)c_{jj'}h(j'),$$

[28] And independent of the initial state j_1.

[29] To obtain a limiting covariance, substitute $h'(j')$ for $h(j')$ in the formula to follow.

where

$$c_{jj'} = p_j{}^*\tau_{jj'} + p_{j'}{}^*\tau_{j'j} - p_j{}^*\delta_{jj'} - p_j{}^*p_{j'}{}^*;$$

$$[\tau_{jj'}] = [I] + \sum_{t=1}^{\infty}\{[M] - [P^*]\}^t = [I] + \sum_{t=1}^{\infty}\{[M]^t - [P^*]\};$$

$$[P^*] = \begin{bmatrix} p_1{}^* & p_2{}^* & \cdots & p_j{}^* & \cdots \\ p_1{}^* & p_2{}^* & \cdots & p_j{}^* & \cdots \\ \cdot & \cdot & \cdots & \cdot & \cdots \\ \cdot & & \cdot & & \\ \cdot & & & \cdot & \end{bmatrix}.$$

If $[\tau_{jj'}]$ is of finite dimension, then

$$[\tau_{jj'}] = \{[I] - [M] + [P^*]\}^{-1}.$$

Helpful numerical checks on the computations of these matrices are the fact that each of the rows of $[\tau_{jj'}]$ sum to one, as do each of the rows of $\{[I] - [M] + [P^*]\}$, and the fact that each of the rows of $[c_{jj'}]$ sum to zero. Numerical examples are given in Section 3.4.1 and Section 4.3.1.

In the following sections we demonstrate how to define $h(j)$ to yield important operating statistics; the analysis given may then be applied to obtain the associated exact probability distribution for small values of T and the asymptotic probability distribution for large values of T.

The asymptotic results are pertinent to an analysis of the accuracy of the Monte Carlo estimates in Section 2.4. For example, consider the states of $[T_X]$. For any state j^*, by letting $h_t(j_t)$ be the indicator function of j^*

$$h_t(j_t) = 1 \text{ if } j_t = j^*$$
$$= 0 \text{ if } j_t \neq j^*,$$

we may conclude that the statistic

$$\frac{\text{Number of times state } j \text{ is observed}}{\text{Number of simulated periods}}$$

is approximately normally distributed with mean equal to the stationary probability of j^* and variance[30] given by $(1/T)c_{j^*j^*}$. With reference to

---

[30] We mention an alternative representation [Fe, p. 298] of $c_{j^*j^*}$ involving the mean $1/p^*_{j^*}$ and variance Var_{j^*} of the distribution of "recurrence time" [Fe, Ch.13] or "first passage time" [KS, Ch. 4] from j^* to j^*

$$c_{j^*j^*} = (\text{Var}_{j^*})(p^*_{j^*})^3.$$

The calculation of Var_{j^*} is given in [KS, p. 83].

$[T_V]$, we aggregate several of the states to obtain $q_{V,\lambda}(v)$, Section 2.3.2. For a particular value v^*, let $\{j\}$, or alternatively for notational purposes $\{j'\}$, be the set of states so aggregated; then the asymptotic distribution of the Monte Carlo estimates of $q_{V,\lambda}(v^*)$ is normal with mean $q_{V,\lambda}(v^*)$ and variance $(1/T) \sum\limits_{\{j\}} \sum\limits_{\{j'\}} c_{jj'}$.

2.7.2 Shortages

In Section 2.5.4 we established that for Sequence β under $\lambda = 1$, shortages can be identified with the negative values of W, which by Section 2.2.7 can be equated to the negative values of X. For this model we let the state j be defined as the value of X, and

$$h(j) = 0 \qquad 0 \leq j \leq S$$
$$= -j \qquad j < 0.$$

In Table 2.7.1 we give the values for Prob $(h, 2 \mid j_2)$, $h = 0, 1, 2, 3$, assuming $\pi_{j_1} = p_X(j)$. Utilizing these values, the computations of Prob $(3, 3 \mid j_3)$ according to Proposition 2.7.1 are shown in Table 2.7.2. In general, to calculate Prob $(h, T \mid j_T)$ from Prob $(h^*, T-1 \mid j_{T-1})$, we need tables of the latter values that have $(h + 1)(S + 1 + .5h)$ entries in toto. There does not seem to be any simple manner for handling accumulated shortages occurring in more complicated backlog models so as to employ Proposition 2.7.1.

For the no-backlog situation we illustrate the technique in a formal manner by presenting the appropriate Markov transition matrix $[M]$ and the function $h(j)$ defined on its states; the actual computation process does not necessitate explicitly writing $[M]$. In Sequence α, we expand the number of states $(v \mid r, \tau)$ so as to exhibit the occurrence of a shortage.[31] We add the states $(-v' \mid r, \tau)$ for each existing pair (r, τ), and $(v, -v' \mid 0)$ for $D \leq v \leq S$, where $v' = 1, 2, \cdots$. In the example of Table 2.3.5, the new states are

$$(-1 \mid 0, 0) \qquad (-1 \mid 4, 2) \qquad (-1 \mid 5, 2) \qquad (-1 \mid 6, 1)$$
$$(-2 \mid 0, 0) \qquad (-2 \mid 4, 2) \qquad (-2 \mid 5, 2) \qquad (-2 \mid 6, 1)$$
$$\vdots \qquad\qquad \vdots \qquad\qquad \vdots \qquad\qquad \vdots$$

---

[31] In this section and those to follow, we confine our attention to the no-backlog model under Sequence α. Because of the relations between V and Z discussed in Section 2.3.5, an analogous approach can be utilized under Sequence β.

TABLE 2.7.1

j_2	Prob $(3, 2 \mid j_2)$	Prob $(2, 2 \mid j_2)$
-3	$\displaystyle\sum_{x=s+1}^{S} p_X(x)\phi(3+x) + \sum_{x=0}^{s} p_X(x)\phi(S+3)$	
-2	$p_X(-1)\phi(S+2)$	$\displaystyle\sum_{x=s+1}^{S} p_X(x)\phi(2+x) + \sum_{x=0}^{s} p_X(x)\phi(S+2)$
-1	$p_X(-2)\phi(S+1)$	$p_X(-1)\phi(S+1)$
0	$p_X(-3)\phi(S)$	$p_X(-2)\phi(S)$
1	$p_X(-3)\phi(S-1)$	$p_X(-2)\phi(S-1)$
$\;\cdot$		
$\;\cdot$		
$\;\cdot$		
S	$p_X(-3)\phi(0)$	$p_X(-2)\phi(0)$

j_2	Prob $(1, 2 \mid j_2)$	Prob $(0, 2 \mid j_2)$
-1	$\displaystyle\sum_{x=s+1}^{S} p_X(x)\phi(1+x) + \sum_{x=0}^{s} p_X(x)\phi(S+1)$	
0	$p_X(-1)\phi(S)$	$\displaystyle\sum_{x=s+1}^{S} p_X(x)\phi(x) + \sum_{x=0}^{s} p_X(x)\phi(S)$
1	$p_X(-1)\phi(S-1)$	$p_X(0)\phi(S-1)$
$\;\cdot$		
$\;\cdot$		
$\;\cdot$		
S	$p_X(-1)\phi(0)$	$p_X(0)\phi(0)$

and

$$(6, -1 \,|\, 0) \qquad (5, -1 \,|\, 0) \qquad (4, -1 \,|\, 0) \qquad (3, -1 \,|\, 0)$$
$$(6, -2 \,|\, 0) \qquad (5, -2 \,|\, 0) \qquad (4, -2 \,|\, 0) \qquad (3, -2 \,|\, 0)$$

In the expanded transition matrix, the $(-v' \,|\, r, \tau)$ row has the same entries as the $(0 \,|\, r, \tau)$ row, and similarly the $(v, -v' \,|\, 0)$ row has the same entries as the $(v \,|\, 0, 0)$ row. Table 2.7.3 summarizes the non-zero transition probabilities in the columns associated with the new states.

To apply Proposition 2.7.1 to the consecutive sum of shortages we let

$$h(j) = 0 \text{ for states in } [T_V]$$
$$= v' \text{ for newly appended states.}$$

TABLE 2.7.2

j_3	Prob $(3, 3 \,|\, j_3)$
-3	$\displaystyle\sum_{j_2=s+1}^{S} \phi(j_2 + 3)\,\text{Prob}\,(0, 2 \,|\, j_2) + \sum_{j_2=0}^{s} \phi(S + 3)\,\text{Prob}\,(0, 2 \,|\, j_2)$
-2	$\displaystyle\sum_{j_2=s+1}^{S} \phi(j_2 + 2)\,\text{Prob}\,(1, 2 \,|\, j_2) + \sum_{j_2=-1}^{s} \phi(S + 2)\,\text{Prob}\,(1, 2 \,|\, j_2)$
-1	$\displaystyle\sum_{j_2=s+1}^{S} \phi(j_2 + 1)\,\text{Prob}\,(2, 2 \,|\, j_2) + \sum_{j_2=-2}^{s} \phi(S + 1)\,\text{Prob}\,(2, 2 \,|\, j_2)$
0	$\displaystyle\sum_{j_2=s+1}^{S} \phi(j_2)\,\text{Prob}\,(3, 2 \,|\, j_2) + \sum_{j_2=-3}^{s} \phi(S)\,\text{Prob}\,(3, 2 \,|\, j_2)$
1	$\displaystyle\sum_{j_2=s+1}^{S} \phi(j_2 - 1)\,\text{Prob}\,(3, 2 \,|\, j_2) + \sum_{j_2=-3}^{s} \phi(S - 1)\,\text{Prob}\,(3, 2 \,|\, j_2)$
$\vdots$	$\vdots$
$s + 1$	$\displaystyle\sum_{j_2=s+1}^{S} \phi(j_2 - s - 1)\,\text{Prob}\,(3, 2 \,|\, j_2) + \sum_{j_2=-3}^{s} \phi(S - s - 1)\,\text{Prob}\,(3, 2 \,|\, j_2)$
$s + 2$	$\displaystyle\sum_{j_2=s+2}^{S} \phi(j_2 - s - 2)\,\text{Prob}\,(3, 2 \,|\, j_2) + \sum_{j_2=-3}^{s} \phi(S - s - 2)\,\text{Prob}\,(3, 2 \,|\, j_2)$
$\vdots$	$\vdots$
S	$\phi(0)\,\text{Prob}\,(3, 2 \,|\, S) + \displaystyle\sum_{j_2=-3}^{s} \phi(0)\,\text{Prob}\,(3, 2 \,|\, j_2)$

TABLE 2.7.3
Transition probability $= \phi(v + v')$

Condition	Period t	Period $t + 1$
$s + 1 \leq v \leq S$	$(v \mid 0, 0)$	$(-v' \mid 0, 0)$
$0 \leq v \leq s$	$(v \mid 0, 0)$	$(-v' \mid S - v, \lambda - 1)$
$\tau > 1$	$(v \mid r, \tau)$	$(-v' \mid r, \tau - 1)$
$\tau = 1$	$(v \mid r, 1)$	$(r, -v' \mid 0)$

2.7.3   Inventory Holding

Just as we were able to employ $[T_X]$ directly for the analysis of shortages in the backlog model, Sequence β with $\lambda = 1$, we can follow a parallel approach for inventory holdings:

$$h(j) = j \qquad 1 \leq j \leq S$$
$$= 0 \qquad j \leq 0.$$

In the no-backlog model, we let

$$h[(v \mid r, \tau)] = v;$$

thus $h(j)$ is defined on the states for matrix $[T_V]$.

In both the backlog and the no-backlog models, it is relatively simple to deal with the statistic inventory on hand and on order, considered either as X or as U. We summarize the possibilities in Table 2.7.4.

TABLE 2.7.4
Definition of $h(j)$ for Inventory on Hand and on Order

Model	Variable	Conditions	$h(j) =$
Backlog	X	$1 \leq x \leq S$	x
		$x \leq 0$	0
	U	$s + 1 \leq u \leq S$	u
No-backlog Sequence α	X		$v + r$
	U	$0 \leq v \leq s$ $r = 0$	S
		otherwise	$v + r$

2.7.4 Purchases and Number of Orders

To obtain the sum of the quantities purchased in the backlog case, we define on the states $j = x$ of $[T_X]$,

$$h(j) = 0 \qquad\qquad s + 1 \le j \le S$$
$$= D + s - j \qquad j \le s.$$

Note that either $h = 0$ or $h \ge D$ with a non-trivial probability, and for $h > 0$, $S - h \le j_t \le S$. In Table 2.7.5 we illustrate the values of Prob $(7, 2 \mid j_2)$ under the model (9, 12) and with $p_X(j)$ as the *a priori* probability of j_1.

An alternative formulation to that in Section 2.6.3 for the probability distribution of the number of orders in the backlog model is to lump together [KS, Ch. 6] the states $x \le s$ into a state j^* so as to form the transition matrix[32]

$$[T_X^*] = \begin{bmatrix} 0 & 1 & \cdots & D-2 & & & D-1 \\ & 0 & \cdots & D-3 & & & D-2 \\ & & \cdot & & & & \cdot \\ & & & \cdot & & & \cdot \\ & & & \cdot & & & \cdot \\ & & & & 0 & & 1 \\ 1 & 2 & \cdots & D-1 & & 0 & D \\ 1 & 2 & \cdots & D-1 & & 0 & D \end{bmatrix},$$

where j^* is associated with the last row and column. We let

$$h(j) = 1 \qquad j = j^*$$
$$= 0 \qquad \text{otherwise.}$$

If the stationary distribution of X is used for the *a priori* probabilities of the states of $[T_X^*]$, then the appropriate vector is

$$[p_X(S) \cdots p_X(s + 1) \quad \sigma].$$

In the no-backlog model, the purchase quantities may be represented as

$$h[(v \mid 0, 0)] = D + s - v \qquad 0 \le v \le s$$
$$= 0 \qquad\qquad \text{otherwise.}$$

---

[32] Note the similarity between $[T_X^*]$ and $[T_U]$ in Section 2.2.2.

TABLE 2.7.5

(9, 12) BACKLOG

j_2	Prob $(7, 2 \mid j_2)$
5	$\sum_{x=10}^{12} p_X(x)\phi(x-5)$
6	0
7	0
8	$p_X(9)\phi(4)$
9	$p_X(8)\phi(3)$
10	$p_X(5)\phi(2)$
11	$p_X(5)\phi(1)$
12	$p_X(5)\phi(0)$

By substituting 1 for $D + s - v$ above, we can obtain the distribution of the number of orders in a consecutive sequence of periods.

2.7.5   *Net Demand*

The fundamental observation permitting us to handle sums of net demand (Section 2.6.1) by the method of Proposition 2.7.1 is that

$$n_t = U_t - U_{t+1},$$

for both the backlog and the no-backlog models. If $U_t \geq U_{t+1}$, then the difference is the amount of filled and backlogged demand not replenished by a new order; if $U_t < U_{t+1}$, then the difference is the excess of the new order over filled and backlogged demand.

Proceeding formally, we relate the above observation to a Markov chain analysis. In the backlog model we expand the $[T_U]$ matrix of Section 2.2.2 so that the new states represent a consecutive pair of the original states [KS, p. 140]. For example, if the following values of U are observed, $S, S - 5, S - 8, S, S - 2$, in the new characterization of states these observations are $(S, S - 5), (S - 5, S - 8), (S - 8, S), (S, S - 2)$. The new transition matrix appears in Table 2.7.6 and the corresponding stationary probabilities are components of $[p_U]$, each multiplied by the

TABLE 2.7.6

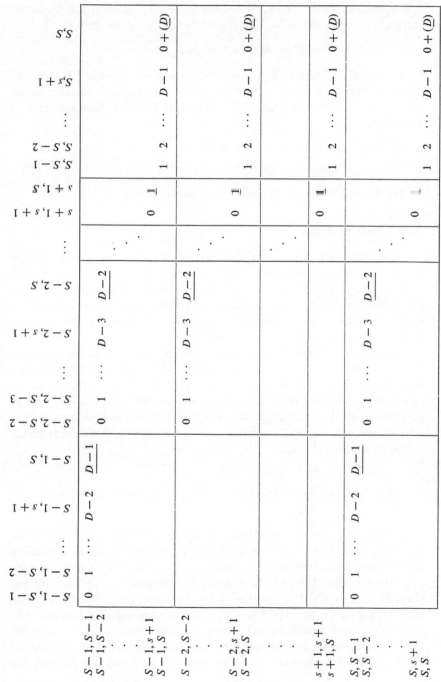

appropriate entry in $\lfloor T_U \rfloor$. The dimension of the enlarged transition matrix is $.5(D^2 + 3D - 2)$. On the states (U_t, U_{t+1}) we define

$$h(j) = U_t - U_{t+1}.$$

In a similar fashion, the no-backlog transition matrix $[T_V]$ can be expanded to represent consecutive pairs of states, and the associated values of U are as indicated in Table 2.7.4. The enlarged transition matrix is of dimension

$$.5D(D + 1) + D(s + 1) + .5(s + 1)(s + 2)$$
$$+ (\lambda - 1)[.25(s + 1)(3s + 4) + \tfrac{1}{12}s(s + 1)(2s + 1)];$$

for the illustration in Table 2.3.5, this dimension is 48.

2.7.6 Sampled Sums

If we desire the probability distribution of a sum of $h_t(j_t)$ where the sampled states j_t are observed in not necessarily consecutive time periods, then the principle of Proposition 2.7.1 is modified to refer to the appropriate higher-order transition probabilities (Section 2.1.6). For example, if the system is to be sampled in alternate periods, then for part (1) of Proposition 2.7.1 we would employ the entries of $[M]^2$.

As the time interval between successive observations increases, there is less dependence of one observation on its predecessor, and the stationary probabilities for the states serve as good approximations for the likelihood of $h(j) = h$. In other words, the stationary probabilities may be used to derive the probability that $h(j) = h$ in any of the observed periods, and, as a result, convoluting this distribution of h provides the probability distribution of a sampled sum.

2.8   THE PRESENCE OF NON-STATIONARY CONDITIONS

Until now, whenever we referred to unconditional probabilities of the states of the system or of functions thereupon, we employed stationary distributions. We complete this chapter with a brief discussion of state probabilities when the previously assumed stationary conditions are not present. The postulates which lead to the equilibrium distributions included specifying a single (s, S) policy and the distribution of demand $\phi(\xi)$. In relaxing these assumptions we may consider both the policy and the demand distribution as varying over time, either in a deterministic manner or in a way that may itself be described by a stochastic process, the parameters of which we are able to specify (perhaps on purely subjective bases) [Kar, KF, KI].

Some instances under which such non-stationary conditions occur are the introduction of an item, later followed by its gradual removal, thereby causing average demand to increase and then to decrease; or the presence of seasonal factors causing cyclical fluctuations in average demand. These variations in the parameters of the demand distribution may induce additional variations in the (s, S) policy. To illustrate, suppose for each period t, we have a transition matrix $[T_{Xt}]$ as shown in Table 2.2.1, and that every k periods the matrices are identical $[T_{Xt}] = [T_{X,t+k}]$. If S varies, each $[T_{Xt}]$ must be constructed so that the first row and column refer to the maximal S; this process involves straightforward revisions of Table 2.2.1. Then we have k vectors of stationary probabilities $[p_{Xt}]$ defined by

$$(1) \qquad [p_{Xt}][T_{Xt}][T_{X,t+1}] \cdots [T_{X,t+k-1}] = [p_{Xt}].$$

It is only necessary to calculate (1) for a single value of t and then use the recursion

$$(2) \qquad [p_{X,t+1}] = [p_{Xt}][T_{Xt}].$$

Similarly the results of Proposition 2.2.8 generalize where the product of as many as λ different $[\Phi]$ matrices are employed instead of $[\Phi]^\lambda$.

Another class of instances is that where the distribution $\phi(\xi)$ is not known exactly, but it is reasonable to specify a time dependent probability distribution on the parameters of $\phi(\xi)$.[33] A further illustration of our abandoning the use of a stationary distribution is when we have some special information about the likelihood of the current state of the system, and consequently we postulate an *a priori* distribution of the initial states different from the stationary probability distribution.

We note that any previously derived stationary probability distribution for the states of the system can be viewed as the limiting vector of the process of multiplying, period by period, the current unconditional state probability vector by the appropriate Markov transition matrix, such as $[T_X]$ or $[T_Y]$; the entries in these transition matrices depend on the (s, S) policy and $\phi(\xi)$. Equivalently, the limiting process may be thought of as the multiplication of a vector of *a priori* probabilities of the initial states times the product of a series of identical transition matrices. Without going into unnecessary detail, if in each period the values (s, S) and the

---

[33] If the distribution for the parameters is identical and independent over time, then in a straightforward way we can compute a resultant demand distribution $\tilde{\phi}(\xi)$ and apply the previous analysis.

distribution $\phi(\xi)$ are determined, we can describe the analysis under relaxed assumptions as involving the multiplication of a vector of *a priori* probabilities of the initial states times the product of a series of not necessarily identical matrices, the variation in the transition matrices being due to and completely summarizing the changes in (s, S) and the distribution $\phi(\xi)$. If in each period (s, S) and the distribution $\phi(\xi)$ are specified in terms of a probability distribution, then a repeated application of conditional probability analysis yields the desired results; we analyze the problem for each possible (s, S) and distribution $\phi(\xi)$ and then weight these probabilities (or expectations) so derived by the probability of the particular (s, S) and distribution $\phi(\xi)$ occurring.

In summary, by employing the above analysis, all the propositions in this chapter, other than those pertaining to the properties of the stationary distributions per se, can be properly interpreted to yield the probability distributions of the operating statistics in the presence of non-stationary conditions, and the consequent mode of computation is vector and matrix multiplication.

Chapter 3

CONTROL OF (s, S)
POLICY DECISIONS

O UR DETAILED STUDY of the usefulness of statistical aggregates for control purposes begins in this chapter. Throughout we postulate that the inventory system is comprised of a multitude of items, each of which is demanded and stocked according to any one of the (s, S) models in Chapter 2. Specifically, we assume that the demand distribution for each item i, $\phi_i(\xi)$, is known and is independent of the demands for other items in the system, and that the delivery time lag λ_i is given. In the next chapter we consider situations in which the $\phi_i(\xi)$ are not known with certainty. The organizational structure is that contained in Section 1.1.1 and illustrated in Section 1.3.1. In particular, we assume top management has devised a set of recommended (s, S) inventory policies for a lower echelon to follow.

A potentiality for control arises because lower management, without the imposition of a surveillance scheme, may be motivated to adopt stockage rules differing from those recommended. Reasons for this divergence of policy, of course, depend on the facts of a real situation, but a list of typical influences would include[1] a desire of the lower echelon (a) to meet any demand contingency, a motive leading to uneconomical surpluses of inventory, (b) to avoid surpluses of inventory, leading to uneconomical shortages of stock on hand, and (c) either to keep inventory on hand varying within a narrow range or to avoid handling small shipments, leading to an uneconomical frequency of ordering. Scientific approaches to the derivation of inventory rules seek to strike an economic balance between these cost factors, each being measured from the view of top management and not of the lower echelon. A natural question to pose in

---

[1] The enumeration to follow is not to be interpreted as a set of internally consistent factors; on the contrary, the influences are opposing. The idea to be conveyed is that, in real situations, any one of these motivations may arise.

examining a particular control scheme is whether the control device encourages lower management to adopt the recommended policies; if it does, we call the control consistent.

We elaborate on the idea of consistency in Section 3.1. There we also explain the two elementary types of management techniques, *barometer* and *quota* controls. The former may be likened to an incentive scheme in which lower management is rewarded or penalized according to its performance as measured in terms of an aggregate index; the latter may be likened to a management-by-exception scheme in which the lower echelon is audited whenever an aggregate index value falls outside a range acceptable to top management. Most real control systems are a composite of these elementary types; having analyzed the consistency of the elements, we can draw conclusions regarding the more elaborate schemes. Typical control indices are listed in Section 3.1.3, and their probability distributions may be obtained directly from the derivations in Chapter 2.

In Section 3.2 we examine barometer control, and show how to construct a consistent scheme by employing a comprehensive index. We also comment on the connection between the design of optimal inventory policies and of a consistent barometer scheme; we illustrate the discussion with an example based on a geometric probability distribution of demand. In Section 3.3 we study quota control, and indicate the attendant difficulty in constructing a consistent device. In particular, we demonstrate that the approach yielding a consistent control for a barometer scheme does not do likewise for a quota scheme, unless the number of inventory review periods comprising a single control period is large. We also examine a quota control on purchases and on net demand; the former is not consistent, and the latter is either not consistent or ineffective. We complete the analysis by demonstrating the connection between determining action probabilities under quota control and error probabilities in the testing of composite statistical hypotheses.

Section 3.4 explores the implications of our results in terms of the model of economic evaluation in Section 1.2. We focus attention (1) on the selection of the number of inventory review periods to be encompassed within a control period, and (2) on the impact of imposing an inconsistent control on the *a priori* probabilities of the states of the inventory system. We stress that the evaluation of a control scheme always involves a comparison of the proposal with at least one other alternative, such as maintaining the status quo. Realizing this principle, we may find in some actual situations that imposing a particular inconsistent device is preferable to imposing a consistent device or to having no additional control.

3.1 INTRODUCTION

We define the notion of a consistent control in Section 3.1.1, and elaborate on the ways lower management may take inconsistent actions. We also comment on the manner by which we can approach the study of control schemes, the extreme cases being an investigation of consistency for a precisely defined control device and the construction of a consistent control scheme. In Section 3.1.2, we review the notions of "quota" and "barometer control," and in Section 3.1.3 we list a collection of indices which may be contained in a control device. In Section 3.1.4, we discuss the general mathematical method for obtaining the behavior of a statistical index comprised of control numbers for a multitude of inventoried items.

3.1.1 Consistency Criterion for an Inventory Model

In Section 1.1.2 we stressed two important aspects of a control scheme: the ability of the device (1) to guarantee or encourage the fulfillment of certain standards, and (2) to ensure or make likely the detection of deviation from these standards. In our present context the standards are to be interpreted as lower management's observance of a set of (s, S) policies which are specified by top management for each item in the system.[2] We say a control scheme is *strongly consistent* if it positively encourages the exact fulfillment of these standards, and *weakly consistent* if it does not positively encourage a violation of the standards; weak consistency admits the joint possibility of positive encouragement neither to fulfill nor to violate standards.[3] Deviations from the specified (s, S) rules are termed inconsistent actions,[4] which may arise under the following circumstances:

Inconsistency type 1. At some period in time, lower management, having full knowledge of the state of the inventory system and the control constraints, violates top management rules.

Inconsistency type 2. Period after period, lower management, having full knowledge of the current state of the inventory system and the control constraints, violates top management rules; the nature of the violation depends on the particular state of the system.

[2] The specification procedure, of course, may be a computing algorithm for the determination of (s, S) from data inputs such as average demand per review period, inventory cost, outage cost, purchase price, etc.

[3] The distinction between *strongly* and *weakly* consistent is analogous to the mathematical distinction between a positive ($x > 0$) and a non-negative ($x \geq 0$) variable.

[4] A scheme is *strongly inconsistent* if it positively encourages a violation of standards.

Inconsistency type 3.   Period after period, lower management violates top management rules by employing (s, S) policies differing from those recommended. Clearly this type of inconsistency may be subsumed as a special case of type 2, but it is significantly important to justify a separate identification.

In each of these instances, top management may have certain *a priori* beliefs about the nature of the inconsistent actions; to illustrate, top management may suppose that the reorder point s, if it is altered by lower management, is revised upward. The third type of inconsistency yields naturally to the mode of analysis in Chapter 2, namely, to a consideration of stationary probability distributions. The other types of inconsistencies involve analyses of transient behavior, except for the possible use of the stationary probabilities for the *a priori* distribution of initial states.

An investigation of the consistency of control schemes may progress at three levels of inquiry:

Level 1.   Given an inventory policy, a control scheme, and a specific set of values for the economic parameters utilized in the scheme, is the resulting situation consistent?

Level 2.   Given an inventory policy, and a control scheme, can specific values for the set of parameters utilized in the scheme be chosen so that the resulting situation is consistent?

Level 3.   Given an inventory policy, can a top management control scheme be devised so that the resulting situation is consistent?[5]

As we shall discover (in Section 3.3.1), a control device may be strongly consistent in a single-item inventory system, but its analog in a multi-item system may be strongly inconsistent.

Our concentrating on the property of consistency is warranted because, whenever a control device is suggested, we are at once confronted with the question of whether the system possibly misdirects operating personnel. But determining whether a system is either consistent or inconsistent is not sufficient to ascertain its full merit. For reasons which we elaborate in Section 3.4, we cannot say that a consistent system is to be preferred unequivocally to an inconsistent control.

[5] We shall avoid misunderstanding if we recall a basic argument advanced in Section 1.1.1. Top management, by its very nature, cannot know the state of the system in as much detail as lower management can; therefore, we omit from consideration suggestions for control system design predicated on a necessity for top management to know such detail. For example, if top management knew the current amount of inventory of a particular item, it could establish a purchase quota which would ensure for the period at hand that the prescribed policy would be followed; such a scheme is functionally equivalent to detail control.

3.1.2 Elementary Control Schemes

We focus attention on two generic types of control schemes.

Barometer control: lower management is rewarded or penalized according to the magnitude of deviation of a control index number from a preset target value.

Quota control: lower management is assumed to be meeting standards as long as the control index number remains under a preset quota limit.[6]

Most real control systems are a combination of several of these devices. In Section 1.3 we described a system comprised of quota controls on both purchase costs and net demand, Section 2.6.1, as well as a barometer index control on consumption. In this chapter we analyze examples of each of the generic types; from these results, it is possible to draw conclusions in a straightforward manner concerning the consistency of composite schemes.[7] Because the number of potential control schemes is sizeable, we necessarily must forego any detailed taxonomic approach; we must be content to investigate those devices which are commonly employed or seem promising.

Throughout we postulate that the inventory records accurately indicate the status of the system. To assume otherwise is to admit for consideration the possibility of apparent fulfillment of standards by means of willful "adjusting" of such data which would otherwise indicate an out-of-control state. A study of this aspect goes beyond our intended scope.

3.1.3 Control Indices

A sufficient condition to establish that the aggregation process in computing any control index number is well defined, insofar as timing considerations are concerned, is that the inventory review periods assumed for each of the (s, S) policies coincide. Reflection on the matter shows that there are many other possible timing configurations for the composite of (s, S) policies which also permit an index aggregation. We shall not attempt to give a necessary condition regarding this timing consideration,

---

[6] If the index number can take negative as well as positive values, or if small values are possibly indicative of inconsistent actions, the quota restriction may be given in terms of an allowable range for the index.

[7] We caution that probability analyses of a combined system—for example, determination of the over-all probability that any one of the quotas is exceeded during a period—can be genuinely difficult. Such complexity is not peculiar to inventory control; analogous problems exist in some statistical quality control procedures which simultaneously employ several control charts and rules for deciding out-of-control situations.

and mainly for convenience of presentation, our discussion in the remainder of this chapter and the next will proceed as if all the review intervals do coincide. But we note that more general configurations can be encompassed in a conceptually obvious way.

The control period and inventory review period may or may not coincide. For example, purchases may accumulate for several review periods before a quota is applied; or shortages may be averaged during a certain number of sampled periods and then compared to a target value. The mathematical analysis underlying such situations is contained in Section 2.7.

Control numbers[8] commonly employed include as elements:

(1) value of inventory on hand (Sections 2.2, 2.3, and 2.7.3)
(2) value of inventory on order (Sections 2.2, 2.3, and 2.7.3)
(3) value of inventory on hand and on order (Sections 2.2, 2.3, and 2.7.3)
(4) number of orders placed (Sections 2.6.2, 2.6.3, and 2.7.4)
(5) number of orders outstanding (Sections 2.6.2, 2.6.3, and 2.7.4)
(6) number or value of current purchases (Sections 2.5.1 and 2.7.4)
(7) number or value of shortages (Sections 2.5.2 and 2.7.2)
(8) number or value of backorders (Sections 2.2, 2.3, and 2.5.2)
(9) number of outages (Section 2.5.2)
(10) net demand (Sections 2.6.1 and 2.7.5).

Items (1), (2), (3), (5), (8), and (9) may be thought of as representing summary status variables at the end of the control period, and the remainder of items as representing movements occurring within the control period. Shortages comprise the actual excess of current demand over available supply on hand, the excess being backlogged if such action is permitted; outages comprise items of inventory usually stocked but which currently are at a zero inventory level. We are also interested in certain schemes which sum several of these indices to provide a super-index for control.

3.1.4 Mathematical Tools

From a formal point of view, we may derive the probability distribution for an index of the sort listed in Section 3.1.3 first by obtaining from Chapter 2 the appropriate probability distribution of the control number for each item to be included in the index, and then by convoluting these distributions. If the index is to be an aggregate over a number of review periods so that the normal distribution approximations in Section 2.7.1

---

[8] We speak of a control number with reference to each item, and of an index number with reference to a systemwide summation of the control numbers.

may be employed, the convolution process is considerably simplified; only the proper mean and variance contributions from each item are required. To illustrate, a Level 1 investigation in Section 3.1.1 of the consistency of a quota scheme involves comparing the probability of the index remaining under the quota when the specified (s, S) rules are observed as against when they are violated.

In the following sections we proceed beyond this formal prescription to a probability analysis of specific control schemes and, in particular, to a judgment concerning their consistency. We rely heavily on the results in Chapter 2.

3.2 BAROMETER CONTROL

We begin our discussion of barometer controls in Section 3.2.1 with an explanation of the general statistical properties of such index devices and of the necessity for using a comprehensive aggregate in order to avoid inconsistent and ineffective controls. Section 3.2.2 outlines a method for constructing a consistent scheme for both the backlog and no-backlog models. The approach is first to compute a control number for each item stocked, the number being a linear function, roughly, of the level of inventory on hand, of the amount of shortage, and of the placing of a replenishment order. The parameters of the linear function yielding a consistent device are called rationalized values. Then the individual rationalized control numbers are summed to form the aggregate index.

Section 3.2.3 presents the fundamental principles of the computational techniques for deriving rationalized parameters; these methods are illustrated with numerical examples. Section 3.2.4 gives special attention to an inventory model with either a geometric or exponential demand distribution, backlogging of excess demand, and a delivery lag of one period. Here we exhibit the specific connection between deriving an optimal (s, S) rule and determining a rationalized control number.

3.2.1 *Index Design and Random Behavior*

We consider as indices the quantities cited in Section 3.1.3 weighted and summed over the various items in the system and perhaps over several consecutive or sampled inventory review periods. In the spirit of Section 1.1.1., we postulate here that lower management's objective is to optimize [9]

---

[9] That is, to maximize or minimize, depending on the nature of the particular control scheme.

the expected value of the deviation between the index and the target value. Since the latter is preset, the problem focuses upon optimizing the expected value of the index number per se. Our analysis in Section 2.7.1 yields the stationary expectation of such a sum; since the demands for the items are independent, the variance of the index sum is the sum of the variances associated with each item, and these also are given in Section 2.7.1 for small and large values of T, the number of inventory review periods encompassed by a control period. In most real situations, if the number of items comprising the index is large, the central limit theorem may be applied on this account to yield the conclusion that the index number is approximately normally distributed with the aforementioned mean and variance.

Considerable difficulty is encountered in providing consistent control by means of fragmentary indices, that is, indices which focus on only one aspect of the system's operating behavior. For example, if the inventory model permits backlogging and the sole index is the value of inventory on hand, we may conclude that lower management, being strongly motivated to reduce the index figure below a target value, would tend to diminish the values of s and D in the (s, S) rules.[10] Similarly for the same model, if the sole index is value of shortages or backlogs, there is a strong motivation to increase s and D; or, if the sole index is the number of orders placed, there is a tendency to increase D. Thus fragmentary control may lead to strong inconsistencies in an obvious way, and these may be either of types 1, 2, or 3 in Section 3.1.1.

Assume that a normal distribution is an adequate representation of the probability distribution of the index number. Then it is simple to demonstrate that under fragmentary control the aggregation process may hide or confound violations which are offsetting. For example, it may occur that the reorder point s from one item is shifted upward, causing an increase in the mean and variance of the probability distribution of the item's control number; that for another item, the point is shifted downward, with a similar change in the mean and variance of the probability distribution of the control number; and that the result is no net change in the parameters of the normal distribution of the index number. A simple example of this situation is where two items both have the same demand distribution $\phi(\xi)$ but differing (s, S) policies due to the composite of economic factors involved. If the index number weights each of these items equally, then an interchange of the two (s, S) policies has no effect on the distribution of the index; this conclusion follows irrespective of the form of the probability distribution of the index number.

---

[10] This conclusion and those to follow are predicated on the results of Sections 2.2.3, 2.2.5, 2.2.8, and 2.5.2.

Finally, a fragmentary index may be ineffective as a control against certain kinds of violations of the (s, S) rules. A striking example is the use of net demand as an index with a target value zero. From Section 2.6.1 we know that for all the inventory models considered, the expected value of net demand is zero, regardless of the (s, S) rule being observed. Therefore, such a barometer index is weakly consistent in that it neither encourages nor discourages the use of the prescribed (s, S) rules.

We conclude by posing a Level 3 investigatory problem, to be discussed in the next section. Is it possible to devise a top management barometer control index[11] which is strongly consistent for the composite of the (s, S) policies?

3.2.2 Rationalizing (s, S) Policies

Barometer control involves rewarding or penalizing lower management by the amount[12]

(1) $\qquad \theta$ (index number − target), where $\theta > 0$.

The target is set at the expected value of the index number and, therefore, is merely the sum of the expected value of each item's control number in a single review period times the number of periods comprising the control interval.

For each item stocked, we seek a set of weighting or pricing factors to be assigned to the various states describing the status of the item at the end of an inventory review period, such that the expected value of the associated control number is a strict *minimum* whenever the specified (s, S) rule is being followed.[13] Thus, even after system aggregation, the index is strongly consistent, since the best course of action for lower management to follow is to obey, item by item, the prescribed stockage policies[14] which may differ.

Of course, prior to assigning weights, we must decide upon those characteristics of the inventory state which are to be priced. We explore

---

[11] If it is possible to make use of full item-by-item detail, then the design problem becomes trivial—ascertain the number of items for which the recommended (s, S) policies have been violated and penalize lower management proportional to this number. This suggested control, of course, is not in keeping with our notion of top management control. We return to this suggestion in Section 3.4.1.

[12] For example, suppose shortage costs are being controlled, the index number is 50, the target number is 100, and θ is .5. Then lower management is rewarded 25. If the values 50 and 100 are interchanged, lower management is penalized 25.

[13] That is, the expected value of the control number with these weights strictly increases with *any* change from the prescribed (s, S) rule.

[14] Note that this conclusion follows irrespective of the value assigned to the target. We return to this point in Section 4.4.

two such possibilities. For the backlog model of Chapter 2 we employ the variable X, the amount of inventory on hand (or backlogged) and on order, and a variable indicating the placing of an order. Then we let:

(2)   control number $= C_{in}x$ $s + 1 \leq x \leq S$,

$C_{fix} + C_{in}x$ $0 \leq x \leq s$,

$C_{fix} - C_{out}x$ $x < 0$,

where C_{in}, C_{out}, and C_{fix} are positive constants to be determined, and (s, S) is the *actual* policy being employed.[15] This scheme has the advantage that the relevant probability distribution $p_X(x)$ is independent of the presence of any time-lag λ. This independence between λ and the rationalizing values of the economic parameters is to be sharply contrasted with the dependence we must usually observe in selecting a preferred (s, S) policy. In most inventory models leading to the selection of optimal stockage policies, the variables Y, V, Z, or W are typically of interest, and we know from Proposition 2.2.8, Algorithm 2.3.2, and Proposition 2.3.5 that these variables do depend on λ. Thus, when a significant delivery lag is present, in general we cannot expect an agreement between the rationalizing economic values and the economic parameters leading to the selection of the preferred (s, S) policy. Making use of the basic result in [Scar] and the continuity properties of s and S in terms of C_{in}, C_{out}, and C_{fix}, we can be assured of the existence of rationalizing values for these control constants.

For the no-backlog model, we utilize the variable V in Sequence α, or the variable W in Sequence β, the number of shortages, and the indicator of placing an order, so that for Sequence α:

(3)   control number $= C_{in}v$ $s + 1 \leq v \leq S$,

$C_{fix} + C_{in}v + C_{out}$ (shortages)

$0 \leq v \leq s$, order placed,

$C_{in}v + C_{out}$ (shortages)

$0 \leq v \leq s$, no order placed.

We are not able to guarantee the existence of rationalizing values for C_{in}, C_{out}, and C_{fix} in the no-backlog model [AKS, Ch. 10]. A variety of other possibilities is easily envisaged, one notable case involving the adding of purchase costs to the control number in the no-backlog model.[16] Much

---

[15] In other words, at the end of a period each unit of inventory on hand (or backlogged) is costed at C_{in}, if the amount is positive, or at $-C_{out}$ if the amount is negative, and if an order is then placed, a further charge of C_{fix} is added.

[16] In Section 2.5.3 we observed that E(purchase costs) in the backlog model is independent of the (s, S) policy being followed. Consequently, adding purchase costs to the control number in this situation is of no assistance in the rationalization process.

current research in the establishment of "optimal inventory rules" [AHM, AKS, B, DKW, FD, H, HMMS, M, Mo, Wh] proceeds in the fashion of defining a pertinent top management utility index for each item's stockage policy, and the rule derived is that which optimizes the expected value of this utility function. For such situations, the control number can be (although it need not be) the same as the utility evaluation;[17] we present an illustration in Section 3.2.4 in which this approach and the control number (2) yield identical results.

If it is possible to find a set of values for C_{in}, C_{out}, and C_{fix} such that the stationary value E (control number) is strictly minimized for the *prescribed* values of (s, S), we say that the given (s, S) rule is rationalized. Observe that inconsistencies of type 1 are possible, of type 2 are sometimes possible, but of type 3 are not possible, that is, it is not possible to violate the (s, S) rules period after period by using alternative (s, S) rules.[18]

If the index number chosen to rationalize each (s, S) policy does, in fact, represent top management's total utility of the situation, and, according to our postulate in Section 1.1.1, top management is interested solely in the expected value of the index, then by setting $\theta = 1$, top management has obtained a control device which provides a complete hedge against inconsistent actions. In other words, if the index number can be treated as a cardinal utility indicator, then management's total utility is the sum of the expected value of the index, and the reward or penalty on lower management is

$$E(\text{index}) - \theta E(\text{index} - \text{target}) = \text{target for } \theta = 1;$$

this constant is independent of the actual (s, S) policies being followed.

If lower management violates the rules despite the consistent situation, then top management will suffer a utility loss whenever it is not practicable to employ a complete hedge. It is plausible that after a number of periods top management would notice a persistent tendency to exceed, say, the target, and would institute corrective action; but this consideration carries us beyond our present realm of discussion of barometer control into that of quota control. We return to this latter subject in Section 3.3. Thus, aside

[17] The objective of many inventory models is to minimize time-discounted expected utility rather than statistical-equilibrium expected utility; in these instances, it is generally true that the economic parameters in the former objective function cannot be used for our purposes here.

[18] A resolution of the issue as to whether type 2 inconsistencies are possible hinges upon whether an (s, S) type policy in fact minimizes the expected value of the control number; i.e., it may be that there is a policy which prescribes a different amount to order for different amounts of inventory on hand and on order, depending on the delivery dates of the amount on order, and such that the expectation of the control number is thereby reduced under the rationalized value [AKS, Ch. 10].

from any possible hedging operation, barometer control in its strict meaning does not admit considerations of "management by exception."

3.2.3   Computational Aspects of the Rationalization Process

In the backlog model we use the suggested scheme (2) in Section 3.2.2, and we may write the expected control number as

(1) $E(\text{control number}) = C_{\text{fix}} \sum\limits_{x=-\infty}^{s} p_X(x) + C_{\text{in}} \sum\limits_{x=1}^{S} x p_X(x)$

$$- C_{\text{out}} \sum\limits_{x=-\infty}^{0} x p_X(x).$$

Since (1) is a homogeneous function of the first degree in the economic parameters, we may, without loss of generality, introduce a normalization $C_{\text{in}} = 1$.

The analysis of Section 2.5.3 may be employed[19] to derive bounds on C_{out}, resulting in relation (2) below. We use the normalization $C_{\text{in}} = 1$ and obtain the result

(2) $\dfrac{1 - \text{Prob(out)}}{\text{Prob(out)}} \leq C_{\text{out}} \leq \dfrac{1 - \text{Prob(short)}}{\text{Prob(short)}},$

where

$$\text{Prob(out)} = \sum\limits_{x=-\infty}^{0} p_X(x \mid \text{specified policy}),$$

and

$$\text{Prob(short)} = \sum\limits_{x=-\infty}^{-1} p_X(x \mid \text{specified policy}).$$

To illustrate the rationalization process in the backlog model, consider the policy $(0, 3)$ with $\phi(\xi)$ a uniform distribution as given in Table 2.4.1. We seek values of C_{fix} and C_{out} so that $E(\text{control number})$ is a strict minimum for the policy $(0, 3)$. To derive bounds on these constants we compare the expectation for $(0, 3)$ with that for $(0, 2)$ and $(0, 4)$. The data in Table 2.4.1 yield

$$E[\text{control number} \mid (0, 3)] = \tfrac{8}{27} C_{\text{fix}} + \tfrac{33}{27} + \tfrac{3}{27} C_{\text{out}},$$

$$E[\text{control number} \mid (0, 2)] = \tfrac{4}{9} C_{\text{fix}} + \tfrac{7}{9} + \tfrac{1}{9} C_{\text{out}},$$

and

$$E[\text{control number} \mid (0, 4)] = \tfrac{16}{69} C_{\text{fix}} + \tfrac{119}{69} + \tfrac{5}{69} C_{\text{out}}.$$

[19] It is readily verified that in Proposition 2.5.3 the conclusion is valid for $p_X(x)$ as well as for $p_{V,\lambda}(v)$.

The inequalities E[control number $\mid$ (0, 3)] $<$ E[control number $\mid$ (0, 2)] and E[control number $\mid$ (0, 3)] $<$ E[control number $\mid$ (0, 4)] give

$$3 < C_{\text{fix}} \quad \text{and} \quad 5C_{\text{fix}} + 3C_{\text{out}} < 39.$$

Using the inequality (2) in our example, where

$$\text{Prob(out)} = 8/27 \quad \text{and} \quad \text{Prob(short)} = 3/27,$$

we obtain

$$2\tfrac{3}{8} \leq C_{\text{out}} \leq 8.$$

Consequently, a set of rationalizing values is $C_{\text{in}} = 1$, $C_{\text{out}} = 4$, and $C_{\text{fix}} = 4$, with E[control number $\mid$ (0, 3)] $= 77/27 = 2.85$.

For the no-backlog model, we illustrate the rationalization procedure by means of an example. Consider the model in Table 2.4.10, where the probability of demand is given by a Poisson distribution with mean 1 (tabulated in Table 2.4.2). We wish to rationalize a (3, 8) policy using the control number (3) suggested in Section 3.2.2, that is, by finding positive values of the control parameters C_{in}, C_{out}, and C_{fix} such that

$$E[\text{control number} \mid (s, S)] \equiv C_{\text{fix}}\sigma(s, S) + C_{\text{in}}E[v \mid (s, S)]$$
$$+ C_{\text{out}}E[\text{shortage} \mid (s, S)]$$

is a minimum for (3, 8). The relations which must be satisfied are E[control number $\mid$ (3, 8)] $<$ E[control number $\mid$ (s, S)] for $s \neq 3$ and $S \neq 8$. As above, we may let $C_{\text{in}} = 1$. We summarize in Table 3.2.1 for neighboring

TABLE 3.2.1

(s, S)	σ	E(shortage)	$E(v)$	$(E - E^*)^a$
(2, 5)	.0992	.6644	1.0008	.1755
(2, 6)	.0908	.5988	1.3594	.0397
(3, 6)	.1565	.4985	1.4413	.3082
(2, 7)	.0836	.5485	1.7356	.0277
(3, 7)	.0990	.5736	1.5012	.1287
(4, 7)	.1711	.4388	1.7682	.4521
(2, 8)	.0771	.4999	2.1297	.0522
(3, 8)	.0904	.5000	1.9173	0
(4, 8)	.1436	.4063	2.0762	.2351
(2, 9)	.0715	.4587	2.5628	.1709
(3, 9)	.0837	.4584	2.3228	.0755
(4, 9)	.0980	.4543	2.1407	.0404
(4, 10)	.0901	.4175	2.5740	.1581

$^a E^* \equiv E$[control number $\mid$ (3, 8)] $= 6.0021$ for $C_{\text{in}} = 1$, $C_{\text{fix}} = 12$, $C_{\text{out}} = 6$. $E \equiv E$[control number $\mid$ (s, S)]

(s, S) policies the relevant statistics that are needed to compute E[control number $| (s, S)$]; these are obtained from the Monte Carlo simulations employed in Table 2.4.10. The resulting inequalities that are to be satisfied to ensure rationalization appear in Table 3.2.2.

TABLE 3.2.2.

Neighboring Policy	C_{fix}	C_{out}	>
(2, 5)	.0088	.1644	.9165
(2, 6)	.0004	.0988	.5579
(3, 6)	.0661	−.0015	.4760
(2, 7)	−.0068	.0485	.1817
(3, 7)	.0086	.0736	.4161
(4, 7)	.0807	−.0612	.1491
(2, 8)	−.0133	−.0001	−.2124
(4, 8)	.0532	−.0937	−.1589
(2, 9)	−.0189	−.0413	−.6455
(3, 9)	−.0067	−.0416	−.4055
(4, 9)	.0076	−.0457	−.2234
(4, 10)	−.0003	−.0825	−.6567

For example, from Table 3.2.1 the comparison between (3, 8) and (4, 7) is

$$.1711C_{\text{fix}} + .4388C_{\text{out}} + 1.7682 \geq .0904C_{\text{fix}} + .5000C_{\text{out}} + 1.9173,$$

or, from Table 3.2.2,

$$.0807C_{\text{fix}} - .0612C_{\text{out}} \geq .1491.$$

We may utilize an algebraic method of linear programming or a geometrical representation of the set of inequalities for a solution[20] [DSS]. In this example, rationalizing values are $C_{\text{in}} = 1$, $C_{\text{fix}} = 12$, and $C_{\text{out}} = 6$. The final column of Table 3.2.1 gives the excess by which the left-hand sides of the inequalities in the chart exceed the right-hand sides.

[20] Briefly, the manner of solution by geometrical means is to graph the set of relations in the chart as equalities, where the variables on the axes are labeled C_{fix} and C_{out}, and to find the polygonal region of feasible values for the two economic parameters implied by the inequality relationships, provided such a region exists. Using, say, the simplex computational method of linear programming, we can define as an objective function the sum of the slack values of Table 3.2.2 constraints (viewed as inequalities), and then obtain an optimal solution to the dual of this set of constraints. We employ the corresponding "shadow prices" for the optimal dual solution as the rationalizing values of the economic parameters, after, perhaps, making any slight correction needed to ensure that E [control number $|$ (3, 8)] is a strict minimum.

3.2.4 Analytic Examples

We turn to the backlog models, Sequence β, $\lambda = 1$, that were considered in Sections 2.5.3 and 2.5.4. Notice that $L(s, S \mid \text{backlog}, \lambda = 1)$ and $E(\text{control number})$ in relation (2) of Section 3.2.2 differ only in the term $C_{\text{pur}}E(\text{purchase})$, and that this term is independent of the (s, S) policy being adopted. Consequently, for the geometric distribution $\phi(\xi) = pq^{\xi}$, the value of s which minimizes

$$E(\text{control number}) = C_{\text{fix}} \frac{\mu}{\mu + D} + \frac{C_{\text{in}}}{\mu + D}$$

$$\times \left[\mu s - \mu^2 + \mu^2 q^s + Ds + \frac{D^2 + D}{2} \right]$$

$$- \frac{C_{\text{out}}}{\mu + D} [-\mu^2 q^s],$$

for given values of the economic parameters, remains that which satisfies

(1a) $$\frac{\mu q^s}{\mu + D} \geq \frac{C_{\text{in}}}{C_{\text{in}} + C_{\text{out}}} \geq \frac{\mu q^{s+1}}{\mu + D};$$

for the exponential density $\phi(\xi) = \tau e^{-\tau\xi}$, the value of s which minimizes[21]

$$E(\text{control number}) = C_{\text{fix}} \frac{\mu}{\mu + D} + \frac{C_{\text{in}}}{\mu + D}$$

$$\times \left[\mu s - \mu^2 + \mu^2 e^{-\tau s} + \frac{D(2s + D)}{2} \right]$$

$$- \frac{C_{\text{out}}}{\mu + D} [-\mu^2 e^{-\tau s}]$$

is

(1b) $$\frac{\mu e^{-\tau s}}{\mu + D} = \frac{C_{\text{in}}}{C_{\text{in}} + C_{\text{out}}}.$$

We may also derive the value of $D = S - s$ which minimizes $E(\text{control number})$ given that s satisfies (1). Rearranging the inequalities (1a) we have

(2) $$q^s \geq \frac{C_{\text{in}}}{C_{\text{in}} + C_{\text{out}}} \left(\frac{\mu + D}{\mu} \right) \geq q^{s+1}.$$

---

[21] **Recall** that for the geometric distribution, $E(\xi) = \mu = q/(1 - q)$, and for the exponential density, $E(\xi) = \mu = 1/\tau$.

For the minimizing value of D, we apply the difference operator Δ (see Section 2.4.2) to E(control number), to get ΔE(control number) ≥ 0 at D. Upon application of the principle [Go, p. 47]

$$\Delta\left(\frac{u}{v}\right) = \frac{v\,\Delta u - u\,\Delta v}{vEv},$$

we obtain the result

(3) $(\mu + D)\left[\dfrac{C_{in}(D+1)^2 - D^2}{2} + C_{in}s + \dfrac{C_{in}}{2}\right]$

$\quad - \left[C_{fix}\mu + (C_{in} + C_{out})\mu^2 q^s + C_{in}\left(\mu s - \mu^2 + \dfrac{D^2}{2} + sD + \dfrac{D}{2}\right)\right] \geq 0.$

Simplifying (3) by means of the left side of (2) yields

(4a) $$D^2 + D - 2\mu\left(\frac{C_{fix} - C_{in}}{C_{in}}\right) \geq 0.$$

When we apply Δ to E(control number) at $D - 1$, we set ΔE(control number) ≤ 0, eventually resulting in

(4b) $$D^2 - D - 2\mu\left(\frac{C_{fix} - C_{in}}{C_{in}}\right) \leq 0.$$

Finally utilizing the quadratic formula on (4) gives

(5) $-.5 + \sqrt{.25 + \dfrac{2\mu(C_{fix} - C_{in})}{C_{in}}} \leq D \leq .5 + \sqrt{.25 + \dfrac{2\mu(C_{fix} - C_{in})}{C_{in}}}.$

For the exponential density, the result is [AKS, Ch. 14]

(6) $$D = \sqrt{\frac{2C_{fix}\mu}{C_{in}}}.$$

At the values (1b) and (6)

$$E(\text{control number}) = C_{in}s + \sqrt{2C_{fix}C_{in}\mu}.$$

For any value of (s, S), we may derive the variance of the control numbers for the above cases as follows. We note

(7) Var(control number) $\equiv E[\text{control number} - E(\text{control number})]^2$
$\qquad\qquad\qquad\qquad = E(\text{control number})^2 - [E(\text{control number})]^2.$

We have already derived the bracketed final term in (7) and consequently, it remains for us to find E(control number)^2. We first apply the normalization[22] $C_{in} = 1$. For the geometric distribution we have

---

[22] When $C_{in} = 1$ for the exponential density, E(control number) $= S$.

E(control number)^2

$$= \frac{1}{\mu + D} \sum_{x=s+1}^{S} x^2 + \frac{1}{\mu + D} \sum_{x=0}^{s} (C_{\text{fix}} + x)^2 q^{s+1-x}$$

$$+ \frac{1}{\mu + D} \sum_{x=-\infty}^{-1} (C_{\text{fix}} - C_{\text{out}}x)^2 q^{s+1-x}$$

$$= \frac{1}{\mu + D} \left[\frac{S(S+1)(2S+1) - s(s+1)(2s+1)}{6} \right]$$

$$+ \frac{1}{\mu + D} \left[C_{\text{fix}}^2 \left(\frac{q^{s+1} - 1}{1 - Q} \right) + 2C_{\text{fix}} \left(\frac{q^s - s - 1 + sQ}{(1 - Q)^2} \right) \right.$$

$$+ \left. \frac{q^s + q^{s-1} - (s+1)^2 + (2s^2 + 2s - 1)Q - s^2 Q^2}{(1 - Q)^n} \right]$$

$$+ \frac{q^{s+2}}{(\mu + D)(1 - q)} \left[C_{\text{fix}}^2 + \frac{2C_{\text{fix}}C_{\text{out}}}{1 - q} + \frac{C_{\text{out}}^2(1 + q)}{(1 - q)^2} \right],$$

where $Q = 1/q$.

In an analogous manner, the value of E(control number)^2 for the exponential density can be shown to be

$$E(\text{control number})^2 = \frac{S^3 - s^3}{\mu(3 + D)}$$

$$+ \frac{1}{\mu + D} \left[C_{\text{fix}}^2 \mu (1 - e^{-rs}) + 2C_{\text{fix}}(\mu s - \mu^2 + \mu^2 e^{-rs}) \right.$$

$$+ \left. \mu s^2 - 2s\mu^2 + 2\mu^3 - 2\mu^3 e^{-rs} \right]$$

$$+ \frac{e^{-rs}}{\mu + D} \left[C_{\text{fix}}^2 \mu + 2C_{\text{fix}}C_{\text{out}}\mu^2 + 2C_{\text{out}}^2 \mu^3 \right].$$

In Figs. 3.2.1a to 3.2.1n, we give a number of examples of (s, S) rules computed by relations (1a) and (5);[23] in addition we exhibit E(control number), and the square root of Var(control number), namely, Standard deviation (control number). Specifically we examine

C_{in}	C_{fix}	C_{out}
1	4	10
1	4	30
1	4	100
1	4	1000
1	100	30
1	100	100
1	100	1000

[23] We use $D = \sqrt{.25 + \dfrac{2\mu(C_{\text{fix}} - C_{\text{in}})}{C_{\text{in}}}}$

From (5) we recognize that the curve for D depends only on C_{in} and C_{fix}, and not on C_{out}. Given values for C_{in}, C_{fix}, and μ, we see that S, E(control number) and Standard deviation (control number) are increasing functions and s is a decreasing function of C_{fix}. Thus when C_{fix} increases, the increase in D occurs through a change in both s and S. Having deter-

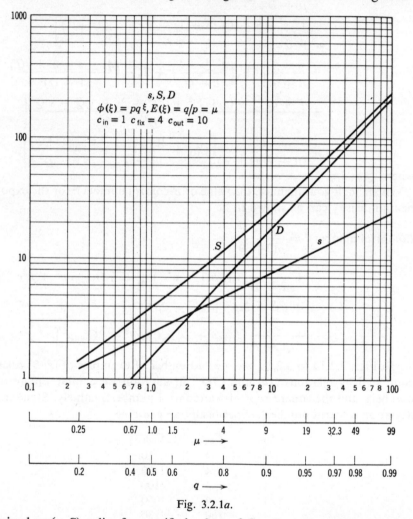

$$s, S, D$$
$$\phi(\xi) = pq^{\xi}, E(\xi) = q/p = \mu$$
$$c_{in} = 1 \quad c_{fix} = 4 \quad c_{out} = 10$$

Fig. 3.2.1a.

mined an (s, S) policy for specified values of C_{in}, C_{out}, C_{fix}, and μ, we **may** wish to know the sensitivity of E(control number) and Var(control **number)** to changes in s, S, and μ. In other words, we may wish to observe the change in the magnitudes of E(control number) and Var(control number) as changes are made in s, S, and μ. This analysis appears in Section 3.3.2

and Section 4.3.2. Such an investigation provides insight to the effect of lower management's adopting an alternative (s, S) policy and of a change in average demand μ.

To summarize our development so far, we have shown that if top management's utility index is the function $L(s, S)$ with given values of the

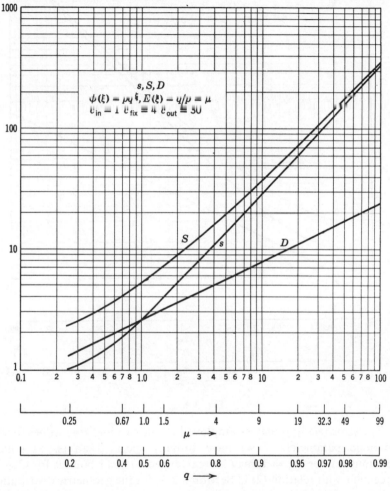

Fig. 3.2.1*b*.

economic parameters, then for the probability distributions in this section, relations (1), (5), and (6) provide the optimal (s, S) policies, and for these policies, the specified parameters are rational.[24]

[24] Except, perhaps, for a slight perturbation to ensure that a strict minimization occurs.

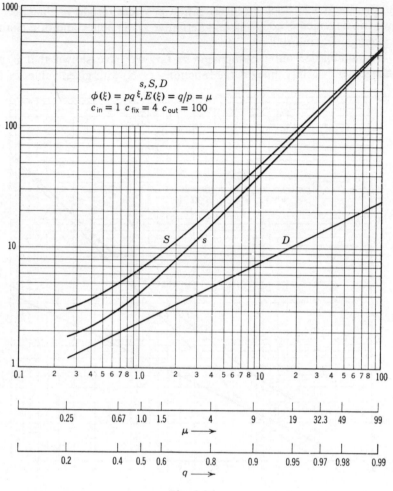

Fig. 3.2.1c.

The same relations may be employed to find rationalizing values for the economic parameters if we have initially specified an (s, S) policy. Relations (1), for $C_{in} = 1$, may be rearranged to yield bounds for C_{out} in agreement with relation (2) in Section 3.2.3; for the geometric distribution and exponential density we have:

$$(8a) \qquad \frac{\mu + D - \mu q^s}{\mu q^s} \leq C_{out} \leq \frac{\mu + D - \mu q^{s+1}}{\mu q^{s+1}}$$

$$(8b) \qquad C_{out} = \frac{\mu + D - e^{-\tau s}}{e^{-\tau s}}.$$

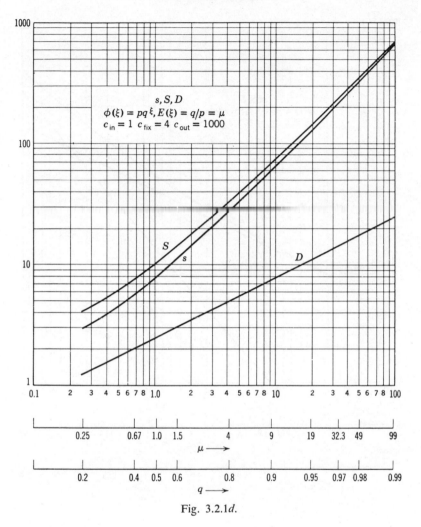

Fig. 3.2.1*d*.

Similarly, (4) and (6) may be rearranged as:

$$(9a) \qquad C_{in}\left[\frac{D^2 - D}{2\mu}\right] + C_{in} \leq C_{fix} \leq C_{in}\left[\frac{D^2 + D}{2\mu}\right] + C_{in},$$

$$(9b) \qquad C_{fix} = C_{in}\frac{D^2}{2\mu}.$$

For example, if (2, 12) is the policy to be rationalized for a geometric distribution with $q = .8$, then (8*a*) and (9*a*) may be employed to yield $C_{in} = 1$, $C_{out} = 5$, and $C_{fix} = 12.5$.

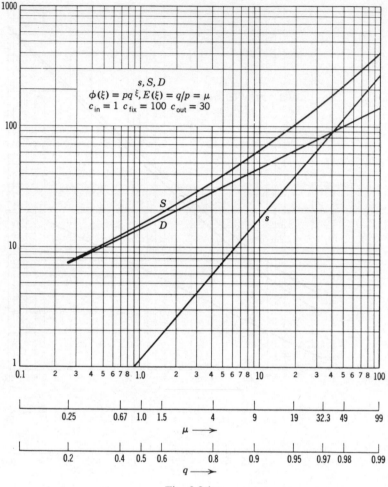

s, S, D

$\phi(\xi) = pq^{\xi}, E(\xi) = q/p = \mu$

$c_{in} = 1 \quad c_{fix} = 100 \quad c_{out} = 30$

Fig. 3.2.1e.

For arbitrary demand distributions under a backlog model, finding a rationalizing value for C_{fix} may require consideration of a system of bounding inequalities as in Section 3.2.3. But we mention that the asymptotic results of Section 2.2.6 imply that for large values of D, the values of $p_X(x)$, for x within the domain $s + 1 \leq x \leq S$, are well approximated by those for the geometric distribution with the same mean. Consequently, in such situations a good first approximation for C_{fix} can be obtained from (9a). In the example (0, 3) of Section 3.2.3, where we chose $C_{fix} = 4$, (9a) gives $4 \leq C_{fix} \leq 7$. Conversely, if top management's utility index is $L(s, S)$ with specified parameters and with C_{fix} relatively large, application

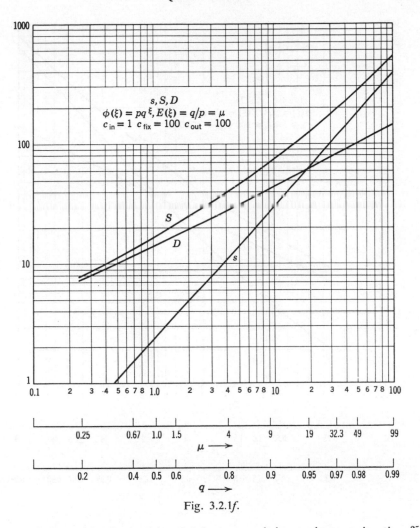

Fig. 3.2.1*f*.

of (5) followed by Proposition 2.5.3 may result in good approximations[25] for the optimal s and D.

3.3 QUOTA CONTROL

The mathematical operations involved in studying quota control are more complex than those of barometer control, as we explain in Section 3.3.1. We demonstrate in Section 3.3.2, both by numerical examples and by

---

[25] Measured in terms of the index $L(s, S)$.

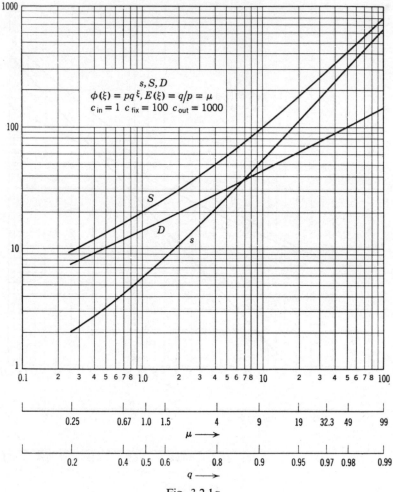

Fig. 3.2.1*g*.

analytic derivation, that the use of a control number rationalized as in Section 3.2 in general does not yield a consistent quota control. We go on to show the genuine difficulty involved in constructing such a consistent device.

One way of exhibiting the inherent complexity is to examine the tradeoff existing between the mean value and variance of a control number, that is, the possibility of diminishing the variation in the control number at the expense of increasing its expectation. The variance contribution is important in determining the probability that the aggregate index remains below the quota value. We present a numerical illustration of this tradeoff based

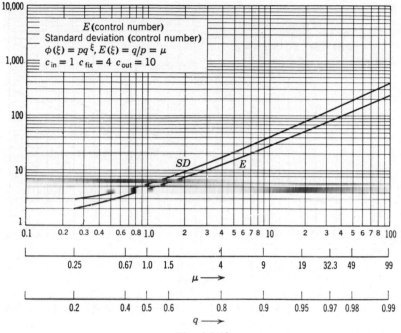

Fig. 3.2.1*h*.

on a backlog model with a geometric distribution of demand and a single-period delivery lag. If the number of inventory review periods comprising a control period is sufficiently large, then rationalized control numbers do produce a consistent scheme, as we demonstrate in Section 3.3.3. We consider a quota control on purchases and on net demand in Section 3.3.4, and conclude that these devices do not generally yield consistent schemes.

Finally, Section 3.3.5 explores the problem of determining the actual probability that an index will exceed a quota limit; such a calculation is needed in the evaluation of a control scheme. If a complete specification of the current operations of the inventory system is made, then the computation may be likened to that of determining error probabilities in testing a simple statistical hypothesis. But a more likely occurrence in real situations is a specification of operations leading to calculations associated with testing composite hypotheses. We discuss a technique for deriving bounds on the probability of interest for the composite case.

3.3.1 Assessment of Analytic Difficulties

The *modus operandi* of quota control is for top management at the beginning of a control period to set a limit (or limits) on the value of the

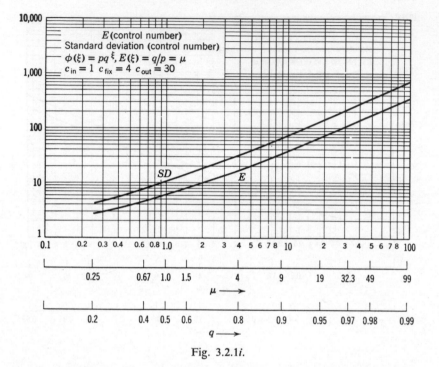

Fig. 3.2.1*i*.

index which is calculated at the end of the period;[26] if the actual index value exceeds the preset quota, top management presumes that the rules or standards have been violated[27] and investigates the situation in further detail. As in virtually every application of statistical techniques to problems of inference, in general there exists a chance that the index exceeds the quota when the standards are being followed. A consistent control scheme is one in which the probability of exceeding the index limit is greater when violations of standards are present than when they are not. With a quota scheme, it is extremely difficult[28] to provide a system which guards against types 1 and 2 inconsistencies of Section 3.1.1; we illustrate the difficulty below. Therefore we must be content to search for systems which protect against type 3 inconsistencies.

Whereas under barometer control schemes we needed only the first moment [Cra, Fe] of the probability distribution of the control numbers

[26] The calculation may entail a summing or averaging of index values during several intervening inventory review periods.

[27] Recall throughout this chapter we postulate that the $\phi_i(\xi)$ are known.

[28] That is, as long as we maintain that an important distinction between top and lower management is the differing amount of factual detail available to each for control purposes.

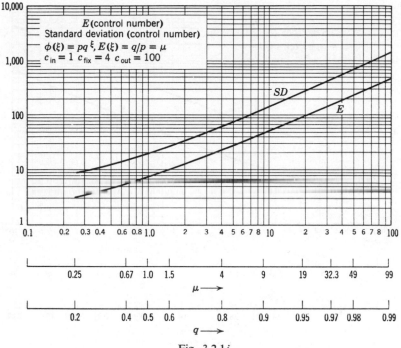

Fig. 3.2.1*j*.

for our analysis of consistency, we now require at least a second moment, namely, the variance and, in certain instances, the entire probability distribution. We investigate the consistency of a quota scheme by examining the procedure when only a single item is in the system; we impose as a necessary condition for consistency of a quota controlled index that an analogous limitation on a control number be consistent in a single-item system. Consequently, if a quota control is inconsistent when applied to a single-item system, we will not consider it for a multi-item system.

Violations of specified (s, S) policies alter the stationary probability distribution of the control number in such a way that both the mean and variance change. As a consequence, lower management, faced with a quota controlled index which top management would like to assume small values, may find it beneficial to violate the prescribed rules in such a way that the variance of the index is decreased despite the fact that, contrary to top management's over-all intentions, the mean value is thereby increased. In general terms, this tradeoff between mean and variance is the fundamental difficulty to be faced in quota schemes.

Our discussion in Section 3.2.1 of the problems connected with establishing a consistent barometer scheme which utilizes fragmentary indices

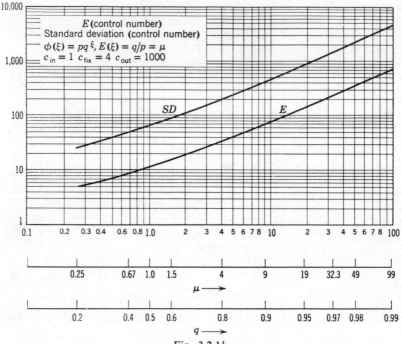

Fig. 3.2.1*k*.

applies equally well here. These difficulties may be illustrated with reference to a system comprised of a single item; for the sake of example, we continue the analysis in Section 3.2.4 for the exponential density. Suppose in selecting fragmentary index quotas we limit our attention to schemes controlling either inventory on hand, shortages, or the placing of an order, where each item on hand is worth C_{in}, each shortage C_{out}, and each order placed C_{fix}, and the quotas are set at C_{in}^*, C_{out}^*, and C_{fix}^*, respectively. The corresponding distribution functions depending on the quotas are

$$\text{Prob(value of inventory on hand} \leq C_{in}^*)$$

$$= \frac{\mu}{\mu + D} \exp\left[-\tau\left(s - \frac{C_{in}^*}{C_{in}}\right)\right] \qquad C_{in}^* \leq C_{in}s$$

$$= \frac{\mu}{\mu + D} + \frac{\dfrac{C_{in}^*}{C_{in}} - s}{\mu + D} \qquad C_{in}s \leq C_{in}^* \leq C_{in}S$$

$$= 1 \qquad C_{in}^* \geq C_{in}S;$$

$$\text{Prob(value of shortages} \leq C_{out}^*) = 1 - \frac{\mu \exp\left[-\tau\left(\dfrac{C_{out}^*}{C_{out}} + s\right)\right]}{\mu + D};$$

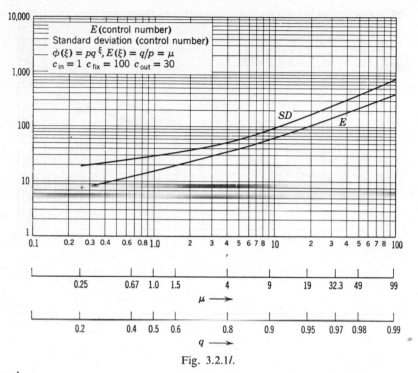

Fig. 3.2.1*l*.

and

$$\text{Prob(ordering charge} \leq C^*_{\text{fix}}) = \frac{D}{\mu + D} \qquad C^*_{\text{fix}} < C_{\text{fix}}$$

$$= 1 \qquad C^*_{\text{fix}} \geq C_{\text{fix}}.$$

Strong inconsistencies are detected by partially differentiating these expressions with respect to s and to D and by noting whether the derivatives are non-zero thereby implying that proper adjustments in the policy variables increase the probability of remaining under the quota. Similarly, weak inconsistencies are observed when the derivatives are zero independent of the values of the policy variables.

Finally we point out that the difficulties raised in Section 3.2.1 with respect to the aggregation process have direct parallels in a quota scheme. To cite a plausible quote control index scheme for which gross violations in the specified policies can occur with no corresponding change in the probability distribution of the index number, we consider a backlog model with $C_i x_i$, $C_i > 0$, as the control number for item i. The rationale of the scheme is that if s and D are increased for many items, many of the X will take on relatively high values; similarly, if s and D are decreased, many of

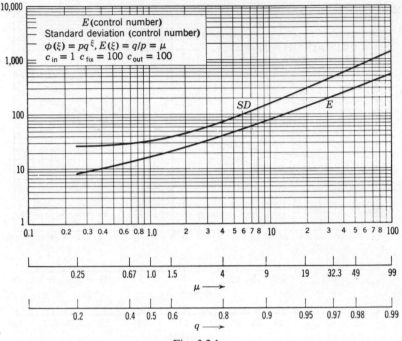

Fig. 3.2.1*m*.

the X will take on relatively low values.[29] Assuming that the number of items comprising the index is sufficiently large for the probability distribution of the index to be well approximated by a normal distribution, we may argue that considerable violations in the prescribed values of s can occur with a completely offsetting effect; as a result, the scheme is at best only weakly consistent. The underlying reason is that changing s merely shifts the distribution of X but does not change its shape, as we proved in Section 2.2.3; consequently only $C_i E(x_i)$ changes, but not the variance of the control number $C_i x_i$. Thus, increasing s for some items and decreasing it for others in a way that leaves constant the sum of the expected values $C_i E(x_i)$ has no visible effect on the probability distribution of the index.

More sophisticated schemes encounter similar or more sophisticated difficulties. For example, control might be attempted in a backlog model by means of quotas on two separate indices: (1) stock on hand or backlogged, and (2) value of current orders. At first look this suggestion seems promising, since for a single-item inventory system a consistent control might be devised. But in a multi-item system, increasing some D values and

[29] As usual, X is the amount of inventory on hand (backlogged) plus on order before placing any order in the current period.

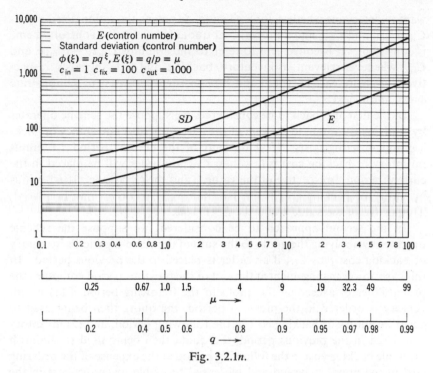

Fig. 3.2.1*n*.

decreasing others may have offsetting tendencies for both indices due to the effect on the variance of the control numbers. Further if the $\phi_i(\xi)$ are different, lower management may be motivated positively to alter several (s, S) rules to obtain a mean-and-variance tradeoff among the various items.

We summarize our discussion by stating that quota control has at least all the hazards with respect to consistency as does barometer control. In addition the analytic complexity increases because more than the first moments of the constituent control number distributions are needed to determine the requisite probability information concerning the distribution of the index. In the next two sections we explore the extent to which it is possible to construct a consistent quota scheme.

3.3.2 *Quota on Index of Rationalized Control Numbers*

A plausible quota scheme to test for consistency is setting a limit on the index comprised of rationalized control numbers such as those suggested in Section 3.2.2. To investigate this suggestion we consider a one-item system under the backlog case and with control number (2) in Section 3.2.2. We want to determine whether, for a given (s, S) policy, the rationalized values C_{in}, C_{out}, and C_{fix}, and a properly set quota value L^*, the control scheme is consistent. It is convenient to refer to the amounts $C_{in}x$, $-C_{out}x$, and C_{fix}, whenever relevant, as inventory, backlog, and ordering costs, respectively. The presence of types 1 and 2 inconsistencies is easy to demonstrate as we show next.

In the first approach to be considered, we suppose the scheme operates by applying the quota to the sum of the current period's inventory or backlog and ordering costs. If at the end of the current period L^* minus inventory or backlog cost is less than C_{fix}, no order will be placed in the current period, irrespective of the value x and the (s, S) rule. If L^* minus inventory or backlog cost is greater than C_{fix}, an order may be placed, irrespective of the value x and the (s, S) rule.

In the second approach to be considered, we suppose the scheme operates by applying the quota to the sum of the current period's inventory or backlog cost plus C_{fix} if an order is placed in the previous period. In this case, lower management at the end of the previous period computes the probabilities of exceeding the quota in the following period if (1) no inventory is ordered in the previous period, the quota then being used to cover inventory or backlog cost in the following period, and (2) inventory is ordered in the previous period, the quota then being used to diminish probable backlog cost in the following period at the expense of the ordering cost in the previous period and increased probable inventory cost in the following period. Let y be the amount of inventory on hand (backlog) plus on order *after* the opportunity to order has occurred in the previous period. Then y is selected according to

$$\min \left[\begin{array}{l} \text{Prob}\left(x - \xi > \dfrac{L^*}{C_{in}}\right) + \text{Prob}\left(\xi - x > \dfrac{L^*}{C_{out}}\right) \quad \text{Action 1 } y = x \\[2ex] \min_{y > x} \left[\text{Prob}\left(y - \xi > \dfrac{L^* - C_{fix}}{C_{in}}\right) + \text{Prob}\left(\xi - y > \dfrac{L^* - C_{fix}}{C_{out}}\right) \right] \\[2ex] \hspace{6cm} \text{Action 2 } y > x. \end{array} \right.$$

In selecting the action having the higher probability of remaining under the quota, there is no need for the result to agree with the recommended (s, S) policy.

We turn next to a consideration of type 3 inconsistency, that is, we ask whether lower management's objective is better met if, period after period, upon facing the same quota, lower management adopts an (s, S) policy different from the prescribed (s, S) rule. In other words, is the stationary probability of remaining under the quota increased by violating the suggested inventory policy through the adoption of another (s, S) rule? The

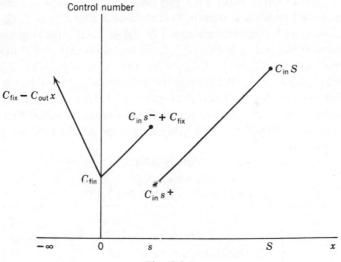

Control number

$C_{\text{fix}} - C_{\text{out}} x$

$C_{\text{in}} s^- + C_{\text{fix}}$

$C_{\text{in}} S$

C_{fin}

$C_{\text{in}} s^+$

$-\infty$ 0 s S x

Fig. 3.3.1.

mathematical analysis required to answer these questions involves the probability distribution of the control number, given the stationary probability distribution for X. For this stationary analysis, we assume the control number is calculated by adding all the costs incurred in the current period. In Fig. 3.3.1 we illustrate the transformation from values of X to values of the control number. Depending on the values of C_{in}, C_{out}, and C_{fix}, and on the prescribed (s, S) policy, the line segments have different orientations, each of which corresponds to one of the cases below:[30]

(1)	$C_{\text{fix}} > C_{\text{in}}S$	$C_{\text{fix}} + C_{\text{in}}s > C_{\text{in}}S$
(2a)	$C_{\text{in}}s < C_{\text{fix}} \le C_{\text{in}}S$	$C_{\text{fix}} + C_{\text{in}}s \le C_{\text{in}}S$
(2b)	$C_{\text{in}}s < C_{\text{fix}} \le C_{\text{in}}S$	$C_{\text{fix}} + C_{\text{in}}s > C_{\text{in}}S$
(3a)	$0 \le C_{\text{fix}} \le C_{\text{in}}s$	$C_{\text{fix}} + C_{\text{in}}s \le C_{\text{in}}S$
(3b)	$0 \le C_{\text{fix}} \le C_{\text{in}}s$	$C_{\text{fix}} + C_{\text{in}}s > C_{\text{in}}S.$

Figure 3.3.1 corresponds to (2a).

By means of several examples previously studied, we show that in general we cannot assume it is possible to set a quota yielding a consistent situation. Consider the policies (0, 3) and (1, 5) assuming, respectively, the

---

[30] We note that certain configurations, e.g., (1), (2b), and (3b), can give rise to situations which might appear anomalous to lower management, viz., for certain seemingly reasonable values of L^*, there will be some "middle" values of X, i.e., neither very high nor very low, which will exceed the quota, whereas higher or lower values of X will not.

uniform distribution in Table 2.4.1 and Poisson distribution in Table 2.4.2. In Section 3.2.3 we derived that (0, 3) is rationalized by $C_{in} = 1$, $C_{out} = 4$, and $C_{fix} = 4$, with $E[\text{control number} \mid (0, 3)] = 77/27$; making use of the suggestions at the end of Section 3.2.4, we find (and can verify) that (1, 5) is rationalized by $C_{in} = 1$, $C_{out} = 20$, and $C_{fix} = 8$, with $E[\text{control number} \mid (1, 5)] = 5.07$. We exhibit the corresponding cumulative probability distributions for the control numbers in Tables 3.3.1 and 3.3.2. In these tables we demonstrate that for each possible quota value, there exists an alternative (s, S) policy[31] with a higher probability of remaining under the limiting value.

TABLE 3.3.1

Backlog, (0, 3)

Uniform, $E(\xi) = 1$, Table 2.4.1

L^*	$C_{in} = 1$	$C_{out} = 4$	$C_{fix} = 4$
	Prob(control number $\leq L^*$)		(s', S')
	(0, 3)	(s', S')	
8–5	1.0000	1.0000	(0, 2)
4	.8889	.9275	(0, 4)
3	.7037	.7681	(−1, 3)
2	.5555	.6522	(−1, 3)
1	.3333	.4783	(−1, 3)

We might ask whether the following weakened version of the consistency property holds: Suppose, for some value of L^*, lower management's objective is better met by the recommended policy than by some alternative policy having $E(\text{control number}) = E^*$. Does this consistent situation extend to the class of all alternative policies having $E(\text{control number}) \geq E^*$? The answer is no. A counter example is provided by the model in Table 3.3.1. For $L^* = 3$, the probability of not exceeding the quota is .7037 for (0, 3) as compared to .5556 for (0, 2), where under the latter policy $E(\text{control number}) = 3$. But as we show in Table 3.3.1, under (−1, 3) the probability of remaining under the quota $L^* = 3$ is .7681 and for this alternative policy $E(\text{control number}) = 3.10$.

Turning to the analytic examples we have considered, suppose the demand distribution is the exponential density $\phi(\xi) = \tau e^{-\tau\xi}$. To illustrate how a potential inconsistency is ascertained, we examine one particular

---

[31] A policy with a negative value for s merely implies that backlogs accumulate before a replenishment order is placed.

TABLE 3.3.2

Backlog, (1, 5) Policy

Poisson, $E(\xi) = 1$, Table 2.4.2

L^*	$C_{\text{in}} = 1$ $\quad C_{\text{out}} = 20$ $\quad C_{\text{fix}} = 8$		$C_{\text{fix}} = 8$
	Prob(control number $\leq L^*$)		(s', S')
	(1, 5)	(s', S')	
87–68	.9998	.9999	(2, 5)
67–48	.9990	.9997	(2, 5)
47–28	.9948	.9987	(2, 5)
27–11	.9770	.9933	(2, 5)
10	.9770	.9933	(2, 5)
9	.9770	.9810	(1, 6)
8	.8365	.8661	(1, 6)
7	.7778	.8181	(1, 6)
6	.7778	.8181	(1, 6)
5	.7778	.8181	(0, 5)
4	.6485	.8181	(−1, 4)
3	.4439	.7123	(−1, 4)
2	.2225	.5449	(−1, 4)
1	.0000	.3638	(−1, 4)

configuration of the parameter values, $C_{\text{in}}s \leq L^* \leq C_{\text{in}}S$ and $L^* \leq C_{\text{fix}} + C_{\text{in}}s$ under case (2a) above, where (s, S) is the prescribed policy. Let

$$\underline{C} = \frac{C_{\text{fix}} - L^*}{C_{\text{out}}} \quad \text{and} \quad \bar{C} = \frac{L^*}{C_{\text{in}}}.$$

Then

$$\text{Prob(control number} \leq L^*) = \int_{\underline{C}}^{\bar{C}} p_X(x)\, dx$$

$$= \int_{\underline{C}}^{s} \frac{e^{-\tau(s-x)}}{\mu + D}\, dx + \int_{s}^{\bar{C}} \frac{1}{\mu + D}\, dx$$

$$= \frac{1}{\mu + D} [\mu - \mu e^{-\tau s} e^{\tau \underline{C}} + \bar{C} - s].$$

Taking the first partial derivative of this probability with respect to D, we find it is negative. Consequently, for any s, lower management is motivated to reduce D in this range of the economic parameters. It is important to note that the argument producing the inconsistency does not require that the values of C_{in}, C_{out}, and C_{fix} rationalize the preferred (s, S) policy. As a result, no values exist for the economic parameters leading to a strongly consistent control scheme of this form.

For another pair of analytic examples, consider for $\phi(\xi)$ the uniform distributions in Section 2.4.4. Assume that the prescribed policy is (s, S), the economic parameters and L^* have values such that $s - (1/\mu) < \underline{C} < S -(1/\mu)$ and $\bar{C} > s$, and these ratios of the economic parameters are integers in the discrete case. Then

$$\text{Prob}(\text{control number} \leq L^*) = 1 + \mu\left(s - \frac{1}{\mu} - \underline{C}\right) + e^{-\mu D} - e^{-1+\mu s - \mu \underline{C}}$$

$$+ 1 - e^{-\mu(\bar{C}-s)}, \qquad \textit{uniform density}$$

$$\text{Prob}(\text{control number} \leq L^*) = 1 + \mu\left(s - \frac{1}{\mu} - \underline{C}\right) + (1 - \mu)^D$$

$$- (1 - \mu)^{(1/\mu)-1-s+\underline{C}} + 1 - (1 - \mu)^{\bar{C}-s},$$

discrete uniform distribution.

Taking the partial derivative in the density case and the partial first difference in the discrete case of these expressions with respect to D yields

$$-\mu e^{-\mu D} < 0, \qquad -\mu(1 - \mu)^D < 0;$$

thus for these values of the parameters, lower management is motivated to reduce D. Once again this result does not require that the values for the economic parameters rationalize the specified (s, S) policy.

As a final indication of the factors producing inconsistency, we give evidence in Tables 3.3.3a–d of the tradeoff between the mean and variance of the control numbers in the backlog model illustrated in Fig. 3.2.1, where demand is geometric $\phi(\xi) = pq^{\xi}$, $\xi = 0, 1, 2, \cdots$. In the table, selected values for C_{in}, C_{fix}, C_{out}, and μ appear; these values are rational for the policy (s^*, S^*). We compute for the policy (s^*, S^*) and an alternative policy $(s^*, s^* + 2D^*)$, where $D^* = S^* - s^*$, the values of $E(\text{control number})$ and $\text{Var}(\text{control number})$ according to the relations derived in Section 3.2.4. Notice that the alternative policy has a smaller $\text{Var}(\text{control number})$ than that for the corresponding rationalized policy.

We summarize informally the rationale for producing inconsistent policies by stating that when the quota is relatively large, lower management is motivated to increase s and D; when it is relatively moderate, to increase D; and when it is relatively low, to decrease s.

Before resolving the question of whether there exists any generally consistent top management quota control scheme, we mention that if there is only a single alternative (s, S) rule which lower management may adopt,

TABLE 3.3.3*a*

q	$C_{in} = 1$	$C_{fix} = 4$		$C_{out} = 10$	
	Rationalized policy (s^*, S^*)			$(s^*, s^* + 2D^*), D^* = S^* - s^*$	
	(s^*, S^*)	E(cont. no.)	Var(c.n.)	E(cont. no.)	Var(c.n.)
.4	1, 3	3.69	17.49	4.04	10.26
.5	1, 4	4.63	38.48	5.21	22.74
.6	2, 5	6.15	68.45	6.49	41.51
.8	7, 12	12.77	289.32	13.56	187.85
.9	17, 24	25.22	1,352.42	26.07	943.66
.95	37, 48	49.54	5,897.30	50.74	4,321.69
.97	66, 80	81.74	16,612.21	83.08	12,767.13
.98	103, 120	121.86	37,607.67	123.32	29,918.12
.99	216, 240	241.97	151,286.07	243.69	126,609.32

q	$C_{in} = 1$	$C_{fix} = 1$		$C_{out} = 30$	
	Rationalized policy (s^*, S^*)			$(s^*, s^* + 2D^*), D^* = S^* - s^*$	
	(s^*, S^*)	E(cont. no.)	Var(c.n.)	E(cont. no.)	Var(c.n.)
.4	2, 4	4.78	56.42	5.09	32.47
.5	2, 5	6.19	165.03	6.54	94.75
.6	4, 7	8.18	222.03	8.51	133.65
.8	11, 16	17.40	1,143.33	17.97	736.30
.9	27, 34	35.06	4,616.99	35.96	3,214.86
.95	58, 69	69.74	19,742.31	71.15	14,453.70
.97	100, 114	115.76	58,040.86	117.09	44,582.47
.98	155, 172	173.14	129,497.73	174.75	102,989.08
.99	320, 344	345.05	523,787.13	346.92	438,296.58

TABLE 3.3.3*b*

	$C_{in} = 1$		$C_{fix} = 4$	$C_{out} = 100$	
q	Rationalized policy (s^*, S^*)			$(s^*, s^* + 2D^*), D^* = S^* - s^*$	
	(s^*, S^*)	*E*(cont. no.)	Var(c.n.)	*E*(cont. no.)	Var(c.n.)
.4	3, 5	6.04	246.7339	6.23	141.15
.5	4, 7	7.83	460.2986	8.33	263.65
.6	6, 9	10.52	909.5910	10.71	546.08
.8	17, 22	22.71	3,479.7923	23.53	2,238.93
.9	38, 45	46.27	16,921.15	47.10	11,774.03
.95	81, 92	92.77	70,948.91	94.17	51,921.89
.97	139, 153	154.53	206,946.17	155.92	158,935.65
.98	213, 230	231.61	469,302.37	233.12	373,194.02
.99	437, 461	462.58	1,890,579.5	464.36	1,581,937.6

	$C_{in} = 1$		$C_{fix} = 4$	$C_{out} = 1000$	
q	Rationalized policy (s^*, S^*)			$(s^*, s^* + 2D^*), D^* = S^* - s^*$	
	(s^*, S^*)	*E*(cont. no.)	Var(c.n.)	*E*(cont. no.)	Var(c.n.)
.4	6, 8	8.64	1,588.11	9.01	907.78
.5	7, 10	11.21	5,836.21	11.55	3,335.42
.6	11, 14	14.98	7,221.10	15.39	4,333.17
.8	27, 32	32.97	38,467.03	33.69	24,730.46
.9	60, 67	68.04	171,838.52	68.94	119,542.91
.95	125, 136	137.48	766,184.20	138.69	560,629.27
.97	215, 229	229.84	2,109,120.0	231.38	1,619,722.7
.98	327, 344	345.14	4,839,873.0	346.75	3,848,588.7
.99	665, 689	690.79	19,726,355.0	692.54	16,505,748.0

TABLE 3.3.3*c*

q	$C_{in} = 1$		$C_{fix} = 100$	$C_{out} = 30$	
	Rationalized policy (s^*, S^*)			$(s^*, s^* + 2D^*)$, $D^* = S^* - s^*$	
	(s^*, S^*)	E(cont. no.)	Var(c.n.)	E(cont. no.)	Var(c.n.)
.4	0, 12	12.47	706.25	15.41	377.54
.5	1, 15	15.63	801.57	18.95	434.22
.6	1, 18	19.52	1,250.83	23.10	677.30
.8	6, 34	34.75	2,393.35	41.17	1,353.95
.9	16, 58	58.89	6,699.24	68.20	3,845.34
.95	38, 99	100.79	23,673.32	113.43	13,775.15
.97	71, 151	152.50	61,653.82	168.72	36,600.45
.98	115, 214	214.59	133,918.72	234.39	81,156.44
.99	253, 393	394.70	534,315.41	420.11	338,648.90

q	$C_{in} = 1$		$C_{fix} = 100$	$C_{out} = 100$	
	Rationalized policy (s^*, S^*)			$(s^*, s^* + 2D^*)$, $D^* = S^* - s^*$	
	(s^*, S^*)	E(cont. no.)	Var(c.n.)	E(cont. no.)	Var(c.n.)
.4	1, 13	13.80	1,014.89	16.57	535.06
.5	2, 16	17.28	1,317.50	20.28	698.96
.6	4, 21	21.85	1,500.97	25.75	810.27
.8	11, 39	40.03	5,190.32	46.31	2,843.81
.9	27, 69	70.09	19,029.58	79.31	10,605.07
.95	61, 122	123.82	77,242.41	136.45	44,168.57
.97	110, 190	191.28	210,191.74	207.59	123,359.08
.98	173, 272	273.05	473,961.21	292.67	284,895.62
.99	371, 511	512.22	1,894,476.2	537.81	1,196,391.1

TABLE 3.3.3*d*

q	$C_{in} = 1$		$C_{fix} = 100$	$C_{out} = 1000$	
	Rationalized policy (s^*, S^*)			$(s^*, s^* + 2D^*), D^* = S^* - s^*$	
	(s^*, S^*)	E(cont. no.)	Var(c.n.)	E(cont. no.)	Var(c.n.)
.4	4, 16	16.29	2,688.31	19.31	1,395.93
.5	6, 20	20.64	3,827.82	23.95	1,999.49
.6	8, 25	26.30	9,095.85	29.99	4,766.38
.8	21, 49	50.30	42,771.38	56.46	22,885.18
.9	49, 91	91.87	173,872.64	101.19	95,521.27
.95	106, 167	168.53	764,391.40	181.28	434,044.49
.97	185, 265	266.58	2,173,130.0	282.77	1,269,818.2
.98	287, 386	386.59	4,846,895.7	406.39	2,905,126.5
.99	599, 739	740.43	19,713,134.0	765.95	12,432,954.0

then whenever the preferred (s, S) policy can be rationalized, there always exists a limit value which is consistent; that is, it is possible to establish a quota such that lower management is motivated to adopt the recommended policy rather than the alternative policy. We sketch a proof of the assertion. Since the control number is a non-negative integer, its expectation may be represented as the sum of the values Prob(control number $> L^*$), $L^* = 0, 1, 2, \cdots$; furthermore, because the policy is assumed to have been rationalized,[32] this expected value is a strict minimum for the recommended (s, S) policy. Suppose, contrary to the assertion, it is not possible to find a value of L^* such that Prob(control number $> L^*$) is strictly smaller for the recommended policy than for the alternative policy; then the expected value of the control number for the recommended policy would be at least as large as that for the alternative rule, a conclusion which contradicts the rationalization process.

3.3.3   The Existence of a Consistent Quota Scheme

In this section we turn to the question of whether for a given inventory system a consistent top management quota scheme exists. In answering affirmatively, we emphasize that our argument mainly describes from a formal mathematical approach how it is possible to construct a consistent quota device. However, we do not argue that in real situations the scheme need be economically advantageous,[33] nor do we attempt to be precise

---

[32] Note that if there is only one alternative policy to the recommended rule, there are many values of the economic parameters which yield a rationalization.

about quantifying the proposal; the latter task in any case seems to be essentially dependent upon the composition of the actual inventory system.

As in the previous section, we start by considering a single-item inventory system and assuming that a control number has been derived from a rationalization process of Section 3.2.2. The law of large numbers and the central limit theorem [Fe, D] assert that, if we average the observed control number over T periods, as T grows large the distribution of the average tends to a normal distribution with a mean equal to the expectation of the control number and variance as given in Section 2.7.1.[34]

Postulating that violations of the recommended (s, S) rule can only involve revising either s or S or both by integral amounts, there is an alternative policy (s', S') such that the associated expected value of the control number is closest to the expected value of the control number for the recommended policy; because we have assumed the parameters of the control number are rationalized values, the two expected values are distinct. We then can view the problem of establishing a consistent control scheme as analogous to a problem of testing statistical hypotheses concerning the mean of a normal distribution [Cra, Ch. 35]. If T is sufficiently large so that the normal approximation to the distribution of the index number fits well for any set of (s, S) policies being followed, a quota slightly larger[35] than the expected control number for the recommended rule produces a consistent control scheme; for any such quota limit, a further increasing of T reduces the probability that the sample average of the control numbers exceeds the quota when the recommended policy is being observed.

A similar line of reasoning may be followed to demonstrate the existence of a consistent quota control on an index number. That is, if the index is the sum of the control numbers for the various items in the system averaged over T periods, and if T is sufficiently large, then the index is approximately normally distributed, and it is possible to place a quota on this index to produce a consistent situation.

However, it is still an open question whether there are alternative (and

---

[33] Judged in the manner of Sections 1.2 and 3.4.

[34] That is, the control number schemes suggested in Section 3.2.2 may be viewed as functions defined on the states of a Markov process and, consequently, the analysis in Section 2.7 is immediately applicable.

[35] Since the variance of the control number for the recommended policy may very well be larger than the variance for alternative policies, we cannot ensure that a consistent situation is present if the quota is relatively large. But this guarantee certainly holds if the control number is between the expected value of the control number for the recommended policy and that for (s', S').

hopefully simpler) approaches to the design of general quota controls that are consistent.[36]

3.3.4   Quota Control for Purchases and Net Demand

A common quota control is one imposed on the value of orders placed, the constituent control number for each item being $C_{pur}r$, where the purchase quantity r is mathematically defined in Section 2.5.1. From this previous analysis we know that in the backlog model the expected value of an order during an inventory review period is $C_{pur}E(\xi)$, a number which is independent of the (s, S) rule being observed. But altering a stockage policy does change the shape (and variance) of the corresponding distribution of $C_{pur}r$ and, consequently, a quota on this index may very well lead to inconsistent actions.[37] In the no-backlog model, a change in the prescribed (s, S) policy brings about both a change in the shape of the distribution of $C_{pur}r$ and a change in its mean.

In Section 1.3 we described the operation of a control scheme predicated on setting a quota for net demand, defined mathematically in Section 2.6.1. As usual, we initiate our analysis of this possibility under the assumption that the inventory system consists of a single item. At the end of an inventory review period, the system is said to be in control if net demand n, weighted by an economic parameter assigned to the item, is above a certain (negative) limit $-L^*$. Since in many real applications of this scheme the economic parameter equals the purchase cost, we use the notation C_{pur} for the weighting coefficient. The quota is then

$$C_{pur}n \geq -L^*.$$

From our analysis in Section 2.6.1 we know that $1 - D \leq n \leq D - 1$. Consequently, if $L^* \geq C_{pur}(D - 1)$, the control is consistent because lower management is not strongly motivated to adopt a different stockage policy. But the consistency is only weak, for lower management, period after period, facing the same control quota, may also adopt the policy $(s + \delta, S)$, for $1 \leq \delta \leq D - 1$. If $L^* < C_{pur}(D - 1)$, the quota easily

---

[36] We remark that throughout we have approached the analysis from a probabilistic, as distinguished from a statistical, point of view. In the actual implementation of such schemes, it may be possible to adopt statistical techniques such as those employed in quality control [BL, Gr] to estimate the parameters of the probability distribution of the index number from time series data. In such applications, the role played by our analysis is to indicate the general form that the index number distribution may be expected to take and the dependence of its parameters on the random variables associated with the underlying (s, S) policies.

[37] In Section 4.2 we examine a related situation pertaining to control of demand.

may be inconsistent. A negative value of n which would result in a violation of the control limit may be avoided by ordering an amount equal to satisfied demand during the period, instead of a larger amount implied in observing the parameter S, or by not ordering at all.

A sophisticated but not uncommon variation of the above scheme is to let L^* vary from one inventory review period to the next, depending on the previous period's L^* and net demand

$$L^*_{t+1} = L_t^* + C_{\text{pur}}n_t.$$

If $C_{\text{pur}}(S - u_t) > L_t^*$ at the start of period t, where u_t is defined in Section 2.1.3 as inventory on hand plus on order, then in some period the control number is certain to exceed the control limit if lower management follows the recommended rule. By reducing D, that is, by adopting a type 3 inconsistent policy, this eventuality can be avoided entirely.

The above analysis directly extends to the control of an index number which is calculated by summing the weighted net demands for the items in the system. If the control period coincides with the inventory review period, and if the number of items in the system is sufficiently large, then the probability distribution of the index number is approximately normal with zero mean and variance equal to the sum of the variances for each distribution of weighted net demand, numbers which can be calculated from the probability distribution of n as derived in Section 2.6.1. If the control period is comprised of several inventory review periods, and again if the number of items in the system is sufficiently large, then the analysis in Section 2.7 is applicable including a reference to the property of asymptotic normality.

It is of some interest to note the qualitative effect of item aggregation when the control quota is in fact sufficiently restrictive so as to induce inconsistent actions. To illustrate the nature of the underlying analysis, we suppose that the same (s, S) policy and demand distribution $\phi(\xi)$ apply to every item potentially included in the system. If we let $(k_i)(i)$ be the aggregate quota, where i is the number of items to be aggregated and k_i a constant depending on i, then given a value α for the probability that the index exceeds the quota, k_i is a decreasing function of i Loosely, doubling the number of items i in the system and maintaining the same probability of surpassing the quota does not require a doubling of $(k_i)(i)$. These assertions follow from an application of the Chebycheff theorem [Cra, Ch. 15].

To summarize, a quota control on an index for net demand at best provides a weakly consistent scheme and may very well lead to inconsistency, usually through encouraging the placement of orders in amounts less than prescribed by the recommended policies.

3.3.5 Commentary on Management by Exception

At the start of Section 3.3 we stated that whenever a quota control index exceeds its limit value, top management observes a statistical signal to investigate the current operations of the system in further detail; we have referred to this procedure as "management by exception." We now comment upon the ability of quota schemes to detect violations in standards when they occur.[38]

Assume that a quota scheme is completely specified. In particular, we are given the composition of the index in terms of the control number and the items encompassed, the number of inventory review periods comprising a control period, and the quota limit. We defer to the next section a discussion of the considerations which must be made in determining such control scheme parameters.

As usual, our approach relies upon stationary probabilities. The reader may wish to review Section 2.1.5, where several arguments justifying this approach appear. The issue involved in analyzing a scheme's ability to detect violations in standards is summarized as follows: suppose inconsistent actions of type 3 commence at some time period. We ask what is the probability of detection under the specified control device.[39] The answer provided from stationary analysis may be interpreted as the detection probability if the control is imposed after the system is allowed to operate for a number of inventory review periods and thereby to attain statistical equilibrium. The accuracy of this answer depends in part on the assumed *a priori* distribution of the states of the system when inconsistent action commences, on the number of inventory review periods comprising a control period, and on the extent to which the review periods are sampled. But even if this answer is somewhat inaccurate, we suggest that the approach nevertheless provides helpful qualitative results.[40]

First we consider the control mechanism functioning under the prescribed rules, as compared to its operating under a different but completely specified set of rules. In the literature of mathematical statistics, this situation is referred to as testing a simple hypothesis against a simple alternative [Cra, Ch. 35]. The results of Chapter 2, especially Sections 2.5, 2.6, and 2.7, are applicable for deriving the probability distribution of each

---

[38] We point out there is a close parallel between the notions of management by rule and by exception in our analysis and the concepts of unbiasedness and power in the theory of statistical testing of hypotheses.

[39] In Section 1.2.2 we referred to such probabilities as $p(a_j \mid N_i, c)$.

[40] From a purely mathematical point of view, an analysis following the remarks in Section 2.8 may be employed to determine precise probabilities. But the amount of computations necessary to take into account the precise effect of non-stationary factors is likely to be large.

constituent control number; the convolution of these distributions gives the distribution of the index number. From a formal point of view, it is a simple matter to extract the probability information needed, once we have the index number distribution.

If the parameters of the control scheme are such that the probability distribution of the index for either alternative is well described as a normal distribution, then the ordinary "type 1 and type 2 error analysis" [K, Ch. 26] provides the probability α_1 that the index will exceed the quota when the standards are being followed, and the probability α_2 that the index will not exceed the quota when the standards are being violated; furthermore, if the situation is consistent, $1 - \alpha_1 > \alpha_2$. As we have mentioned previously, the parameters of the normal distribution, namely, the mean and variance, are computed by adding, respectively, the mean and variance of the distributions of the constituent control numbers.

A more likely case of interest, especially when each control number is of a rationalized sort as in Section 3.2.2, is the probability that the index number exceeds its limit L^*, given that the violation of standards results in E(index number) $= I^*$, where I^* is greater than the expected value of the index number when the recommended policies are being observed. The difficulty we face is that specification of I^* is not sufficient to characterize uniquely the set of rules being followed; in statistical terminology, we are testing a simple hypothesis against a composite alternative [Cra, Ch. 35]. In viewing the detection ability of the control scheme in such instances, we may be conservative and determine that set of rules in which the probability of detection is a minimum,[41] the rules being taken from the class for which E(index number) $= I^*$.

We now illustrate the considerations involved. We assume that the parameters of the control scheme are such that the probability distribution of the index number is well described by a normal distribution. In Fig. 3.3.2 we exhibit two cases which are to be distinguished, namely, $L^* > I^*$ and $L^* < I^*$. In the former instance, the most unfavorable set of rules is that which minimizes the variance of the index distribution; in the latter, that which maximizes the variance. If $L^* = I^*$, the probability of detection is 0.5 regardless of the value of Var(index number). To keep the exposition simple, we postulate that, for the value of I^* in the following formulas, a set of rules does in fact exist such that E(index number) $= I^*$, and that each E(control number) is non-negative; the reader will have little trouble in supplying the additional details needed when these postulates are

[41] Of course, we can complement the study by investigating the alternative assumption that the probability of detection is a maximum, the rules being taken from the class for which E(control number) $= I^*$. Having both conservative and optimistic values of the probability, we then have bounds for any contingency.

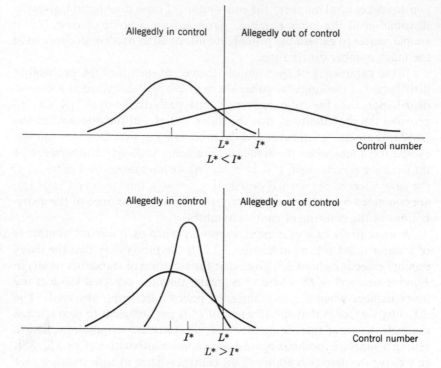

Fig. 3.3.2. Density of control number distribution.

dropped. Suppose the various (s, S) rules are indexed so that we may refer to $R_{j(i)}$ as the jth stockage rule for item i in the system.[42]

If $L^* > I^*$, we determine the most unfavorable mixture of alternative rules, that is, the set which is most difficult to detect when using the specified quota, by solving the following mathematical problem:

(1a)   Minimize $\sum_i \sum_{j(i)} \delta_{ij(i)} \text{Var}[\text{control number} \mid R_{j(i)}]$,
subject to

(1b) $\sum_i \sum_{j(i)} \delta_{ij(i)} E[\text{control number} \mid R_{j(i)}] = I^*$,

(1c) $\sum_{j(i)} \delta_{ij(i)} = 1$ for each i,
and

(1d) $\delta_{ij(i)} = 0, 1.$

[42] Actually we need refer only to a subset of all possible stockage rules. That subset has the property that for each possible value of E, two policies are included, each satisfying $E(\text{control number}) = E$, and one having $\text{Var}(\text{control number})$ equal to $\max_{R_{j(i)}} \text{Var}(\text{control number})$, and the other to $\min_{R_{j(i)}} \text{Var}(\text{control number})$.

If $L^* < I^*$, the minimization criterion is replaced by maximization. For computation purposes, (1) may be viewed as an integer linear programming problem and presumably may be solved by currently suggested techniques [Gom].

An alternative computational attack to (1) is through a functional equation approach [B].[43] For any value of $I \leq I^*$, let $F_i(I)$ be the value of (1a) subject to the previous constraints when we consider only items 1, 2, $\cdots$, i. We start with

$$F_1(I) = \min_{\substack{R_{j(1)} \\ E(\text{control number} \mid R_{j(1)}) = I}} [\text{Var}(\text{control number} \mid R_{j(1)})], \quad \text{if there exists an } R_{j(1)} \text{ such that } E(\text{control number} \mid R_{j(1)}) = I,$$

$$= M, \quad \text{otherwise,}$$

where M is arbitrarily large. In a recursive fashion, we characterize $F_i(I)$ as

$$F_i(I) = \min_{\substack{R_{j(i)} \\ E(\text{control number} \mid R_{j(i)}) \leq I}} \{\text{var}(\text{control number} \mid R_{j(i)})$$

$$+ F_{i-1}[I - E(\text{control number} \mid R_{j(i)})]\}$$

$$\text{if there exists an } R_{j(i)} \text{ such that } E(\text{control number} \mid R_{j(i)}) \leq I,$$

$$= M, \quad \text{otherwise.}$$

The determination of the mixture of policies occurs when we have computed $F_{i'}(I^*)$ for the last item i' in the system.

The connection between ascertaining the probability of detection in our analysis and the probability of error in the statistical testing of a composite hypothesis suggests that the apparent technical complexities we face are not peculiar to statistical inference in inventory systems but are inherent in the underlying structure of the problem.[44] In the following section we state the policy conclusions that are to be drawn from this commentary.

3.4 POLICY IMPLICATIONS

Section 3.4.1 summarizes the relation between the previous analysis in this chapter and the evaluation model of Section 1.2. We draw attention to the definition of the various possible situations describing the inventory

[43] The problem is closely related to the "knapsack" or "cargo loading" model [Dan, B], the difference here being the additional constraints (1c); our functional equation formulation resembles that suggested for these models.

[44] We feel there is at least a modicum of value in recognizing such a problem for what it is even though this classification underscores the attendant difficulties.

system, the setting of the value θ in a barometer scheme and the action limit in a quota device, and the determination of the number of inventory review periods comprising a single control period. The specification of control-period length to some extent resembles the choice of a sample size in statistical hypothesis testing in that, under suitable restrictions, probabilistic accuracy increases as the number of observations increases; one point deserving special mention is that augmenting the number of observations for control purposes implies that the inventory system operates and thereby incurs the consequent costs for a longer period of time.

The imposition of an inconsistent control has impact in part on the evaluation of *a priori* probabilities of various system situations, and in part on the probability of detecting an out of control situation, as we comment in Section 3.4.2. We discuss in Section 3.4.3 whether top management should aim at adopting consistent controls, despite the difficulties of designing such devices, and whether management may find it better to employ an inconsistent control than to leave the system relatively uncontrolled.

3.4.1 Economic Design of Control Scheme Parameters

In Section 1.2 we outlined a general model for evaluating control schemes. Here we make the connection between that analysis and the material in this chapter. The elements comprising the model are a list of possible system situations and their *a priori* probabilities for each control system considered, the set of terminal actions available to top management, the economic worth associated with a situation described by a system situation and a terminal action, and the economic cost stemming from the operation of the control device *per se*. We discuss the relevance of these points in the evaluation of a particular control scheme; a comparison of different schemes involves comparing the individual evaluations.

We commented briefly in Section 1.2 that there is generally some discretion in setting down the exact definition of a system situation. With regard to the subject matter of this chapter, we could conceptually define a situation as being the complete array of (s, S) rules being observed. For large-scale inventory systems, such a definition provides little hope of having real operational significance. In keeping with our argument that top management is interested mainly in aggregate operational characteristics of the system, we postulate instead that the situations be defined in terms of the control indices employed. It is necessary that the indices are not of a fragmentary sort for this to be a reasonable postulate. For example, a situation may be defined as the expected value of an index comprised of rationalized control numbers. We discussed in Section 3.3.5 that such a definition is not equivalent to a complete specification of the array of (s, S) rules being observed. Therefore, in order to adopt such an approach, the economic worth of a situation as valued by top management must be well defined in terms of the expected value of the index number. Our position is enhanced insofar as the policies were originally derived by an optimization process which is in consonance with the chosen control numbers. We readily recognize that there may be a number of persuasive theoretical arguments against this suggested approach. Nevertheless, if top management is committed to employing some sort of aggregate control, as we assume, then we believe that our course is best as compared with competing alternatives. We postpone to the next section a discussion of the *a priori* probabilities to be attached to these situations.

When control is attempted solely by means of a barometer scheme, there are no terminal actions in addition to the decision to impose the control itself with some value of θ chosen. Under quota control and the assumptions in Section 3.1.1, the terminal actions for top management at the end of any control period are (1) to suppose that the inventory policies being observed are not significantly different from those recommended, and (2) to suspect that significant violations are occurring and to initiate a detailed investigation.

For a fixed value T of the number of inventory review periods comprising a control period, top management must select a value for the quota L^*. Then if the index remains below the quota limit, action (1) is taken; otherwise, action (2) is taken. The economic calculation to be made in this instance is a standard one in statistical decision theory [CM, Ch. 5], namely, to compute

$$\max_{L^*} \left[\sum_i q_i{}^*(L^*, T) \sum_j W(N_i, a_j, L^*, T) p(a_j \mid N_i, L^*, T) \right]$$

where each of the above terms has been defined in Section 1.2.2, the computation of $p(a_j \mid N_i, L^*, T)$ has been discussed in Section 3.3.5, and it is assumed that a single situation N_i holds throughout the T periods.

Next we comment upon the considerations involved in a choice of T. The influence of T is somewhat but not completely analogous to the influence of the sample size in ordinary statistical inference problems. One factor relates to economic worth. In statistical applications, the marginal cost of an additional item in a sample is usually assumed to be constant [CM, Ch. 9; Sch, Ch. 35] and independent of the system situation.[45] In

[45] One illustrative exception is when the quality of manufactured items is being tested by a mechanism which destroys only defectives; the cost of testing then depends in part on the underlying state, that is, on the percentage defective.

our case a unit increase in T means that the system operates for an additional inventory review period and, therefore, the associated cost depends on the actual system situation. Because the selection of T is integral to the decision of adopting a control scheme, we must have a framework for evaluating the economic worth of various devices, each of which may differ with regard to the length of the control period. The tenor of our previous analysis, namely the emphasis on statistical equilibrium, suggests that we compare schemes according to their economic worth per unit of time.[46]

A further distinction between T in our analysis and the sample size in most statistical problems is that the stockage policies being observed may change as T increases.[47] There is no guarantee that the system situation remains fixed over T inventory review periods.

A final factor in the analysis of the effect of T relates to the concomitant increase in statistical accuracy. We illustrate this effect by means of two examples. First, consider the model in Table 3.3.1 (and Table 2.4.1). For the numbers rationalizing the policy (0, 3), the values of E(control number) are $E(0, 3) = 2.8518$, $E(0, 2) = 3$, and $E(0, 4) = 2.9420$; the corresponding variances of the distribution of the control number are $\text{Var}(0, 3) = 4.4968$, $\text{Var}(0, 2) = 4.6667$, and $\text{Var}(0, 4) = 3.2142$. If we would sample the control number for T inventory review periods, each a sufficiently large number of periods after its predecessor so that the stationary probabilities hold for each sampled period, the variance of the distribution of the average value of the control number would be $\text{Var}(s, S)/T$ [Cra, Ch. 27]. But if the T periods are successive in time, we might expect less variation than this number indicates. From Section 2.7.1, where we give the mathematical method for finding this variance for large values of T, we compute the numerical calculations for our example, as exhibited in Tables 3.4.1a–c.

The first step in the computations is to find $[P^*]$, which is comprised of identical rows, each being the stationary probabilities $[p_X]$ defined for $[M] \equiv [T_X]$. Then the matrices $[\tau_{jj'}]$ and $[c_{jj'}]$ are formed, according to the formulas in Section 2.7.1. The function $h(j)$ represents the possible values for the control number as defined by relation (2) in Section 3.2.2. For

---

[46] The above statement is admittedly vague because we do not wish to repeat the discussion in Section 1.2 concerning the decision criterion for selecting one control scheme from among those available. We are suggesting that whatever selection criterion is employed, it should be applied to a scheme's worth prorated over the length of the control period.

[47] An analogous situation in quality control procedures occurs in a sampling inspection of the output from a continuous line of production. If the sampled items are separated by large intervals of time, the quality of the production process may fluctuate considerably.

TABLE 3.4.1*a*

Uniform $E(\xi) = 1$ (Table 2.4.1)
Backlog $D = 2$

$$9 \times \{[I] - [M] + [P^*]\}$$

8	0	0	1
2	9	0	-2
-1	0	9	1
-1	0	0	10

$$9^{-1} \times [\tau_{jj'}]$$

.1235	0	0	-.0123
-.0247	.1111	0	.0247
.0123	0	.1111	-.0123
.0123	0	0	.0988

$$[c_{jj'}]$$

.2222	-.1481	-.0370	-.0370
-.1481	.2222	-.1111	.0370
-.0370	-.1111	.2222	-.0741
-.0370	.0370	-.0741	.0741

$$h(j)$$

2	1	4	8

$C_{in} = 1$ $\quad C_{fix} = 4$ $\quad C_{out} = 4$

example, if the policy is (0, 3) and $C_{in} = 1$, $C_{fix} = 4$, $C_{out} = 4$, we have

$$h(3) = 3 + 0 + 0 = 3$$
$$h(2) = 2 + 0 + 0 = 2$$
$$h(1) = 1 + 0 + 0 = 1$$
$$h(0) = 0 + 4 + 0 = 4$$
$$h(-1) = 0 + 4 + 4 = 8.$$

Having $[c_{jj'}]$ and $h(j)$, we can compute $\text{Var}\left[\sum_T \frac{h(j)}{T}\right]$ as T grows large by the relation given in Section 2.7.1.

TABLE 3.4.1*b*

Uniform $E(\xi) = 1$ (Table 2.4.1)

Backlog $D = 3$

$27 \times \{[I] - [M] + [P^*]\}$

22	−3	0	5	3
4	24	0	−4	3
4	6	27	−4	−6
−5	−3	0	32	3
−5	−3	0	5	30

$27^{-1} \times [\tau_{jj'}]$

.0425	.0041	0	−.0055	−.0041
−.0069	.0412	0	.0069	−.0041
−.0027	−.0082	.0370	.0027	.0082
.0055	.0041	0	.0316	−.0041
.0055	.0041	0	−.0055	.0329

$[c_{jj'}]$

.1701	−.0576	−.0741	−.0219	−.0165
−.0576	.2222	−.1481	.0206	−.0370
−.0741	−.1481	.2222	−.0370	.0370
−.0219	.0206	−.0370	.0960	−.0576
−.0165	−.0370	.0370	−.0576	.0741

$h(j)$

3	2	1	4	8

$C_{in} = 1$ $\qquad$ $C_{fix} = 4$ $\qquad$ $C_{out} = 4$

The results in our example are Var[average control number $\mid (0, 3)$] = 1.6268/T, Var[average control number $\mid (0, 2)$] = 2/T, and Var[average control number $\mid (0, 4)$] = 1.3818/T. Thus as T grows large, these are the values which may be employed for the analysis in Section 3.3.5. Observe there is more than a 35% reduction in the corresponding variances when consecutive rather than sample periods are used, and that the variance for the policy (0, 4) is less than that for the policy (0, 3).

For our second example, we employ the model in Table 3.3.2 (and Table 2.4.2). The policy (1, 5) is rationalized by $C_{in} = 1$, $C_{fix} = 8$, and

TABLE 3.4.1*c*

Uniform $E(\xi) = 1$ (Table 2.4.1)

Backlog $D = 4$

$$69 \times \{[I] - [M] + [P^*]\}$$

54	−11	−5	15	11	5
8	58	−5	−8	11	5
8	12	64	−8	−12	5
8	12	18	61	−12	−18
−15	−11	−5	15	80	5
−15	−11	−5	15	11	74

$$69^{-1} \times [\tau_{jj'}]$$

.0170	.0025	.0019	−.0025	−.0025	−.0019
−.0032	.0158	0	.0032	−.0013	0
−.0013	−.0032	.0151	.0013	.0032	−.0006
0	−.0013	−.0038	.0145	.0013	.0038
.0025	.0025	.0019	−.0025	.0120	−.0019
.0025	.0025	.0019	−.0025	−.0025	.0126

$$[c_{jj'}]$$

.1428	−.0378	−.0378	−.0454	−.0109	−.0109
−.0378	.1739	−.1021	−.0189	−.0151	0
−.0378	−.1021	.2155	−.0907	.0359	−.0208
−.0454	−.0189	−.0907	.1701	−.0435	.0284
−.0109	−.0151	.0359	−.0435	.0785	−.0449
−.0190	0	−.0208	.0284	−.0449	.0483

$$h(j)$$

4	3	2	1	4	8

$C_{in} = 1$ $\qquad$ $C_{fix} = 4$ $\qquad$ $C_{out} = 4$

$C_{out} = 20$, so that the values of E(control number) are $E(1, 5) = 5.0714$, $E(1, 4) = 5.2412$, and $E(1, 6) = 5.1571$, where the control number is defined as relation (2) in Section 3.2.2. The corresponding variances of the distribution of the control numbers are Var$(1, 5) = 26.9125$, Var$(1, 4) = 34.7438$, and Var$(1, 6) = 22.5614$. As with the first example, we exhibit in Tables 3.4.2*a–i* the numerical calculations needed to find the variance of the distribution of the average value of the control number over T consecutive periods. We obtain Var[average control number $| (1, 5)] = 18.3389/T$, Var[average control number $| (1, 4)] = 24.0961/T$, and Var

TABLE 3.4.2a

Poisson $E(\xi) = 1$ (Table 2.4.2)

Backlog $D = 3$

$\{[I] - [M] + [P^*]\}$

.7984	−.1047	.1007	.1195	.0601	.0198	.0048	.0009	.0001
.1663	.8952	−.0831	−.0030	.0141	.0075	.0023	.0005	.0001
.1663	.2631	.9168	−.1870	−.1085	−.0384	−.0099	−.0020	−.0003
−.2015	−.1047	.1007	1.1195	.0601	.0198	.0048	.0009	.0001
−.2015	−.1047	.1007	.1195	1.0601	.0198	.0048	.0009	.0001
−.2015	−.1047	.1007	.1195	.0601	1.0198	.0048	.0009	.0001
−.2015	−.1047	.1007	.1195	.0601	.0198	1.0048	.0009	.0001
−.2015	−.1047	.1007	.1195	.0601	.0198	.0048	1.0009	.0001
−.2015	−.1047	.1007	.1195	.0601	.0198	.0048	.0009	1.0001

TABLE 3.4.2b

Poisson $E(\xi) = 1$ (Table 2.4.2)

Backlog $D = 3$

$[\tau_{jj'}]$

1.1844	.1386	−.0922	−.1308	−.0692	−.0234	−.0059	−.0011	−.0002
−.2318	1.0620	.1159	.0462	.0082	.0000	.0004	.0001	.0000
−.0786	−.2776	1.0393	.1650	.1023	.0373	.0098	.0020	.0004
.1844	.1386	−.0922	.8691	−.0692	−.0234	−.0059	−.0011	−.0002
.1844	.1386	−.0922	−.1308	.9307	−.0234	−.0059	−.0011	−.0002
.1844	.1386	−.0922	−.1308	−.0692	.9765	−.0059	−.0011	−.0002
.1844	.1386	−.0922	−.1308	−.0692	−.0234	.9940	−.0011	−.0002
.1844	.1386	−.0922	−.1308	−.0692	−.0234	−.0059	.9988	−.0002
.1844	.1386	−.0922	−.1308	−.0692	−.0234	−.0059	−.0011	.9997

TABLE 3.4.2c

Poisson $E(\xi) = 1$ (Table 2.4.2)

Backlog $D = 3$

$[c_{jj'}]$

.2000	−.0817	−.0851	−.0184	−.0101	−.0034	−.0008	−.0001	−.0000
−.0817	.2265	−.1234	−.0103	−.0072	−.0028	−.0007	−.0001	−.0000
−.0851	−.1234	.2260	−.0211	.0007	.0020	.0007	.0001	.0000
−.0184	−.0103	−.0211	.1008	−.0360	−.0113	−.0027	−.0005	−.0001
−.0101	−.0072	.0007	−.0360	.0592	−.0050	−.0012	−.0002	−.0000
−.0034	−.0028	.0020	−.0113	−.0050	.0212	−.0003	−.0000	−.0000
−.0008	−.0007	.0007	−.0027	−.0012	−.0003	.0053	−.0000	−.0000
−.0001	−.0001	.0001	−.0005	−.0002	−.0000	−.0001	.0010	.0000
−.0000	−.0000	.0000	−.0001	−.0000	−.0000	−.0000	.0000	.0001

$h(j)$

4	3	2	9	8	28	48	68	88

$C_{in} = 1$ $\qquad$ $C_{fix} = 8$ $\qquad$ $C_{out} = 20$

TABLE 3.4.2d

Poisson $E(\xi) = 1$ (Table 2.4.2)

Backlog $D = 4$

$$\{[I] - [M] + [P^*]\}$$

.7614	−.1632	.0374	.1611	.1251	.0556	.0173	.0041	.0008	.0001
.1293	.8367	−.1465	.0385	.0791	.0433	.0147	.0037	.0007	.0001
.1293	.2046	.8534	−.1454	−.0434	−.0026	.0025	.0011	.0003	.0000
.1293	.2046	.2213	.8545	−.2273	−.1252	−.0434	−.0111	−.0022	−.0004
−.2385	−.1632	.0374	.1611	1.1251	.0556	.0173	.0041	.0008	.0001
−.2385	−.1632	.0374	.1611	.1251	1.0556	.0173	.0041	.0008	.0001
−.2385	−.1632	.0374	.1611	.1251	.0556	1.0173	.0041	.0008	.0001
−.2385	−.1632	.0374	.1611	.1251	.0556	.0173	1.0041	.0008	.0001
−.2385	−.1632	.0374	.1611	.1251	.0556	.0173	.0041	1.0008	.0001
−.2385	−.1632	.0374	.1611	.1251	.0556	.0173	.0041	.0008	1.0001

TABLE 3.4.2e

Poisson $E(\xi) = 1$ (Table 2.4.2)

Backlog $D = 4$

$$[\tau_{jj'}]$$

1.2097	.2127	.0418	−.1762	−.1704	−.0824	−.0268	−.0066	−.0013	−.0002
−.2427	1.0788	.1879	.0414	−.0292	−.0239	−.0092	−.0024	−.0005	−.0001
−.1139	−.2992	1.0697	.1876	.1075	.0369	.0091	.0017	.0002	.0000
.0051	−.1109	−.3083	1.0537	.1892	.1156	.0418	.0109	.0022	.0004
.2097	.2127	.0418	−.1762	.8295	−.0824	−.0268	−.0066	−.0013	−.0002
.2097	.2127	.0418	−.1762	−.1704	.9175	−.0268	−.0066	−.0013	−.0002
.2097	.2127	.0418	−.1762	−.1704	−.0824	.9731	−.0066	−.0013	−.0002
.2097	.2127	.0418	−.1762	−.1704	−.0824	−.0268	.9933	−.0013	−.0002
.2097	.2127	.0418	−.1762	−.1704	−.0824	−.0268	−.0066	.9986	−.0002
.2097	.2127	.0418	−.1762	−.1704	−.0824	−.0268	−.0066	−.0013	.9997

TABLE 3.4.2f

Poisson $E(\xi) = 1$ (Table 2.4.2)

Backlog $D = 4$

$$[c_{jj'}]$$

.1668	−.0486	−.0484	−.0504	−.0107	−.0059	−.0020	−.0005	−.0001	−.0000
−.0486	.1950	−.0730	−.0617	−.0048	−.0044	−.0017	−.0004	−.0000	−.0000
−.0484	−.0730	.2032	−.0763	−.0014	−.0023	−.0011	−.0003	−.0000	−.0000
−.0504	−.0617	−.0763	.1968	−.0139	.0023	.0022	.0007	.0001	.0000
−.0107	−.0048	−.0014	−.0139	.0728	−.0298	−.0093	−.0022	−.0004	−.0000
−.0059	−.0044	−.0023	.0023	−.0298	.0455	−.0040	−.0009	−.0001	−.0000
−.0020	−.0017	−.0011	.0022	−.0093	−.0040	.0165	−.0003	−.0000	−.0000
−.0005	−.0004	−.0003	.0007	−.0022	−.0009	−.0003	.0041	−.0000	−.0000
−.0001	−.0000	−.0000	.0001	−.0004	−.0001	−.0000	−.0000	.0008	.0000
−.0000	−.0000	−.0000	.0000	−.0000	−.0000	−.0000	−.0000	.0000	.0001

$h(j)$

5	4	3	2	9	8	28	48	68	88

$C_{in} = 1$ $C_{fix} = 8$ $C_{out} = 20$

TABLE 3.4.2g

Poisson $E(\xi) = 1$ (Table 2.4.2)

Backlog $D = 5$

$$\{[I] - [M] + [P^*]\}$$

.7379	−.2003	−.0027	.1207	.1664	.1117 ·	.0474	.0145	.0034	.0006	.0001
.1058	.7996	−.1866	−.0019	.1204	.0995	.0449	.0140	.0033	.0006	.0001
.1058	.1674	.8133	−.1858	−.0021	.0535	.0326	.0115	.0029	.0005	.0001
.1058	.1674	.1812	.8141	−.1861	−.0690	−.0133	−.0007	.0003	.0001	.0000
.1058	.1674	.1812	.1820	.8138	−.2530	−.1359	−.0467	−.0118	−.0024	−.0004
−.2620	−.2003	−.0027	.1207	.1664	1.1117	.0474	.0145	.0034	.0006	.0001
−.2620	−.2003	−.0027	.1207	.1664	.1117	1.0474	.0145	.0034	.0006	.0001
−.2620	−.2003	−.0027	.1207	.1664	.1117	.0474	1.0145	.0034	.0006	.0001
−.2620	−.2003	−.0027	.1207	.1664	.1117	.0474	.0145	1.0034	.0006	.0001
−.2620	−.2003	−.0027	.1207	.1664	.1117	.0474	.0145	.0034	1.0006	.0001
−.2620	−.2003	−.0027	.1207	.1664	.1117	.0474	.0145	.0034	.0006	1.0001

TABLE 3.4.2h

Poisson $E(\xi) = 1$ (Table 2.4.2)

Backlog $D = 5$

$$[\tau_{jj'}]$$

1.2254	.2591	.1261	−.0517	−.2339	−.1959	−.0910	−.0291	−.0071	−.0013	−.0002
−.2506	1.0878	.2318	.1253	−.0511	−.0809	−.0430	−.0145	−.0036	−.0007	−.0001
−.1447	−.3265	1.0744	.2320	.1259	.0347	.0047	−.0001	−.0002	−.0000	−.0000
−.0393	−.1598	−.3271	1.0746	.2315	.1460	.0550	.0150	.0032	.0005	.0000
.0580	−.0056	−.1603	−.3397	1.0603	.2041	.1239	.0447	.0116	.0024	.0004
.2254	.2591	.1261	−.0517	−.2339	.8040	−.0910	−.0291	−.0071	−.0013	−.0002
.2254	.2591	.1261	−.0517	−.2339	−.1959	.9089	−.0291	−.0071	−.0013	−.0002
.2254	.2591	.1261	−.0517	−.2339	−.1959	−.0910	.9708	−.0071	−.0013	−.0002
.2254	.2591	.1261	−.0517	−.2339	−.1959	−.0910	−.0291	.9928	−.0013	−.0002
.2254	.2591	.1261	−.0517	−.2339	−.1959	−.0910	−.0291	−.0071	.9986	−.0002
.2254	.2591	.1261	−.0517	−.2339	−.1959	−.0910	−.0291	−.0071	−.0013	.9997

TABLE 3.4.2i

Poisson $E(\xi) = 1$ (Table 2.4.2)

Backlog $D = 5$

$$[c_{jj'}]$$

.1423	−.0322	−.0320	−.0319	−.0334	−.0070	−.0038	−.0013	−.0003	−.0000	−.0000
−.0322	.1688	−.0507	−.0385	−.0400	−.0030	−.0028	−.0011	−.0002	−.0000	−.0000
−.0320	−.0507	.1753	−.0504	−.0392	−.0000	−.0017	−.0008	−.0002	−.0000	−.0000
−.0319	−.0385	−.0504	.1760	−.0526	−.0002	−.0012	−.0006	−.0002	−.0000	−.0000
−.0334	−.0400	−.0392	−.0526	.1706	−.0106	.0025	.0020	.0006	.0001	.0000
−.0070	−.0030	−.0000	−.0002	−.0106	.0566	−.0253	−.0078	−.0018	−.0003	−.0000
−.0038	−.0028	−.0017	−.0012	.0025	−.0253	.0369	−.0034	−.0008	−.0001	−.0000
−.0013	−.0011	−.0008	−.0006	.0020	−.0078	−.0034	.0135	−.0002	−.0000	−.0000
−.0003	−.0002	−.0002	−.0002	.0006	−.0018	−.0008	−.0002	.0033	−.0000	−.0000
−.0000	−.0000	−.0000	−.0000	.0001	−.0003	−.0001	−.0000	−.0000	.0006	.0000
−.0000	−.0000	−.0000	−.0000	.0000	−.0000	−.0000	−.0000	−.0000	.0000	.0001

$h(j)$

6	5	4	3	2	9	8	28	48	68	88

$C_{in} = 1$ $C_{fix} = 8$ $C_{out} = 20$

[average control number $|$ (1, 6)] $= 15.2907/T$. Notice that in this case there is more than a 67% reduction in the corresponding variances when consecutive rather than sampled sums are employed, and that the variance for the policy (1, 6) is less than that for the policy (1, 5).

Throughout we have restricted the concept of an index number to the realm of financial-like controls; although in real inventory systems the rationalized control numbers of Section 3.2.2 may have no counterpart in cash outlays, nevertheless we find it suggestive to identify the components of the control number by such terms as inventory, backlog, and ordering costs. There are of course control indices other than financial types which might be useful, notwithstanding our decision to classify them beyond the scope of this study. We mention one such device as an illustration. Periodically the inventory records may be audited to determine the overall percentage of recommended policies actually being observed. Our reservation concerning the merit of this control is that the data requirements seem to be considerably more severe than those for the schemes previously examined in this chapter. To determine whether a recommended stockage rule for an item has been observed, we need to examine a complete history of the transactions, that is, the time sequence of orders and demands during the control period. As a consequence, we believe that the costs associated with such an audit will encourage the employing of a sampling technique, in other words, to the examining of only a portion of the records. For the same reason, we believe that it will be economical to tolerate a few violations in the sample audit and not undertake a further detailed and presumably costly investigation.[48]

3.4.2 Consistency, A Priori and Detection Probabilities

The consistency property affects the relative evaluation of control schemes in two ways, namely, in influencing the values of the *a priori* probabilities of system situations and in determining the ability to detect out-of-control situations. We discuss each of these factors in turn.

The property of consistency is an appealingly plausible requirement;[49] for top management to adopt a control procedure which fails to meet this

---

[48] We also question whether the economic evaluation of the system situations is well described simply in terms of the percentage of recommended inventory rules being violated. Such a percentage figure weights each violation as being equally significant; only in special circumstances is an inventory system comprised of items toward which management takes such an extreme view. Of course a weighting scheme might be devised to account for the relative importance of various kinds of violations.

[49] The reader familiar with mathematical statistics will observe the previously mentioned parallel between our view of consistency and the statistician's notion of an unbiased test of hypotheses [Cra, Ch. 35; K, Ch. 27].

criterion appears to be at variance with top management's prescription of stockage policies. To the extent lower management ascertains the possible benefits in terms of its own objectives to be derived from inconsistent actions, top management is able to foresee that the imposition of an inconsistent control will bring about violations in the recommended policies. This realization, when quantified with regard to the *a priori* probabilities of the situations in our economic model,[50] could very well lead to the rejection of the scheme for control purposes.[51] But if there is reason to believe that the system situations associated with the inconsistency of a control device are unlikely to occur, or if their occurrence entails little economic loss to top management, then our predilection for this criterion is correspondingly weakened. Furthermore, in real situations, the imposition of a consistent control does not automatically ensure that the recommended policies will be followed.

An inconsistent system by its very nature may prove relatively ineffective in detecting the out-of-control situation whenever such occurs.[52] In other words, the scheme may lack the power to detect violations as they occur. But it also must be realized that a consistent control scheme may be ineffective in discovering out-of-control situations.

As we have stated, an acceptance or rejection of a control scheme ought to be made on the basis of a full analysis of the economic model which is composed of the various elements listed at the beginning of Section 3.4.1. Consider, for example, a commonly employed quota scheme on the total value of purchases, a mechanism which in some situations may be inconsistent (Section 3.3.4). Despite the lack of consistency the scheme may be preferable to no quota at all, a possibility which we discussed previously in Section 1.2.2. In essence there are two economic losses to be compared: (1) the expected loss resulting from the imposition of a control which encourages certain violations in the recommended policies, and (2) the expected loss stemming from violations which might occur if the inconsistent control is not imposed. The latter quantity may very well outweigh the former.

Another facet to system design is establishing the criteria for deciding the items encompassed by a single index. In Section 1.1 we listed certain characteristics of importance. Our above discussion touches upon the

---

[50] That is, the probabilities $q_i^*(c)$ in Section 1.2.2.

[51] Here is the crucial difference between our situation and the one usually encountered in the theory of statistical testing of hypotheses. In the latter instance, there is usually no reason to believe that the adoption of a biased test will in and of itself change the likelihood of any hypothesis being true.

[52] Loosely, for an inconsistent control the probabilities $p(a_j \mid N_i, c)$ in Section 1.2.2 may be functions relatively insensitive to changes in N_i.

conceptual aspect of being able to describe a system situation and the economic-worth function depending upon these situations. Here we add that a further aspect is top management's facility in arriving at *a priori* probabilities of the system situations. It is conceivable that inventory records are so arranged as to make it inconvenient to construct aggregates based on functional characteristics. One possible resolution of this difficulty is to construct the indices for each period by sampling at random[53] from the items in the system and then by forming separate aggregates from the sample so as to take into account meaningful aggregation criteria.

3.4.3 Concluding Remarks

Up to this point we have outlined the manner in which quantitative analysis of an index number control scheme may be undertaken. Here we offer a personal critique of the efficacy of index number control *for the purpose stated at the beginning of this chapter*, Section 3.1.1. As usual, we emphasize the two notions "management by rule" and "management by exception." By concentrating on these two ideas we do not intend to give the impression that we are foresaking the economic model in Section 1.2 or in the preceding discussion; rather we are stating that within the confines of our analysis these two elements play a crucial role in the final economic evaluation.[54]

We stress that a sensible discussion of the merits of control schemes must take cognizance of the fact that top management is forced to choose among several broad alternatives: (1) to impose no top management control over lower management's observance of recommended policies; (2) to adopt an index scheme such as the one presented in this chapter; or (3) to devise another type of control method. Because of the aggregation process and the nature of the probability distributions thereby convoluted, it is not surprising if choice (2) turns out to be ineffective for detecting a low or moderate level of violation except when T is large. But choice (1) is trivially ineffective in this respect, and choice (3), insofar as we have envisaged it, is also limited by the nature of the costs associated with such a procedure. Thus in a large-scale inventory system it may be inevitable that top management has no economically advantageous way of maintaining close control

[53] It is likely that some sort of stratification will be required, depending on the organization of the inventory files.

[54] Another important factor in the design of a control scheme is the economic cost associated with its operations, e.g., charges for personnel, document handling, and office equipment. As we indicated in Section 1.3.3, we go no further in our theoretical analysis than to mention this factor, for at present, it appears that such considerations by and large are mainly dependent on whatever real situation is actually involved.

over lower management's observance of the recommended rules.[55] Furthermore, in certain real situations it may be that the principal economic benefit derived from taking an audit when it is in fact called for stems from the future operations of the system;[56] past losses suffered by top management through violations of recommended policies may not be recoverable. In addition, the employment of an aggregate type of control may be necessitated by restrictions imposed by a Board of Directors, a point which we discussed in Section 1.1.1. Consequently, we reaffirm the validity of top management's need to impose aggregate control.

In investigating aggregate control schemes available to top management, we have studied the extent to which it is possible to construct strongly consistent control schemes, and we have determined whether many commonly employed control devices are consistent. We found among the devices considered in this chapter that a barometer control utilizing rationalized control numbers is strongly consistent, in that it positively encourages lower management to follow the prescribed rules; quota control on net demand is at best weakly consistent and often is inconsistent; and most other quota schemes are inconsistent, an exception being one involving an averaging of rationalized control numbers for a sufficiently large number of inventory review periods.

We may ask whether a consistent barometer control is to be preferred to an inconsistent device, other factors such as control costs being equal. In answering we begin by pointing out that in actuality it is not a trivial matter to institute a pure barometer scheme. It is unlikely that top management can ensure itself a barometer control giving a complete hedge, Section 3.2.2, because the index number comprised of rationalized control numbers is not likely to represent top management's utility function, and it is difficult in real situations to set θ at a sufficiently high level.[57] Consequently, as we mentioned at the end of Section 3.2.2, in real applications of barometer control schemes top management is often justifiably motivated to take corrective action if it observes several consecutive periods in which penalties occur; in effect it has thereby combined an element of quota control with the barometer device. Furthermore, lower management, when faced with a nominal barometer device, may not view its own objective as optimizing θ(index number $-$ target),

---

[55] It must be realized that top management is unlikely to be very concerned about a low level of violation. Indeed, it is an advantage that a small number of infringements is obscured in an index, and thus does not tempt top management to investigate in detail.

[56] That is, the benefits may stem in large part from the influence of the function $R(N_i, a_j)$ in Section 1.2.2.

[57] In other words, it is unlikely that top management can enforce a penalty that would fully compensate it for systemwide losses that are possibly incurred.

but rather as minimizing the probability that a penalty exceeds a given amount; once again, the resultant effect is a quota control.

The discussion in the preceding paragraph and in Section 3.4.2 means that imposing a nominally strongly consistent scheme does not guarantee the system operates according to the prescribed management rules. Therefore, we cannot recommend without qualification that consistent systems are to be preferred. Lower management may quickly realize that aggregate control schemes tend to be weak in their power to detect mild violations. Whether in actual situations the consistency motivation will dominate the realization of an ineffective power to detect mild violations is a question which transcends an economic and statistical analysis and falls into the scope of industrial psychology.[58]

Our analysis has led to the conclusions that almost all commonly used aggregate control schemes are inconsistent, and that it may be nearly impossible as well as undesirable to impose a strongly consistent control device. We must not infer from these conclusions that aggregate controls should be rejected entirely. Rather we must face the fact that inconsistency is a price which in most cases will have to be paid whenever aggregate controls are instituted. The ultimate determination of the merit of imposing a control scheme can only be provided by means of evaluating one device relative to another in the fashion prescribed in Section 1.2.2.

[58] Research in this area seems to have already begun [Ste].

Chapter 4

CONTROL UNDER VARYING
DEMAND DISTRIBUTIONS

4.1 INTRODUCTION

I N CHAPTER 3 WE examined control problems under the assumption that
the demand distribution $\phi_i(\xi)$ for each item i is known. Here we investigate questions arising when this particular assumption is modified.[1]
We study three types of control problems.

The first control problem to be considered, which was illustrated in
Section 1.3, deals with encouraging personnel within the organization to
consume inventoried items in an economical fashion, and with planning for
this type of consumption as well as for purchases to restock inventories.
In broad terms, the need for the control on personnel occurs when the
lower echelon does not devote sufficient care to avoiding wastage of costly
resources. When consumption patterns, based on the demand behavior of
either personnel or customers, are found to have changed, top management
may need to revise its allocation of financial resources to allow for replenishment of inventories.

The second control problem deals with providing top management with
information as to the actual demand distributions for the various items.
For example, management may want to undertake a review of the currently
recommended set of stockage rules, if the previously assumed demand
distributions have changed significantly in the aggregate.

The third set of control problems arises when top management is uncertain about both the currently operating stockage policies and the
associated demand distributions in a multi-item inventory system. We
consider, as in Chapter 3, the question of designing a consistent control
scheme that encourages lower management to adopt economical inventory
rules.

[1] We continue the assumptions given in Section 3.1 regarding the employment of
(s, S) policies, fixed delivery lags, control period timing, etc.

With regard to the second and third types of control problems, our results, although suggestive, are rudimentary, since progress to date has been limited in the determination of optimal inventory policies when the probability distributions for demand cannot be stated with certainty. Our discussion below will clarify the reasons why such progress has been slow.

We treat the analysis of internal economic consumption and of replenishment planning in Section 4.2, and show that a barometer control on the value of inventory consumption is consistent, and, under proper operating conditions, so is a quota control. We also discuss the closely allied problem of designing an aggregate index which can be used for planning purposes. What distinguishes our problem in this section from that in Chapter 3 is that now we focus attention on the replenishment quantities as they are influenced by $\phi(\xi)$, whereas in Chapter 3 we concentrated on the influence of selecting the (s, S) policies.

In Section 4.3 we initiate the study of making decisions about the aggregate set of demand distributions by an examination of the control problem for the special case of a single-item inventory system. We point out how the situation can be viewed as a somewhat complicated exercise in statistical inference. Then we extend the discussion to a multi-item inventory system. Here the difficulties found in the single-item case are further complicated by the aspect that, for certain control problems in this category, the use within an index of commonly employed statistical measures may be precluded because of the accompanying property of their confounding significant changes among the components. We go on to explore several alternative statistics which avoid such confounding, and one which does not require knowing the actually employed (s, S) policies.

Turning to situations in which both currently operating stockage policies and the demand distributions are not known with certainty, we explain in Section 4.4 that in some real situations it is possible to devise a consistent barometer control for lower management operations. In contrast, the difficulties we encountered in Chapter 3 in devising a quota control are magnified.

4.2 CONTROL OF CONSUMPTION AND REPLENISHMENT PLANNING

In many instances demands for inventory are generated by outside customers, and, as we have seen in Chapter 3, the operating of a set of (s, S) policies involves making replenishment orders from time to time. In other real situations, similar to the simplified example given in Section 1.3, demand for items is generated by the activities of personnel within an organization. Typical examples are the consumption of stationery supplies by an office staff, of gasoline for a fleet of delivery trucks, and of spare parts in the maintenance of machinery. An alternative way of stating the preceding dichotomous characterization of demand is in terms of drains on inventory and of requests for refilling the inventory. In both these cases, top management needs to provision for the replenishment of inventory. We start our analysis by considering the control problem of motivating personnel responsible for internal consumption to be economical.

4.2.1 Internal Consumption

We postulate that for each item i there exists within a period an incontrovertible and nondiminishable demand value ξ_i' occurring with probability[2] $\phi_i(\xi_i')$. This assumption is quite strong, and the results to follow depend heavily on it; we are ruling out, for example, situations in which the indication of a demand can be postponed until a later period. The actions of the operating personnel transform the basic demand value to a realized demand ξ_i which is at least as large as ξ_i'

(1) $$\xi_i \equiv g_i(\xi_i') \geq \xi_i' \qquad \xi_i' \geq 0.$$

It follows from (1) that

(2a) $$\text{Prob}\,(\xi_i \leq \bar{\xi}) \leq \text{Prob}\,(\xi_i' \leq \bar{\xi}) \qquad \bar{\xi} \geq 0,$$

(2b) $$E(\xi_i') \leq E(\xi_i).$$

The system is defined as in control if $\xi_i = \xi_i'$ for all i. To ensure this equality, top management often desires an aggregate control device, such as those described in Chapter 3.[3]

A plausible and commonly considered control number to be employed in an index is $C_{\text{pur}(i)}\xi_i$, where $C_{\text{pur}(i)} > 0$ is a given weighting factor for item i, usually its purchase price. As in Chapter 3, a barometer control scheme extending over T consecutive or sampled inventory review periods would operate by penalizing lower management by the amount[4]

(3a) $$\theta\left(\frac{\text{Index number}}{T} - \text{Target}\right), \qquad \theta > 0,$$

where

(3b) $$\frac{\text{Index number}}{T} = \sum_T \sum_i C_{\text{pur}(i)}\xi_{i,t}/T$$

(3c) $$\xi_{i,t} = \text{demand for item } i \text{ in period } t.$$

---

[2] As previously, we refer to $\phi_i(\xi_i')$ as a probability distribution, but a similar analysis pertains if $\phi_i(\xi_i')$ is a probability density function.

[3] The analysis below can be generalized to the formulation

$$[\xi_1, \xi_2, \ldots, \xi_i, \ldots] \equiv g(\xi_1', \xi_2', \ldots \xi_i', \ldots) \geq [\xi_1', \xi_2', \ldots, \xi_i', \ldots]$$

without vitiating our conclusions.

[4] If the amount is negative, then in fact lower management would be rewarded.

If lower management, which is subject to this barometer control, views its objective as minimizing the expected value of (3a), then it correspondingly will seek to minimize the expected value of the index number. Because of (2b), operating personnel will be positively encouraged to adopt such actions that $\xi_i' = \xi_i$ for all i, and consequently the barometer control is strongly consistent. The target would likely be set at

$$\sum_i C_{\text{pur}(i)} E(\xi_i'),$$

although the consistency result is independent of the target value assigned. The selection of θ and T will be discussed below in Section 4.2.3.

As previously, a quota control would operate by top management setting a limit L^* on the above index number, and presuming that the system is out of control if the index exceeds L^*. We assume to start that the values of L^* are established independently of the observed past values of the index number. Considerations in determining the numerical values of L^* will be discussed below in Section 4.2.3. If the lower echelon of operation is not allowed to store inventory from one period to the next, there is no incentive to select $g_i(\xi_i')$ so that ξ_i' is revised upward in an effort to weaken effective control in subsequent periods. Consequently, setting a quota in general is strongly consistent, since from (2a), for $L^* > 0$, Prob (index $\leq L^*$) is maximized if $\xi_i' = \xi_i$ for all i. But if operating personnel are permitted to store inventory, which is then not charged against a future quota, a strong inconsistency may arise from the aforementioned motive of attempting to avoid exceeding the quota in future periods through anticipatory provisioning.

If, in fact, L^* is set by top management to reflect previous values of the index number, then a scheme again becomes inconsistent, for lower management, as in the paragraph above, will be motivated to overconsume in the current period so as to lower the probability of exceeding the quota in subsequent periods.

To illustrate, a simple form for the functions g_i is

(4) $g_i(\xi_i') = a_i \xi_i' + b_i$ for all ξ_i', $a_i \geq 1, b_i \geq 0$.

Then

$$E(\xi_i) \equiv E[g(\xi_i')] = a_i E(\xi_i') + b_i$$
$$\text{Prob }(\xi_i \leq \bar{\xi}) = \text{Prob }(a_i \xi_i' + b_i \leq \bar{\xi}).$$

Lower management is motivated to select $g_i(\xi_i')$—in other words, to pick a_i and b_i, so that

$a_i^* E(\xi_i') + b_i^* = \min_{a_i, b_i} [a_i E(\xi_i') + b_i]$ *barometer control*

$a_i^* \xi_i' + b_i^* = \min_{a_i, b_i} (a_i \xi_i' + b_i)$ for all ξ_i *quota control—no lower echelon inventory storage* subject to $a_i \geq 1$, $b_i \geq 0$. The resultant values are $a_i^* = 1$ and $b_i^* = 0$, and thus the schemes are consistent.

4.2.2 Replenishment Planning

We turn to the related situation where top management is interested in planning for replenishment of inventory. Letting r_i be the replenishment amount for item i in a single period, we postulate that top management is concerned with the distribution of

$$\sum_i C_{\text{pur}(i)} r_i,$$

and, specifically, it bases its planning on the value of

(1) $$\sum_i C_{\text{pur}(i)} E(r_i).$$

If the distributions $\phi_i(\xi)$ change appreciably and thereby alter the value of (1), top management wants to revise its previous planning accordingly.

If, as in Section 4.2.1, the drains on inventory that must be planned for emanate from consuming personnel, then $r_i \equiv \xi_i$. If, as in Chapter 3, r_i is determined through the operation of an (s, S) rule, then each r_i may reflect an accumulation of several periods of ξ_i. From Proposition 2.5.1, we know that if demand is backlogged, then

$$E(r_i) = E(\xi_i),$$

and if demand is not backlogged

$$E(r_i) = E(\xi_i) - E(\text{shortage}).$$

Therefore, we suggest in general that, for replenishment planning, top management may well employ the average index number value (3b) in Section 4.2.1. Such an index does not depend on the particular (s, S) policies being observed.[5] If the arithmetic average of T periods of observed ξ_i is a maximum likelihood estimator for $E(\xi_i)$ [Cra, L], then the suggested average index number is the maximum likelihood estimator for (1).[6] Furthermore, if the values for i and T are sufficiently large, the statistical distribution of the averaged index number is approximately normal with mean equal to (1) [Cra]. Thus, in this situation, top management can employ a variety of standard statistical approaches to assist the planning control procedure. To illustrate, analogous to establishing a quota control, top management may set limits on the value of the averaged index so that,

---

[5] Our recommendation in the no-backlog model is predicated on the assumption that the value of $E(\text{shortage})$ is likely to be small relative to the value of $E(\xi_i)$.

[6] Such occurs for $E(\xi_i)$ as the mean of a Poisson, normal, binomial, negative binomial, or gamma distribution.

if the averaged index falls outside these limits, top management assumes it is necessary to change its previous replenishment provisioning plan. This control accords with the procedure of statistical hypothesis testing. To set the control limits, it is not necessary for top management to specify the exact value of the variance of the averaged index. The variance either may be estimated from historical data and a *t*-statistic analysis be employed [BL, Cra], or top management may specify an *a priori* joint probability distribution for the mean and variance of the index [Sch, Ch. 28].

4.2.3 Summary Evaluation

Our commentary in Section 3.4 on the factors influencing the economic design of a control system are equally pertinent to the present situation. Consequently, we shall offer only a brief review of these points here. It is reasonable to believe that top management's interest in inventory consumption can be described well in terms of the index number in Section 4.2.1, especially if $C_{pur(i)}$ represents the cost to the firm of item *i*. In other words, we feel that in carrying out the analysis of Section 1.2, the system situations can be sensibly defined with reference to the behavior of the index number rather than of the separate components of the index. As in Chapter 3, top management must specify T, θ for a barometer control, and L^* for a quota control for the situation in Section 4.2.1. To do this, management has to take into account the aspects of statistical accuracy, of allowing the system to remain out of control for specified periods of time, of the feasible magnitudes of possible penalties and rewards, and of the probabilities of overlooking out-of-control situations and of auditing in-control situations. Similarly, the same kind of considerations are involved in the planning situation in Section 4.2.2, setting the limits for the *t*-statistic, the number of periods of observations to be averaged, and the width parameter in a confidence interval.

It is noteworthy that controlling consumption, in strong contrast to controlling the observance of inventory stockage policies, readily yields to the design of consistent mechanisms, either of the barometer or quota type. With regard to quota controls, top management can ensure the consistency property by demonstrating that the quota limit is set by a mechanism which is independent of the past values of the index. For example, top management could announce in advance the quota for several control periods. If it is infeasible to preclude lower management from storing inventory from one period to the next, then consistency can be preserved by adopting the procedure of assessing at the start of each control period the value of the stored inventory and charging this amount against the current quota. We point out that this procedure as well as the preceding one of pre-announcing quotas is not often practiced, even though the failure to follow such suggestions then produces an inconsistent control system.

We emphasize that an important distinction must be drawn between what we have called a quota control and what is commonly termed a budgetary control. In the latter device, top management places a virtually inviolable limit on the total amount of consumption that can occur, as measured in terms of the index value. Even if the system is operating according to standards—to illustrate in the internal consumption case, $g_i(\xi_i') = \xi_i'$ for all i—it is still possible for the index number to exceed a control value because of the random nature of the demand values. Thus, imposing a budgetary control implies that in some periods a number of these demands may go unsatisfied. Top management can impose a quota control without converting it into a budgetary control. Top management may discover it is desirable to permit consumption to occur without effective upper bound constraint, and then to conduct an audit after finding that the index has exceeded a control limit. Evaluating the desirability of a budgetary control involves considering the feasibility of placing no effective upper bound on current consumption and the economic effect of possibly forcing some demand to go unfulfilled. The latter effect, in turn, depends on the possible decision rules that lower management utilizes and their associated probabilities of being employed.

In conclusion, with regard to internal consumption activity, we believe that because of the difficulties associated with instituting a barometer control, as we have discussed in Section 3.4.3, top management is advised to rely on consistent quota control schemes to encourage economic consumption decisions. With reference to the planning process, typical statistical inference approaches can be embedded in a decision model to assist the provisioning procedure.

4.3 PROBLEMS ASSOCIATED WITH DETERMINING DEMAND DISTRIBUTIONS

In this section we return to inventory systems composed of (s, S) stockage rules. We consider the case where top management does not know with certainty the distributions $\phi_i(\xi)$ for every period. We begin the analysis by assuming the system contains only a single item; then we go on to investigate the further difficulties arising when there is more than one item in the system. In Section 4.3.1 we first explain the fundamental interconnection between the statistical and economic aspects of the inference problem. In brief, the attendant difficulty is that economic costs from the system's operation are being incurred at the same time data on the demand distribution are being collected; thus both the determination of a stockage rule and the collection and interpretation of data are inseparable activities. Then we proceed to give a so-called Bayesian view of the problem, which formally encompasses all the economic and statistical factors to be considered; the approach is beset with difficulty because it usually leads to unwieldy calculations. Finally we discuss a variety of statistics that can be used in lieu of frequently employed statistical measures; these alternative indices entail a loss of statistical accuracy, but they take on significance when we study a multi-item inventory system.

In Section 4.3.2 we explain what additional complications arise when the statistical inference problem is extended to a multi-item system. A particularly serious difficulty is that it is necessary to design special indices that do not permit changes in several components to cancel each other out. We illustrate that the rationalized control numbers we have employed previously do permit offsets, and then go on to show how to construct indices which do not confound changes. One such index does not require a knowledge of the actually operating inventory policies. At the end of the section we argue that a classical hypothesis testing approach, although incomplete in scope, may prove both workable and economically advantageous.

4.3.1 Single-Item System

For a given distribution $\phi(\xi)$, we postulate that top management can specify a preferred (s, S) policy. Because of the uncertainty about the demand distribution, top management sometimes selects an (s, S) policy differing from the preferred policy for the actual, but unknown, distribution $\phi(\xi)$. Thus, as additional demand information is collected, top management may be able to improve its currently adopted policy. How this goal is to be accomplished is the subject we now investigate.

Conceivably the distribution $\phi(\xi)$ might change in some fashion not predictable with certainty in each inventory review period. Without making some very special assumptions about the variations in $\phi(\xi)$, such as that they obey a cyclical or probabilistic pattern [Ka, KF, KI], it would be hopeless to attempt to use evolving statistical data in a precise manner for prediction purposes. We shall restrict our discussion below to the special case in which top management believes a single $\phi(\xi)$ is pertinent for several, say, N inventory review periods but is uncertain as to the precise specification of $\phi(\xi)$. Top management then must decide upon a statistical procedure which selects a set of periods $(t_1, t_2, \cdots, t_k)$, $k \leq N$, such that, in each period, the system data are summarized and an (s, S) policy is adopted, given the information presently available. The latter aspect might be subdivided into a decision whether to maintain the currently used (s, S) rule and, if not, a computation to determine a new stockage rule.

Two factors inhibit our providing a detailed discussion of the above statistical inference problem: (1) the subject matter of this monograph pertains primarily to top management's controlling an inventory system by means of aggregate statistical indices, as distinct from top management's providing rules for preferred stockage policies on an item-by-item basis; and (2) the problem of determining $\phi(\xi)$ in an economic fashion within the present context is sufficiently complex to require a separate monograph. But it will help in our understanding of the inherent difficulties associated with the problem of aggregate control, Sections 4.3.2 and 4.4, to outline briefly the difficulties encountered with this special problem.

A naive approach to the determination of $\phi(\xi)$ is to treat the situation as if it were a typical case of hypothesis testing or of statistical estimation [Cra, L] wherein at review periods $(t_1, t_2, \cdots, t_k)$ the parameters of $\phi(\xi)$ are estimated, or a hypothesis that the underlying demand distribution is $\phi_0(\xi)$ is accepted or rejected at some specified level of significance. Predicated on the parameter estimates, or on the acceptance of $\phi_0(\xi)$ or of some alternative distribution $\phi_1(\xi)$, an (s, S) policy is chosen for a number of future periods.

Operationally the procedure seems simple; but we would argue that the classical approaches of hypothesis testing and statistical estimation appear incomplete in providing criteria for the selection of the periods $(t_1, t_2, \cdots, t_k)$, for the precise utilization of the statistical estimates, and for the choice of a level of significance. A comprehensive statistical procedure should take explicit cognizance of the fact that the item is being stocked and demanded while statistical observations are being collected, and that, as a consequence, there are economic factors to be balanced against each other, such as the costs associated with maintaining an inappropriate (s, S) policy for several periods before and after data collection, with possibly revising the policy after the data collection has occurred, and with the data collection procedure itself. An alternative analytic approach outlined in the next paragraphs seems to reverse the advantages and disadvantages of the classical view; that is, the approach rationalizes the statistical procedure to be followed but is sufficiently involved to make a realization quite difficult.

The essence of a Bayes solution [L, Ch. 1; Sch] to the control problem is to enumerate in an efficient fashion the various statistical procedures potentially available, that is, the designation of the periods $(t_1, t_2, \cdots, t_k)$ in which the available data are to be summarized and of a rule for choosing an (s, S) policy given these data, and then to select a procedure which maximizes the expected economic worth.[7] To make the requisite expected

---

[7] This corresponds to the value $V^*(c)$ in Section 1.2.2.

worth calculation for any statistical procedure, top management first specifies its *a priori* beliefs about the actual demand distribution operating over the next N periods in terms of a probability distribution [Sch, CM, Sa].[8] Then for each possible $\phi(\xi)$ the associated conditional expected worth of the procedure is computed,[9] weighted by the *a priori* probability of $\phi(\xi)$, and summed with the other weighted conditional expected worths.

The expected worth conditional on a particular $\phi(\xi)$ is obtained by adding:

1. The conditional expected worth, using the starting (s, S) policy for the set of initial periods until the first data are summarized.

2. The conditional expected worth for the next set of periods until the data are again summarized. Here we must employ the rule which specifies which (s, S) policy is to be adopted, given an observed value of the statistic.[10] We comment on the selection of the statistic below.

3. Analogous to (2), the conditional expected worths for each succeeding set of periods.

4. The costs due to computing the statistics at periods $(t_1, t_2, \cdots, t_k)$.

The formal approach to finding optimal statistical procedures is well established [DKWo], but, at the present state of knowledge, it seems to require a sizeable number of computations. Only a few special results leading to economically optimal statistical decision procedures have been published to date [Kar, Sca]. The approach in these papers involves as elements a summarizing of the data in each inventory review period, utilizing the associated *a posteriori* probabilities [CM, Sch], accounting for the future variation in the statistical data, and prescribing a stockage policy for each period predicated on the current stock level and the statistical information presently available. An approximate or inexact method, which, although simplified in comparison with [Kar, Sca], is in itself somewhat difficult to apply, is to ignore the influence of future variation in the statistical data. Instead, an (s, S) policy is selected which is economically optimal solely with respect to the current *a posteriori* probabilities of the demand distribution $\phi(\xi)$ and the corresponding stationary probabilities of the inventory states.[11] We illustrate this suggestion by an example below.

[8] These correspond to $q_i{}^*$ in Section 1.2.2.

[9] This corresponds to $\overline{W}(N_i, c)$ in Section 1.2.2.

[10] Specifically, knowing the probability distribution of the statistic for the particular $\phi(\xi)$, we can derive the probability of selecting any (s, S) policy under the procedure being evaluated; this latter distribution corresponds to $p(a_j \mid N_i, c)$ in Section 1.2.2.

[11] To see how ignoring the influence of the future might make an effect, suppose what turns out to be an unusually large demand occurs. Determining (s, S) solely on the basis of the *a posteriori* probabilities, we may significantly raise both s and S and

Suppose the demand density is of the exponential type $\tau e^{-\tau \xi}$, and the inventory model and the economic function to be minimized in terms of the stationary probabilities is that given in Section 2.5.4[12] and Section 3.2.4,

[12] We omit the term $C_{pur}\mu$, since it is independent of (s, S).

$$E(\text{cost} \mid \mu) = C_{\text{fix}} \frac{\mu}{\mu + D} + \frac{C_{\text{in}}}{\mu + D} [\mu s - \mu^2 + \mu^2 e^{-\tau s} + .5 D(2s + D)]$$

$$- \frac{C_{\text{out}}}{\mu + D} [-\mu^2 e^{-\tau s}],$$

where $\mu = 1/\tau$. Letting p_i be the *a posteriori* probability that the demand density parameter is μ_i, where $\sum_i p_i = 1$, $p_i > 0$, the *a posteriori* expected cost is

$$\sum_i p_i E(\text{cost} \mid \mu_i).$$

Differentating this expression with respect to s and to D and setting the results equal to zero yield the following two equations in the unknowns s and D, the solutions of which provide the minimum expected cost policy:

$$\sum_i \frac{p_i \mu_i e^{-\tau_i s}}{\mu_i + D} = \frac{C_{\text{in}}}{C_{\text{in}} + C_{\text{out}}},$$

and

$$\sum_i p_i \left[\frac{C_{\text{in}} \mu_i}{\mu_i + D} + \frac{C_{\text{in}} D^2 - C_{\text{fix}} \mu_i}{2(\mu_i + D)^2} - \frac{(C_{\text{in}} + C_{\text{out}})\mu_i^2 e^{-\tau_i s}}{(\mu_i + D)^2} \right] = 0.$$

If $p_i = 1$ for $i = j$ and $p_i = 0$ otherwise, these expressions of course reduce to relations (1b) and (6) in Section 3.2.4 for that parameter μ_j.

We turn to the question of what data should be collected and how it should be utilized at each control period t. In a real situation, if specifying $\phi(\xi)$ is tantamount to estimating a parameter of the distribution and a sufficient statistic exists for this purpose, then such a statistic embodies all the usable information from the data [Cra, Ch. 32; L, Ch. 1]; that is, with regard to the data that have evolved, only the value of the sufficient statistic need be used in making the decision as to whether the currently employed (s, S) rule is to be maintained.[13] Although for general statistical problems we cannot expect to have sufficient statistics for estimating the probability

---

thereby order a large amount, incurring an ordering cost and possibly high inventory holding charges. If the influence of the future possibility of obtaining more data were taken into account, the revision of the current (s, S) policy might be more moderate and incur less total expense.

[13] Obviously there are the economic factors mentioned above that are pertinent to the decision.

distribution parameter values, we find that we do have sufficient estimators for many of the probability distributions utilized to describe demand patterns. In particular, there exist sufficient estimators of the parameters of Poisson, normal, uniform, binomial, negative binomial, and gamma distributions, as well as for truncated versions of these distributions [K]. Because of institutional reasons it may be more convenient to observe something other than a sufficient statistic, for example, the quantity of orders placed, the number of periods between orders, inventory on hand and backlogged, etc., the probability distributions of which we examined in Chapter 2. As elaborated below, the utilization of these alternative statistics is wasteful of information and, consequently, should be adopted only if corresponding savings accrue from their ready availability.

Because of the difficulties mentioned above in determining optimal statistical decision procedures, we are not able to perform calculations demonstrating the relative effectiveness of different statistics in terms of a complete economic model. But we can obtain some insight to the considerations involved by approaching the problem from a classical statistical inference point of view. Even adopting this approach entails overcoming difficulties, such as deriving the probability distribution of the statistics, and requires making strong assumptions such as to utilize the stationary probabilities of the inventory states. Since our discussion must necessarily be limited and, consequently, our results can only be tentative, we have elected to pose the problem in terms of hypothesis testing[14] and to assume that a sufficient number of periods of data have been collected so that the distributions of the statistics are well approximated by a normal distribution, a property we explored in Section 2.7. In other words, our comparisons are predicated on the asymptotic or large sample properties of the statistics. Almost needless to say, in actual inventory problems the amount of available data usually is not extensive. Nevertheless, for the purpose at hand, the asymptotic analysis will be instructive in highlighting how the degree of statistical accuracy depends on the particular statistic employed.

Our illustrative situation will accord with testing a simple hypothesis against a simple alternative. Specifically we shall assume that top management must decide by statistical data whether demand $\phi(\xi)$ is to be described by a Poisson distribution with mean equal to 1 or with mean equal to 2. Consequently, we may employ the fundamental Neyman-Pearson lemma [L, Ch. 3], so that the procedure to be followed is to select a critical value K and to decide that the Poisson mean is 1 if the statistic falls below K, and

---

[14] Characterizing the problem as one of parameter estimation is a more appealing alternative to the one we have chosen, but the analysis would require deriving a way to transform the statistic value into a parameter estimate. This would carry us too far afield for the intended scope of the discussion.

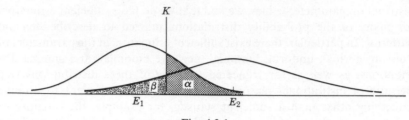

Fig. 4.3.1.

that the mean is 2 otherwise.[15] Making use of our normal distribution assumption, we sketch in Fig. 4.3.1 the distributions of a particular statistic when the Poisson mean is 1 and 2.

The area α of the right-hand tail of the distribution on the left is the probability that top management declares a mean equal to 2 when it is really 1, and the area β of the left-hand tail of the distribution on the right is the probability that top management declares a mean equal to 1 when it is really 2. To give an indication of which of two statistics makes better use of the data available, we shall set K so that the areas of the right-hand tails of the E_1 distributions for each statistic are equal; given our assumption as to the use of a normal distribution, we calculate K as a specified number of standard deviations above the mean of an E_1 distribution. Then a comparison is made by viewing the corresponding areas of the left-hand tails of the E_2 distribution for each statistic. The statistic having the smaller left-hand tail is said to make better use of the data available. This comparison may be characterized in the following algebraic manner. For a given statistic, let the couples (E_1, V_1) and (E_2, V_2) represent the mean and variance of the statistic's distribution when the Poisson mean is 1 and 2, respectively. For an alternative statistic, let (E_1', V_1') and (E_2', V_2') be the corresponding set. Determining an area $\alpha(<.5)$ for the right-hand tail is equivalent to selecting a value of k_α to be employed in the formulas below [BL, Ch. 3].

If

(I) $$\frac{E_1 - E_2 + k_\alpha\sqrt{V_1}}{\sqrt{V_2}} < \frac{E_1' - E_2' + k_\alpha\sqrt{V_1'}}{\sqrt{V_2'}},$$

we say the first statistic makes better use of the data, or, alternatively, the first statistic has more accuracy, or contains more information than the second.[16]

---

[15] For all the statistics we investigate, the expected value of the statistic when the mean is 1 is less than the expected value of the statistic when the mean is 2.

[16] The relation (I) may be derived as follows. In each case the critical values of K are $E_1 + k_\alpha\sqrt{V_1}$ and $E_1' + k_\alpha\sqrt{V_1'}$. The distance k_β of the critical number from

In our first example, we suppose backlogging occurs and that top management knows with certainty that the actual operating stockage policy is $(S - 1, S)$, that is, $D = 1$. We have from Section 2.2.4 that the stationary probabilities are $p_X(S - x) = \phi(x)$, and, therefore, in this example the influence of imbedding the inference problem in an inventory situation is minimal. From Section 2.7.1, we have that for any $h(j)$ defined on the states X and any value of T, $\mathrm{Var}\left[\dfrac{\sum h(j)}{T}\right] = \dfrac{1}{T}\mathrm{Var}[h(j)]$. One implication of these conclusions is that, for this example, our numerical analysis applies equally to the cases of T consecutive or sampled sums of $h(j)$. In our illustration, the values of $\phi(x)$ may be found in Section 2.4.5, Tables 2.4.1 and 2.4.2. We compare five statistics in Table 4.3.1.

TABLE 4.3.1

$$\frac{E_1 - E_2 + k \ \sqrt{V_1}}{\sqrt{V_2}}$$

Statistic	$k_{.30} = .524$			$k_{.10} = 1.282$			$k_{.01} = 2.326$		
	$T = 100$	$T = 900$	$T = 2500$	$T = 100$	$T = 900$	$T = 2500$	$T = 100$	$T = 900$	$T = 2500$
1	-6.70	-20.84	-34.99	-6.16	-20.31	-34.45	-5.43	-19.57	-33.71
2	-5.15	-15.66	-26.16	-5.01	-15.52	-26.02	-4.82	-15.32	-25.83
3	-3.95	-12.27	-20.58	-3.65	-11.96	-20.28	-3.23	-11.55	-19.86
4	-1.55	$- 5.20$	$- 8.84$	-1.17	$- 4.81$	$- 8.46$	-0.63	$- 4.28$	$- 7.92$
5	-2.31	$- 7.31$	-12.31	-2.05	$- 7.05$	-12.05	-1.68	$- 6.68$	-11.68

Statistic 1. Arithmetic mean.
Statistic 2. Average sum of squares.
Statistic 3. Average control number for which (1, 2) policy is rationalized, given Poisson, mean = 1.
Statistic 4. Average control number for which Poisson, mean = 1, is rationalized given (1, 2) policy.
Statistic 5. Rationalize Poisson, mean = 1, with Average $(\xi - 1.5)^2$.

The first is the average amount of demand occurring in T periods

(1)
$$\frac{\sum\limits_{T} \xi_t}{T},$$

which is a sufficient statistic for the Poisson parameter. As we mentioned above, we know from the theory of mathematical statistics that this approach will give the best result according to criterion (I) above. Since the policy is $(S - 1, S)$, this statistic is also the accumulated amount ordered if the T periods are consecutive. The two sets of mean and variance are $(1, 1/T)$, and $(2, 2/T)$ for a Poisson distribution with mean 1 and with mean 2, respectively.

---

the means E_2 and E_2' in terms of the statistic's associated standard deviation is given in the formula above . The smaller (algebraically) that k_β is, the smaller is the area β of the left-hand tail area.

The second is the statistic

(2)
$$\frac{\sum_T \xi_t^2}{T}.$$

By squaring each observation, we have attempted to distinguish between an underlying Poisson distribution with mean 1 and with mean 2 by greatly increasing the magnitude of the larger values of ξ—those occurring more often when the mean is 2. It can be shown that for any Poisson distribution with expectation τ, the mean and variance of this statistic is $[\tau^2 + \tau, \tau(4\tau^2 + 6\tau + 1)/T]$; in our example, the two sets of mean and variance values are $(2, 11/T)$ and $(6, 58/T)$.

The third statistic we investigate is obtained by a rationalizing procedure, exactly analogous to that in Sections 3.2.2 and 3.2.3. Specifically, we let

$$\text{control number} = \begin{array}{ll} C_{in}x & s + 1 \leq x \leq S \\ C_{fix} + C_{in}x & 0 \leq x \leq s \\ C_{fix} - C_{out}x & x < 0; \end{array}$$

then we have the relation

$$E(\text{control number}) = C_{fix} \sum_{x=-\infty}^{s} p_X(x) + C_{in} \sum_{x=1}^{S} x p_X(x) - C_{out} \sum_{x=-\infty}^{0} x p_X(x).$$

As usual, we normalize $C_{in} = 1$; we let $C_{fix} = 0$, since $S = s + 1$. In Section 3.2.3 we discussed finding values for C_{fix}, C_{in}, and C_{out} such that, for the given (s, S) policy and a particular $\phi(\xi)$, the value of E(control number) is smaller than for any other (s, S) policy. Here we let $\phi(\xi)$ be the Poisson distribution with mean 1, and assume the inventory policy to be $(1, 2)$. From relation (2) in Section 3.2.3, we have the constraint

$$\frac{1 - .2642}{.2642} \leq C_{out} \leq \frac{1 - .0803}{.0803}$$

which yields

$$2.79 \leq C_{out} \leq 11.45.$$

We pick $C_{out} = 10$. Our statistic is

(3)
$$\frac{\sum_T \text{control number}}{T} \qquad \begin{array}{l} \textit{control number rationalizes } (1,2) \\ \textit{policy with Poisson, mean} = 1. \end{array}$$

The two sets of mean and variance are $(2.14, 13.35/T)$ and $(5.94, 83.65/T)$. We compute these numbers by evaluating E(control number) above and similarly E(control number)^2; then we employ the relations

$$\text{Var (control number)} = E(\text{control number})^2 - [E(\text{control number})]^2$$

$$\text{Var}\left(\frac{\sum\limits_{T}\text{control number}}{T}\right) = \frac{1}{T}\text{Var (control number)}.$$

The fourth statistic is constructed by a somewhat different rationalizing procedure, again with the policy assumed to be (1, 2). In this instance, we let $C_{in} = 1$, $C_{fix} = 0$, as we did previously, and find a value for C_{out} such that $E(\text{control number})$ is smaller when the Poisson mean is 1 than when it is 2. This yields

$$1.1037 + C_{out}(.1037) < .5413 + C_{out}(.5403)$$

$$C_{out} > 1.29,$$

and we pick $C_{out} = 2$. Our statistic is

(4) $\qquad \dfrac{\sum\limits_{T}\text{control number}}{T} \qquad$ *control number rationalizes Poisson, mean = 1, with (1, 2) policy.*

The two sets of mean and variance are $(1.31, .76/T)$ and $(1.62, 2.91/T)$, which are computed in the same manner as for the third statistic above.

The rationalizing procedures employed in the third and fourth statistics require knowing the actual operating (s, S) policy. In forming the next statistic, a similar rationalization operation is followed but the result is independent of the actually employed (s, S) policy; it, like the first two statistics, utilizes only the emergent demands. We consider the statistical variable $(\xi - c)^2$, where c is a constant to be determined below. From the theory of mathematical statistics [Cra, Ch. 15] we know

(5) $\qquad E(\xi - c)^2 = E(\xi - \tau)^2 + (\tau - c)^2 = \text{Var}(\xi) + (\tau - c)^2,$

with $\tau \equiv E(\xi)$. We wish to select the constant c so that (5) is a minimum if the hypothesized value of the parameter is correct, that is, when the system is in control. In the case of a Poisson distribution, we have

(6) $\qquad E(\xi - c)^2 = \tau + (\tau - c)^2 \quad$ *Poisson, parameter τ.*

Differentiating (6) with respect to the parameter τ, setting the result equal to zero, and solving for c in terms of the hypothesized value of τ yields the proper value for c

(7) $\qquad c = \bar\tau + .5.$

The variance of this control number $(\xi - c)^2$ may be obtained through the following relations. Let $y = (\xi - c)^2$; then

(8a) $\qquad \text{Var}(y) = E(y^2) - [E(y)]^2,$

where

(8b) $E(y^2) = E(\xi - \mu)^4 + 4(\mu - c)E(\xi - \mu)^3 + 6(\mu - c)^2 \text{Var}(\xi) + (\mu - c)^4.$

For the Poisson distribution, we have

(9a) $E(y^2) = (\tau + 3\tau^2) + 4(\tau - c)\tau + 6(\tau - c)^2\tau + (\tau - c)^4,$

and

(9b) $\text{Var}(y) = \tau + 2\tau^2 + 4\tau(\tau - c) + 4\tau(\tau - c)^2.$

In our example, corresponding to the Poisson distribution with mean 1, we let $\bar\tau = 1$, so that $c = 1.5$. Our statistic is

(10) $\dfrac{\sum\limits_{T} (\xi_t - 1.5)^2}{T}$ *control number* $(\xi - c)^2$ *rationalizing Poisson, mean* $= 1$.

The two sets of mean and variance are $(5/4, 2/T)$ and $(9/4, 16/T)$, which are calculated from (6) and (9), and the relation

$$\text{Var}\left[\frac{\sum\limits_{T}(\xi_i - c)^2}{T}\right] = \frac{1}{T}\text{Var}(\xi - c)^2.$$

In Table 4.3.1 we have used three values for k_α, namely, one for $\alpha = .30$, .10, and .01, and three values for T. According to our criterion (I) above, the ordering of the statistics from best to worst is the arithmetic mean, the average sum of squares, the average control number when policy (1, 2) is rationalized, the average $(\xi - c)^2$ for c rationalizing a Poisson distribution with mean $= 1$, and the average control number when Poisson distribution with mean $= 1$ is rationalized.

In our second example, where we continue to test for a Poisson distribution either with mean 1 or with mean 2, we suppose backlogging occurs and the stockage policy is $(S - 3, S)$. The appropriate values for $p_X(x)$ are exhibited in Section 2.4.5, Tables 2.4.1 and 2.4.2. In Table 4.3.2 we examine three statistics under two different assumptions as to the collection of data. Assumption S is that the data are from T sampled periods, in the sense of Section 2.7.6; consequently we may use $p_X(x)$ directly. Assumption C is that the data are from T consecutive periods; here we must employ the analysis in Section 2.7.1, and the relevant $\{[I] - [M] + [P^*]\}$, $[\tau_{jj'}]$, and $[c_{jj'}]$ matrices appear in Section 3.4.1, Table 3.4.2, and in this section, Tables 4.3.3a–c.

The first statistic is average demand

(11)

TABLE 4.3.2

$$\frac{E_1 - E_2 + k_\alpha \sqrt{V_1}}{\sqrt{V_2}}$$

Stat.	Assmptn.	$k_{.30} = .524$			$k_{.10} = 1.282$			$k_{.01} = 2.326$		
		$T = 100$	$T = 900$	$T = 2500$	$T = 100$	$T = 900$	$T = 2500$	$T = 100$	$T = 900$	$T = 2500$
1	S	−6.70	−20.84	−34.99	−6.16	−20.31	−34.45	−5.43	−19.57	−33.71
	C	−6.70	−20.84	−34.99	−6.16	−20.31	−34.45	−5.43	−19.57	−33.71
2	S	−4.25	−13.55	−22.84	−3.68	−12.97	−22.27	−2.88	−12.18	−21.48
	C	−6.70	−20.84	−34.99	−6.16	−20.31	−34.45	−5.43	−19.57	−33.71
3	S	−4.61	−14.67	−24.73	−4.01	−14.07	−24.13	−3.18	−13.24	−23.30
	C	−5.90	−18.61	−31.33	−5.23	−17.95	−30.66	−4.32	−17.03	−29.75

S: sampled periods of data.
C: consecutive periods of data.
Statistic 1. Arithmetic mean.
Statistic 2. Average accumulated purchases.
Statistic 3. Average $(S - x)$.

TABLE 4.3.3a

Poisson $E(\xi) = 2$ (Table 2.4.1)

Backlog $D = 3$

$$\{[I] - [M] + [P^*]\}$$

.9432	−.0891	−.0323	.0379	.0594	.0442	.0230	.0094	.0032	.0009	.0002
.0785	1.0463	−.0323	−.0524	−.0308	−.0099	−.0011	.0008	.0006	.0003	.0000
.0785	.1816	1.1031	−.0524	−.1211	−.1001	−.0552	−.0233	−.0080	−.0023	−.0008
−.0568	−.0891	−.0323	1.0379	.0594	.0442	.0230	.0094	.0032	.0009	.0002
−.0568	−.0891	−.0323	.0379	1.0594	.0442	.0230	.0094	.0032	.0009	.0002
−.0568	−.0891	−.0323	.0379	.0594	1.0442	.0230	.0094	.0032	.0009	.0002
−.0568	−.0891	−.0323	.0379	.0594	.0442	1.0230	.0094	.0032	.0009	.0002
−.0568	−.0891	−.0323	.0379	.0594	.0442	.0230	1.0094	.0032	.0009	.0002
−.0568	−.0891	−.0323	.0379	.0594	.0442	.0230	.0094	1.0032	.0009	.0002
−.0568	−.0891	−.0323	.0379	.0594	.0442	.0230	.0094	.0032	1.0009	.0002
−.0568	−.0891	−.0323	.0379	.0594	.0442	.0230	.0094	.0032	.0009	1.0002

TABLE 4.3.3b

Poisson $E(\xi) = 2$ (Table 2.4.1)

Backlog $D = 3$

$$[\tau_{jj'}]$$

1.0432	.0716	.0284	−.0288	−.0477	−.0362	−.0190	−.0078	−.0026	−.0007	−.0001
−.0759	.9524	.0284	.0506	.0316	.0114	.0021	−.0002	−.0004	−.0002	.0000
−.0475	−.1382	.9091	.0317	.0922	.0795	.0447	.0191	.0066	.0019	.0006
.0432	.0716	.0284	.9711	−.0477	−.0362	−.0190	−.0078	−.0026	−.0007	−.0001
.0432	.0716	.0284	−.0288	.9522	−.0362	−.0190	−.0078	−.0026	−.0007	−.0001
.0432	.0716	.0284	−.0288	−.0477	.9637	−.0190	−.0078	−.0026	−.0007	−.0001
.0432	.0716	.0284	−.0288	−.0477	−.0362	.9809	−.0078	−.0026	−.0007	−.0001
.0432	.0716	.0284	−.0288	−.0477	−.0362	−.0190	.9921	−.0026	−.0007	−.0001
.0432	.0716	.0284	−.0288	−.0477	−.0362	−.0190	−.0078	.9973	−.0007	−.0001
.0432	.0716	.0284	−.0288	−.0477	−.0362	−.0190	−.0078	−.0026	.9992	−.0001
.0432	.0716	.0284	−.0288	−.0477	−.0362	−.0190	−.0078	−.0026	−.0007	.9998

TABLE 4.3.3c

Poisson $E(\xi) = 2$ (Table 2.4.1)

Backlog $D = 3$

$[c_{jj'}]$

.0791	−.0224	−.0278	−.0099	−.0090	−.0056	−.0027	−.0010	−.0003	−.0000	−.0000
−.0224	.1313	−.0710	−.0147	−.0106	−.0067	−.0034	−.0014	−.0005	−.0001	−.0000
−.0278	−.0710	.1382	−.0382	−.0094	.0020	.0033	.0018	.0007	.0002	.0000
−.0099	−.0147	−.0382	.1580	−.0474	−.0277	−.0128	−.0048	−.0015	−.0004	−.0001
−.0090	−.0106	−.0094	−.0474	.1129	−.0212	−.0097	−.0037	−.0011	−.0003	−.0001
−.0056	−.0067	.0020	−.0277	−.0212	.0680	−.0056	−.0021	−.0006	−.0001	−.0000
−.0027	−.0034	.0033	−.0128	−.0097	−.0056	.0324	−.0009	−.0003	−.0000	−.0000
−.0010	−.0014	.0018	−.0048	−.0037	−.0021	−.0009	.0124	−.0001	−.0000	−.0000
−.0003	−.0005	.0007	−.0015	−.0011	−.0006	−.0003	−.0001	.0039	−.0000	−.0000
−.0000	−.0001	.0002	−.0004	−.0003	−.0001	−.0000	−.0000	−.0000	.0010	.0000
−.0000	−.0000	.0000	−.0001	−.0001	−.0000	−.0000	−.0000	−.0000	.0000	.0004

and as in the first example, the two sets of the mean and variance are $(1, 1/T)$ and $(2, 2/T)$ for both Assumptions S and C.

The second statistic is

(12)
$$\frac{\sum_T \text{purchase}}{T},$$

that is, accumulated purchases divided by T, Section 2.7.4. Here the two sets of mean and variance are $(1, 2.66/T)$ and $(2, 4.63/T)$ for Assumption S, and as T grows large $(1, 1/T)$ and $(2, 2/T)$ for Assumption C. To compute the mean, for both Assumptions S and C we employ the results in Section 2.5.1. To compute the variance, for Assumption S we calculate

$$E(\text{purchase})^2 = \sum_{x=-\infty}^{S} (\text{purchase amount} \mid x)^2 p_X(x)$$

$$= \sum_{x=-\infty}^{s} (S - x)^2 p_X(x)$$

$$\text{Var}\left(\frac{\sum \text{purchase}}{T}\right) = \frac{1}{T} \text{Var (purchase)}$$

$$= \frac{1}{T} \{E(\text{purchase})^2 - [E(\text{purchase})]^2\},$$

and for Assumption C we let $h(j)$ be defined as in Section 2.7.4 and calculate the relation (2) in Section 2.7.1.

The third statistic is defined on the states X

(13)
$$\frac{\sum_T (S - x)}{T},$$

that is, it is based on the number of units that stock on hand (backlogged) and on order falls below the value S. The two sets of mean and variance are $(1.83, 1.71/T)$ and $(2.66, 2.70/T)$ for Assumption S, and, as T grows large, $(1.83, 1.30/T)$ and $(2.66, 1.69/T)$ for Assumption C. For Assumption S, we employ the relations

$$E\left[\frac{\sum (S - x)}{T}\right] = E(S - x) = \sum_{x=-\infty}^{S} (S - x)p_X(x)$$

$$E(S - x)^2 = \sum_{x=-\infty}^{S} (S - x)^2 p_X(x)$$

$$\mathrm{Var}\left[\frac{\sum (S - x)}{T}\right] = \frac{1}{T}\mathrm{Var}\,(S - x) = \frac{1}{T}\{E(S - x)^2 - [E(S - x)]^2\},$$

and for Assumption C, we employ $E(S - x)$ above and relation (2) in Section 2.7.1, where $h(x) = S - x$.

As in the previous comparison, we examine three values for k_α and for T in Table 4.3.2. We notice that for any k_α and T, the second and third statistics when based on data for T consecutive periods provide more information than when they are based on data for T sampled periods. Since demand is assumed independent from one inventory review period to the next, equal statistical accuracy occurs when the data are collected either from T consecutive or sampled periods if the arithmetic mean of the observations is utilized. If the data are collected over consecutive periods, then, asymptotically, the arithmetic mean and average accumulated purchases provide the same amount of information[17] and more than that provided by the average $(S - x)$. In contrast, if the data are collected from sampled periods, then the statistic average $(S - x)$ performs better than average accumulated purchases, but, of course, not so well as the sufficient statistic the arithmetic mean.

We now summarize the foregoing discussion. Hopefully future research will evolve optimal decision procedures that combine the problem of statistical inference with that of selecting a prescribed inventory rule. In the meantime, so-called classical statistical approaches can be utilized, recognizing their deficiences in solving the entire economic problem and, in some cases, so can an intermediate approach employing *a posteriori* probabilities. Whenever it is possible to utilize a sufficient statistic to determine $\phi(\xi)$, such a method will ensure that maximum use is being made of the data available. But alternative statistics of the sample average type, which, in some actual situations, may be more easily obtainable, can be

[17] This result can be argued from the observation that, as T grows large, the values of accumulated purchases and accumulated demand over T consecutive periods are nearly identical.

employed with a corresponding loss in statistical accuracy. In choosing between data from T sampled or consecutive periods, the latter approach appears to provide more information when the statistic is defined according to the states of the inventory system.

4.3.2   Multi-Item System

We now explore the multi-item case, which is a generalization of the problem in Section 4.3.1. In our discussion to follow, we retain the assumption as to the stability of every $\phi_i(\xi)$ for N consecutive inventory review periods, and as in the preceding section, we conduct the analysis in terms of hypothesis testing. Specifically, top management is assumed to be interested in whether, for each item i, the demand distribution obeys a specified law $\phi_i(\xi)$. In other words, top management is said to believe, at the same time it selects the current set of (s, S) policies, that the probability distribution for item i is $\phi_i(\xi)$. As time elapses and data accumulate, top management wishes to know whether its initial assumption holds, and if not, wishes to make a general revision of the set of (s, S) rules. In real situations of this sort, it is usually too costly to make this general revision as compared to maintaining the current rules, unless many of the actual demand distributions deviate significantly from the assumed $\phi_i(\xi)$. What we explore is the possibility of constructing a statistic suitable for the purpose of signalling top management whenever the assumptions about $\phi_i(\xi)$ are violated.

Of course an obvious approach to this problem is to conduct a hypothesis test for each item, as in Section 4.3.1, and then to count the proportion of items for which the null hypothesis is rejected. If this proportion is significantly high, a general revision is instituted. Although in this situation the decision of whether to make a large scale overhaul of stockage rules does eventually depend on an aggregate statistic, the underlying basis of the approach is really an item-by-item analysis. We focus the remainder of our attention on devising index controls wherein statistical inference is carried out only at the aggregate stage.

As we discussed in Section 1.2, the essential elements to be considered in a system design analysis are an enumeration of possible system situations, the courses of action available to top management, the economic consequences of taking such actions when any one of the possible situations occurs, and the statistical devices which can aid top management in making economically advantageous decisions. In this instance, the conceivable system situations can be defined as a vector of demand distributions of the specified $\phi_i(\xi)$, one for each item i. But, as with the analogous suggestion in Section 3.4.1, it is unlikely that this characterization yields meaningful results for large-scale inventory systems. As an alternative, we shall adopt a dichotomous characterization, namely, statements as to the presence or absence of the condition that, for all i, the demand distributions obey the specified laws $\phi_i(\xi)$. As we have mentioned, management's decisions are, based in large measure on the index value, whether or not to make a complete system review of the recommended (s, S) inventory rules.

It follows from the nature of the above definitions of situations and actions that we are involved with testing composite statistical hypotheses [Cra, K, L], and furthermore, that the economic evaluation associated with a particular combination of a situation and action is not easily determined. The latter difficulty combines the complexities both of finding an economic evaluation even when precise details are known about the situation and action, and of resolving the apparent non-uniqueness of the evaluation due to the aggregate characterization of the situation and action.

Beyond these economic problems lie the mathematical difficulties of ascertaining the probability distribution of any statistic as a function of the aggregate situations. Our solution might be a conservative approach like that in Section 3.3.5, where we explored the notion of least favorable out-of-control situations. Finally, we are faced with complexities such as those outlined in the previous section, namely, the selection of a particular statistic and the periods for summarizations of the data. The rest of this section examines several of the detailed aspects of selecting a statistic and determining its probability distribution.

Suppose the uncertainty about each $\phi_i(\xi)$ can be stated in terms of uncertainty about $E(\xi_i)$, and that the system is said to be in-control when each $E(\xi_i)$ has the value associated with the $\phi_i(\xi)$ initially specified by top management. If it is true that two items ought to have the same (s, S) policy if they have the same purchase price $C_{\text{pur}(i)}$ and the same $E(\xi_i)$, then the statistical analysis presented in Section 4.2.2 is applicable. But in real situations this condition is likely to be the exception rather than the rule. If, for example, top management selects its recommendation for an (s, S) policy in the manner described in Section 3.2.4, then the penalty for being out of stock is also of importance, and this economic quantity may not be the same for both items. Further, for many probability distributions, specifying $E(\xi_i)$ is not tantamount to completely determining the probability distribution; the shapes of both distributions may vary and, as a result, so should the (s, S) policies. Consequently using the statistic

(1)
$$\frac{\sum\limits_T \sum\limits_i C_{\text{pur}(i)} \xi_{i,t}}{T},$$

which is suggested in Sections 4.2.1 and 4.2.2, and which is the natural generalization of

$$\frac{\sum_{T} \xi_t}{T}$$

in Section 4.3.1, means that if there are two items i and i' such that $C_{\text{pur}(i)} = C_{\text{pur}(i')}$ and $E(\xi_i) = E(\xi_{i'})$, then the two demand distributions $\phi_i(\xi)$ and $\phi_{i'}(\xi)$ can be interchanged and there will be no effect on the expected value of the aggregate statistic (1). In other words, changes in the specified $\phi_i(\xi)$ may have offsetting effects in (1).

Is it possible to design a control number for each item so that the expected value of the statistic

$$(2) \qquad \frac{\sum_{T} \sum_{i} w_i(\text{control number}_{i,t})}{T} \qquad w_i > 0$$

is a minimum only when each $\phi_i(\xi)$ is that which was initially specified by top management? The w_i represent weight factors chosen by top management to allow for the relative importance of the component items. With the exception of statistic (10) in Section 4.3.1, all the other statistics which we have investigated so far suffer from the possibility of their confounding changes that occur in several of the $\phi_i(\xi)$. To illustrate, we examine a control number rationalized as in Section 3.2.2 and employed as statistic (3) in Section 4.3.1. We use the example of the geometric distribution considered in Sections 3.2.4 and 3.3.2. Tables 4.3.4*a–d* show the values of $E(\text{control number})$ and $\text{Var}(\text{control number})$ for various values of μ. The examples in Tables 4.3.4*a–d* are selected optimal (s, S) policies appearing in Table 3.3.3. Notice the value of $E(\xi_i)$ could be increased for several i and decreased for others, possibly resulting in an offsetting effect on both the mean and variance of statistic (2) above.[18]

The control number $(\xi_i - c_i)^2$, which is statistic (10) in Section 4.3.1, is designed so that its expectation is a minimum only for the specified $\phi_i(\xi)$; consequently, utilizing this type of control number in (2) eliminates the problem of possible offsetting changes in the $\phi_i(\xi)$. In the previous section, we showed how to set c_i when $\phi_i(\xi)$ is a Poisson distribution. Other

---

[18] We comment here on the selection of an (s, S) policy according to a minimum cost criterion, an approach discussed in some detail in Sections 2.5.3 and 3.2.4. The one-sided sensitivity of the expectation and variance of the control number to changes in the value of μ, as exhibited in Table 4.3.4 and based on the model in Section 3.2.4, points up that it may be better for top management to overestimate average demand than to underestimate it in selecting an (s, S) rule.

TABLE 4.3.4.*a*

q	$C_{in} = 1$	$C_{fix} = 4$	$C_{out} = 100$	
	Rationalized policy for $q = .4$ (3, 5)		Rationalized policy for $q = .8$ (17, 22)	
	E(cont. no.)	Var(c.n.)	E(cont. no.)	Var(c.n.)
.4	6.04	246.73	20.04	1.90
.5	9.21	1225.08	20.00	2.03
.6	18.95	5332.99	19.89	4.60
.8	141.40	104,003.48	22.71	3479.79
.9	541.36	731,183.82	112.31	171,771.30
.95	1478.18	3,574,884.8	640.96	2,047,190.5
.97	2783.27	10,524,918.0	1678.04	8,154,092.7
.98	4435.12	24,231,937.0	3161.84	21,251,279.0
.99	9419.81	98,715,756.0	7950.08	94,944,062.0

TABLE 4.3.4*b*

q	$C_{in} = 1$	$C_{fix} = 100$	$C_{out} = 100$	
	Rationalized policy for $q = .4$ (1, 13)		Rationalized policy for $q = .8$ (11, 39)	
	E(cont. no.)	Var(c.n.)	E(cont. no.)	Var(c.n.)
.4	13.80	1014.89	24.47	227.26
.5	18.50	2420.71	28.42	301.54
.6	27.82	6406.56	29.80	417.65
.8	110.68	78,312.22	40.03	5190.32
.9	394.33	577,838.24	113.49	134,605.52
.95	1170.51	3,171,848.2	493.64	1,552,261.9
.97	2362.39	9,904,532.9	1306.85	6,687,668.5
.98	3939.16	23,450,222.0	2570.52	18,617,148.0
.99	8831.44	97,717,366.0	6993.69	89,979,668.0

TABLE 4.3.4c

q	$C_{in} = 1$		$C_{fix} = 4$		$C_{out} = 30$	
	Rationalized policy for $q = .4$ (2, 4)		Rationalized policy for $q = .8$ (11, 16)		Rationalized policy for $q = .97$ (100, 114)	
	E(cont. no.)	Var(c.n.)	E(cont. no.)	Var(c.n.)	E(cont. no.)	Var(c.n.)
.4	4.78	56.42	14.04	1.91	107.31	16.32
.5	6.58	219.41	14.00	2.17	107.20	16.56
.6	11.10	783.77	13.92	6.19	107.02	17.23
.8	54.41	11,182.16	17.40	1,143.33	105.83	26.81
.9	183.08	69,923.60	65.00	27,371.17	102.61	83.35
.95	469.52	327,848.94	264.98	232,235.33	96.55	2,252.51
.97	863.56	954,382.72	607.81	819,245.04	115.76	58,040.86
.98	1,360.46	2,188,591.9	1,074.13	2,027,048.8	223.35	408,034.34
.99	2,857.27	8,892,759.1	2,536.40	8,698,890.9	1,001.88	4,693,930.4

TABLE 4.3.4d

q	$C_{in} = 1$		$C_{fix} = 100$		$C_{out} = 30$	
	Rationalized policy for $q = .4$ (0, 12)		Rationalized policy for $q = .8$ (6, 34)		Rationalized policy for $q = .97$ (71, 151)	
	E(cont. no.)	Var(c.n.)	E(cont. no.)	Var(c.n.)	E(cont. no.)	Var(c.n.)
.4	12.47	706.25	22.47	227.67	111.99	557.22
.5	16.00	1,232.46	23.43	304.81	112.22	568.42
.6	21.89	2,280.14	24.88	432.04	112.57	584.28
.8	59.88	13,055.61	34.75	2,393.35	114.14	648.50
.9	162.29	67,080.01	75.17	24,112.50	116.62	728.48
.95	413.16	314,063.90	222.41	187,000.01	122.23	3,985.48
.97	782.14	930,724.66	496.43	698,829.90	152.50	61,653.82
.98	1,262.43	2,157,522.6	900.01	1,823,435.5	252.96	372,813.37
.99	2,738.81	8,851,670.8	2,262.35	8,338,548.7	921.18	4,130,623.2

examples are

(3a) $E(\xi - c)^2 = \sigma^2 + (\mu - c)^2$ *normal, parameter μ; (σ^2 given)*

(3b) $E(\xi - c)^2 = \dfrac{r(1 - p)}{p^2} + \left[\dfrac{r(1 - p)}{p} - c\right]^2$

negative binomial, parameter p; (r given)

(3c) $E(\xi - c)^2 = \dfrac{k}{\tau^2} + \left(\dfrac{k}{\tau} - c\right)^2$ *gamma, parameter τ; (k given).*

Differentiating (3) with respect to the parameter, setting the result equal to zero, and solving for c in terms of the hypothesized value of the parameter, yields the proper values for c:

(4a) $c = \bar{\mu}$ *normal*

(4b) $c = \dfrac{2r(1 - \bar{p}) + 1}{2\bar{p}}$ *negative binomial*

(4c) $c = \dfrac{1 + k}{\bar{\tau}}$ *gamma.*

The variance of the index (2) is

$$\frac{\sum_i w_i^2 \, \text{Var(control number}_i)}{T}$$

where $\text{Var(control number}_i)$ is computed from relation (8) in Section 4.3.1.

As we pointed out in Section 4.3.1, this statistic utilizes only emergent demand and does not entail a knowledge of the actual (s, S) policies being employed. If top management does have knowledge of this type, then it is possible as we demonstrate next, to design other control numbers having the desired property of a minimum expectation for (2).

Our approach, if the (s, S) policies are known, is to utilize control numbers similar to (2) and (3) in Section 3.2.2. Without loss of generality, we let $C_{in} = 1$ and seek a value of C_{out}; since we are rationalizing against changes in a single parameter, we may let $C_{fix} = 0$.[19] Two examples will illustrate the procedure.

First, consider the backlog model where we employ

$$\text{control number} = x \qquad\qquad 0 \le x \le S$$
$$-C_{out}x \qquad x < 0,$$

and assume the exponential density $\tau e^{-\tau \xi}$ for a particular parameter value $\bar{\tau}$ is the demand distribution. Then, analogously to our procedure in Section 3.2.4, we find C_{out} such that for our given (s, S) policy

(5) $\dfrac{1}{\mu + D}\left[\mu s - \mu^2 + \mu^2 e^{-\tau s} + \dfrac{D(2s + D)}{2}\right] - \dfrac{C_{out}}{\mu + D}\left[-\mu^2 e^{-\tau s}\right]$

is a minimum at

$$\bar{\tau} = 1/\bar{\mu}.$$

Differentiating (5) with respect to μ, setting the result equal to zero, and solving for C_{out}, we arrive at the relation

$$C_{out} = \left[\frac{(D + \bar{\mu})^2 - .5D^2}{(e^{-\tau s})(\bar{\mu}^2 + \bar{\mu}s + 2\bar{\mu}D + sD)}\right] - 1.$$

[19] Alternatively we could seek a value of C_{fix} and let $C_{out} = 0$. The choice above is appealing in that it requires measuring only the state X or V, and does not necessitate indicating when an order occurs.

At this value of C_{out}, the value of (5) is a minimum and equal to

$$(6) \qquad \frac{\bar{\mu}s^2 + .5(2\bar{\mu} + s)D(2s + D)}{\bar{\mu}^2 + \bar{\mu}s + 2\bar{\mu}D + sD}.$$

As a numerical example, the policy (11, 16) is rationalized with respect to $\mu = 4$, by $C_{in} = 1$ and $C_{out} = 5.91$,[20] and the value of (6) is 11.40. With this rationalization, the value of (5) at $\mu = 1$ is 12.92, at $\mu = 5$ is 11.66, and at $\mu = 11$ is 34.11.

Our second illustration will be a no-backlog example taken from the policy found in Section 2.4.9, Table 2.4.12. We define the control number as

$$\text{control number} = \begin{array}{ll} C_{in}v & 0 < v \leq S \\ C_{out} & v = 0. \end{array}$$

Letting $C_{in} = 1$, we seek such a value for C_{out} that the value of $E(v \mid \mu) + C_{out}\text{Prob(out} \mid \mu)$ is a minimum for the hypothesized value of $\mu \equiv E(\xi)$. Consider two other values for $E(\xi)$, say, μ_1 and μ_2, where $\mu_1 < \mu < \mu_2$. Then:

$$(7a) \quad E(v \mid \mu) + C_{out}\text{Prob(out} \mid \mu) < E(v \mid \mu_1) + C_{out}\text{Prob(out} \mid \mu_1),$$

and

$$(7b) \quad E(v \mid \mu) + C_{out}\text{Prob(out} \mid \mu) < E(v \mid \mu_2) + C_{out}\text{Prob(out} \mid \mu_2).$$

We assume that $E(v \mid \mu_1) > E(v \mid \mu) > E(v \mid \mu_2)$ and $\text{Prob(out} \mid \mu_1) < \text{Prob(out} \mid \mu) < \text{Prob(out} \mid \mu_2)$. Rearranging the terms in (7), we derive:

$$(8) \qquad \frac{E(v \mid \mu) - E(v \mid \mu_2)}{\text{Prob(out} \mid \mu_2) - \text{Prob(out} \mid \mu)}$$

$$< C_{out} < \frac{E(v \mid \mu_1) - E(v \mid \mu)}{\text{Prob(out} \mid \mu) - \text{Prob(out} \mid \mu_1)}.$$

We rationalize $\mu = 1$, and let $\mu_1 = .75$ and $\mu_2 = 2$ in (8); this yields

$$\frac{1.9173 - 1.3769}{.6566 - .4619} < C_{out} < \frac{2.2816 - 1.9173}{.4619 - .3448}$$

$$2.78 < C_{out} < 3.11;$$

consequently we choose[21] $C_{out} = 3$. For this rationalization, Table 4.3.5 exhibits the expectation of the control number for various values of μ.

---

[20] The numbers which rationalize the (11, 16) policy in the sense of Section 3.2.4 are $C_{in} = 1$, $C_{out} = 30$, and $C_{fix} = 4$, as is seen in Table 3.3.3.

[21] Of course, our choice may only be approximate since the upper and lower limits are calculated from values of μ not extremely close to $\mu = 1$.

TABLE 4.3.5

μ	E(control number) $=$ $E(v \mid \mu) + 3$ Prob(out $\mid \mu$)
.25	4.1811
.50	3.4718
.75	3.3160
1.00	3.3030
2.00	3.3467
4.00	3.4068
8.00	3.4627

In summary, designing and evaluating aggregate control schemes to determine demand distributions in a multi-item system involve all the difficulties associated with the statistical inference problem for a single-item system and several more. Specifically, it is necessary to determine the data summarization periods $(t_1, t_2, \cdots, t_k)$, define the system situations and management action rules, and select an index. As in Section 4.3.1, adopting a classical approach of hypothesis testing seems to neglect a number of economic considerations. Nevertheless, there is a workable simplicity attached to the procedure of testing a null hypothesis, which is predicated on management's specification of the $\phi_i(\xi)$, and possibly using a t-test [BL] in lieu of computing exact variances. Such an approach, of course, pays little attention to the error of accepting the null hypothesis when it is false. But if the statistic does not permit a confounding of several changes in the $\phi_i(\xi)$—we have demonstrated such indices exist—then there is much to be said for rejecting the null hypothesis only when the statistical evidence shows a significant deviation, for such a rejection can entail a fairly expensive review of the entire inventory system stockage policies.

One more point deserves mentioning in this connection. Throughout the monograph we have postulated that the distributions $\phi_i(\xi)$ are mutually independent. This does not preclude their parameters having a functional dependence. It may be that when $E(\xi)$ for one item increases, so does the corresponding expectation for other items. To the extent this is so, the aggregate statistic which does not permit confounding may improve in its ability to detect changes in the $\phi_i(\xi)$.[22]

[22] It is even possible to generalize some of our results to the case where the ξ_i are dependent. The rationalizing process, such as $(\xi_i - c_i)^2$, remains valid in that statistic (2) in this section still has a minimal expectation when each parameter τ_i is that which has been specified initially by management.

4.4   CONTROL OF STOCKAGE POLICIES

The two techniques we studied in Chapter 3 for the control of (s, S) policy decisions are barometer and quota controls. We emphasized determining whether they provided consistent mechanisms. We now extend the discussion for the situation where the $\phi_i(\xi)$ are not known with certainty. Specifically, in Section 3.2.2 we proposed a barometer scheme that rewards or penalizes lower management by the amount

(1) θ(index number $-$ target) $\theta > 0$,

where the target is set at the expected value of the index number computed under the assumptions that the recommended policies are being observed and the demand distributions are known. When the latter assumptions are in fact true, that is, when the system is in-control, the scheme is "fair" [Fe, Ch. 10] in that the expected payoff is zero. Two factors militate against a parallel target setting in the present situation: (1) The demand distributions are not known with certainty. (2) Top management most likely wants lower management to select (s, S) policies according to the current best estimates of the demand distributions in operation, rather than to follow a rigid set of stockage rules. The apparent differences between the situation in Chapter 3 and the present one seem significant, but recall that the factor in the previous barometer scheme leading to consistency is the beneficial effect of lower management's being motivated to minimize the index number, given that the target figure is a preset constant, Section 3.2.1. If we abandon the fairness property in a barometer control, we may be able to devise a consistent control mechanism, provided that we can construct such an index number that lower management, in minimizing the expected value of the index number, is in fact following top management's recommendations. Almost needless to say, the warnings in Section 3.2.1 against employing fragmentary indices are pertinent to the construction of the proper underlying control numbers.

An important example of such a suitable index arises when top management's stockage preferences are expressed in terms of a minimum expected cost criterion, as we have studied in Sections 2.5.3 and 3.2.4. Here top management specifies a set of economic parameters C_{fix}, C_{in}, and C_{out}, for each item and instructs lower management to adopt an (s, S) policy minimizing the expected value of the associated control number. In terms of stationary probability analysis, lower management in fact obtains a minimum expectation of the index number comprised of the various control numbers by adopting the recommended policies. Thus a barometer control scheme may operate as follows. Top management specifies a target figure; this may be fixed with reference to a likely set of distributions $\phi_i(\xi)$ and perhaps so as to make the expectation of (1) favorable to lower management if the assumed values of $\phi_i(\xi)$ occur and the corresponding preferred stockage rules are adopted. Whatever the setting of the target, lower management remains motivated to adopt policies which minimize the expectation of the index number. Since the demand distributions are not known with certainty, lower management faces the difficult statistical decision problem outlined in Section 4.3.1 above; as data emerge and the uncertainty about the demand distributions decreases, the consistency property strongly motivates lower management to follow the preferred policies.

In contrast to the foregoing results pertaining to a barometer control, the conclusion stemming from an examination of our previously considered quota control scheme, based on rationalized control numbers, is that its asymptotic consistency property is relinquished. Recall we found in Section 3.3.3 that if the demand distributions are known, it is possible to design a quota device that at least will be consistent if the number T of review periods of observation is sufficiently large. The idea underlying the analysis was that with sufficient data, the probability distributions of the control number for two different (s, S) policies could be distinguished, and with a quota upon the arithmetic average of an index comprised of rationalized control numbers, lower management's objective would be better met if the recommended policies were followed. One detail of the analysis is that, as T becomes large, it is possible to find a consistent quota despite the fact that the variance of the distribution of the index may be larger when the recommended policies are being followed than when the policies are being violated.

We have seen certain evidence of this effect on variances in Section 3.3.2, Table 3.3.3. Consider as the index number the same one that we discussed above for a barometer scheme and impose a quota, say, on the average of this index value over T periods. Because of the difficulty created by variances being altered when changes in $E(\xi_i)$ occur, we cannot conclude the situation is consistent for an arbitrary value of the quota. In other words, the positive conclusion of Section 3.3.3 depends in an essential way on setting the quota with knowledge of the demand distribution and the associated index number distribution when the system is in-control.

The impediment to finding a consistent quota scheme in the present situation may be mitigated to the extent that the variance of the distribution of the index number averaged over T periods is insensitive to actual changes in the demand distributions and stockage policies observed, and insofar as we can use a normal distribution with a fixed variance as an adequate approximation. Given these assumptions about the probability distribution of the index number, lower management is encouraged to adopt recommended policies. This result follows in part from the preceding analysis of the motivation involved in a barometer scheme, namely, a desire to adopt minimum expected cost (s, S) policies, and in part from the observation that lowering the expected value of a normal distribution shifts the entire distribution toward lower values of the random variable, so that the probability of remaining under an arbitrarily set quota is a maximum when the expected value of the index is a minimum.

As we explored in detail in Section 3.4.3, consistency is not the sole consideration in evaluating a control scheme, and we ask the reader to review that section since much of what is said there is equally applicable to the present case. Of particular importance is our previous conclusion that, for several reasons, it may be nearly impossible in real situations to impose a consistent control scheme. When uncertainty as to the actual $\phi_i(\xi)$ is introduced, we must add the observation that the control problem becomes even more complex because the mechanism for determining the preferred (s, S) policies, given available historical information, is difficult by itself, the opportunity for lower management to cause the system to go out-of-control thereby increases, and the constructs embodied in the control model of Section 1.2 are harder to define since the dimension of system situations and management actions increases. But, as always, a decision to employ a particular control scheme in an actual situation must be made with reference to specific competing alternatives. Consequently, our discussion, which highlights the nature of the problems embodied within any control system, should suggest the critical points of comparison that are to be encountered in an evaluation process.

REFERENCES

AHM   Arrow, K. J., T. Harris, and J. Marschak, "Optimal Inventory Policy," *Econometrica*, Vol. 19, 1951, pp. 250–272.

AKS   Arrow, K. J., S. Karlin, and H. Scarf, *Studies in the Mathematical Theory of Inventory and Production*, Stanford University Press, 1958.

B   Bellman, R., *Dynamic Programming*, Princeton University Press, 1957.

BG   Blackwell, D., and M. A. Girshick, *Theory of Games and Statistical Decisions*, John Wiley and Sons, New York, 1954.

BL   Bowker, A. H., and G. J. Lieberman, *Engineering Statistics*, Prentice-Hall, Englewood Cliffs, N.J., 1959.

CM   Chernoff, H., and L. E. Moses, *Elementary Decision Theory*, John Wiley and Sons, New York, 1959.

Cra   Cramer, H., *Mathematical Methods of Statistics*, Princeton University Press, 1954.

Dan   Dantzig, G. B., "Discrete Variable Extremum Problems," *Operations Research*, Vol. 5, 1957, pp. 266–276.

D   Doob, J. L., *Stochastic Processes*, John Wiley and Sons, New York, 1953.

DSS   Dorfman, R., P. A. Samuelson, and R. M. Solow, *Linear Programming and Economic Analysis*, McGraw-Hill, New York, 1958.

DKW   Dvoretsky, A., J. Kiefer, and J. Wolfowitz, "The Inventory Problem," *Econometrica*, Vol. 20, 1952, pp. 187–222.

DKWo   Dvoretsky, A., J. Kiefer, and J. Wolfowitz, "The Inventory Problem—Case of Unknown Distributions of Demand," *Econometrica*, Vol. 20, 1952, pp. 450–466.

Fe   Feller, W., *An Introduction to Probability Theory and Its Applications*, John Wiley and Sons, New York, 1957.

FD   Fetter, R. B., and W. C. Dalleck, *Decision Models for Inventory Management*, R. D. Irwin, Homewood, Ill., 1961.

Go   Goldberg, S., *Introduction to Difference Equations*, John Wiley and Sons, New York, 1958.

Gom   Gomory, R., "Essentials of An Algorithm for Integer Solutions to Linear Programs," *Bulletin American Mathematical Society*, Vol. 64, 1958, pp. 275–278.

Gr   Grant, E. L., *Statistical Quality Control*, McGraw-Hill, New York, 1952.

H   Hanssmann, F., *Operations Research in Production and Inventory Control*, John Wiley and Sons, New York, 1962.

HMMS   Holt, C. C., F. Modigliani, J. F. Muth, and H. A. Simon, *Planning Production, Inventories, and Work Force*, Prentice-Hall, Englewood Cliffs, N.J., 1960.

Ka   Karlin, S., "Optimal Policy for Dynamic Inventory Process with Stochastic Demands Subject to Seasonal Variations," *Journal of SIAM*, Vol. 8, 1960, pp. 611–629.

Kar   Karlin, S., "Dynamic Inventory Policy with Varying Stochastic Demands,"
           Management Science, Vol. 6, 1960, pp. 231–258.

KF   Karlin, S., and G. Fabens, "A Stationary Inventory Model with Markovian
           Demand," *Mathematical Methods in Social Sciences*, Stanford University
           Press, 1960.

KI   Karlin, S., and D. Iglehart, "Optimal Policy for Dynamic Inventory Process
           with Non-Stationary Stochastic Demands," *Studies in Applied Probability
           and Management Science*, Stanford University Press, 1962.

KR   Karlin, S., and H. Rubin, "The Theory of Decision Procedures for Distribu-
           tions with Monotone Likelihood Ratios," *Annals of Math. Stat.*, Vol. 27,
           1956, pp. 272–299.

KB   Karman, T., and M. Biot, *Mathematical Methods in Engineering*, McGraw-
           Hill, New York, 1940.

KMST   Kemeny, J., H. Mirkil, L. Snell, and G. Thompson, *Finite Mathematical
           Structures*, Prentice-Hall, Englewood Cliffs, N.J., 1960.

KS   Kemeny, J., and L. Snell, *Finite Markov Chains*, Prentice-Hall, Englewood
           Cliffs, N.J., 1960.

K   Kendall, M. G., *Advanced Theory of Statistics*, Vol. II, Griffin and Co.,
           London, 1951.

L   Lehman, E. L., *Testing Statistical Hypotheses*, John Wiley and Sons, New
           York, 1959.

LR   Luce, R. D., and H. Raiffa, *Games and Decisions*, John Wiley and Sons,
           New York, 1957.

M   Magee, J. F., *Production Planning and Inventory Control*, McGraw-Hill, New
           York, 1958.

Mo   Morse, P. M., *Queues, Inventories and Maintenance*, John Wiley and Sons,
           New York, 1958.

Sa   Savage, L. J., *The Foundations of Statistics*, John Wiley and Sons, New York,
           1954.

Sca   Scarf, H., "Bayes Solutions of the Statistical Inventory Problem," *Annals of
           Math. Stat.*, Vol. 30, 1959, pp. 490–508.

Scar   Scarf, H., "The Optimality of (s, S) Policies in the Dynamic Inventory
           Problem," *Mathemetical Methods in the Social Sciences*, Stanford University
           Press, 1960.

Sch   Schlaifer, R., *Probability and Statistics for Business Decisions*, McGraw-Hill,
           New York, 1959.

Ste   Stedry, A. C., *Budget and Control and Cost Behavior*, Prentice-Hall, Engle-
           wood Cliffs, N.J., 1960.

Wh   Whitin, T. M., *The Theory of Inventory Management*, Second Edition,
           Princeton University Press, 1957.

INDEX